BASIC
STATISTICAL
METHODS
for Engineers and Scientists

In accordance with the statistical nature of the book the order of the authors' names was decided by chance and is not significant.

BASIC STATISTICAL METHODS

for Engineers and Scientists

ADAM M. NEVILLE, D. Sc. (Eng.), Ph.D.

Head of Department of Civil Engineering, University of Leeds, formerly Dean of Engineering, University of Calgary

JOHN B. KENNEDY, Ph. D.

Professor and Head of Department of Civil Engineering, University of Windsor

INTERNATIONAL TEXTBOOK COMPANY
Scranton, Pennsylvania

To
N. K. and L. N.

Preface

We should explain at the outset that we are not mathematicians but engineers. This should not, however, be construed as an apology because this book is written to satisfy, we hope, the needs of engineers and scientists who, as is always the case, need statistics but not necessarily the full treatment of the underlying mathematical theory.

We believe that in order to better understand engineering and scientific problems and to be able to draw correct inferences from experiment, a knowledge of statistics is essential in the very early stages of a university program. This book makes the acquisition of such knowledge possible since it does not build upon rigorous mathematics but rather uses an intuitive approach and common sense. Clearly then this is *not* a book on mathematical statistics, but neither is it a cookbook of ready-to-apply formulae. Jargon is down to a minimum; explanation, though full, is kept simple and there is a large number of illustrative solved problems both in the text and at the end of each chapter.

The book should thus prove acceptable as a textbook either for a one-semester course, possibly with some of the more advanced chapters omitted, or as a basis for a one-year junior course taken at a comfortable rate. We have endeavored to make the book suitable also for the engineer or scientist who wants to teach himself the basic statistical methods, as well as for occasional use by the man who is presented with a specific problem requiring statistical treatment, be it in research, in laboratory, or in production.

We hope to have satisfied these aims since the book is written largely from the practical point of view. The manuscript was understood by our wives which makes us confident that it can be understood by anybody.

We are grateful to Dr. June Adam and Mr. T. Lewis for help with some aspects of Problem 18-4, and to Professor D. B. DeLury for help on some aspects of the power curve in Chapter 20. While we are not recording other specific thanks, we wish to acknowledge our obvious debt to the authors of numerous books on statistics from which we ourselves learned the art.

Reproduced material is acknowledged wherever appropriate. We are indebted to the Imperial Chemical Industries Ltd., London, and to Messrs. Oliver and Boyd Ltd., Edinburgh, for permission to reprint Table G from their book by Davies: *Statistical Methods in Research and Production*, and to the Literary Executor of the late Sir R. A. Fisher, F.R.S., Cambridge, and

Dr. F. Yates, F.R.S., and the same publishers for permission to reprint Tables II, III, IV, VI and XXXIII from their book *Statistical Tables for Biological, Agricultural and Medical Research*.

We wish to express our thanks to Mrs. M. Christopherson and Mrs. E. L. Wittig who arranged the typing of the manuscript; to Messrs. D. J. Martin and F. W. Unger who checked the typescript; and to Miss S. M. J. Porter who read the proofs. Last, as well as least, we are grateful to Elizabeth Neville who performed the experiment discussed on page 68.

A. M. NEVILLE
J. B. KENNEDY

Calgary and Windsor, Canada
July, 1964

Contents

Notation

$_nC_r$	number of combinations of r items from n items
d	range coefficient
d_m	mean deviation
f	class frequency
F	cumulative frequency
$F(z)$	area under normal probability curve between $z = 0$ and $z = z$
n	sample size
N	population size
$\binom{n}{r}$	number of combinations of r items from n items
$_nP_r$	number of permutations of r items from n items
p	probability of success of an event
q	$= (1 - p) =$ probability of failure of an event
r	correlation coefficient
R	range
$\bar{R}$	mean range
s	estimate of standard deviation
s^2	estimate of variance
V	coefficient of variation
w	class width
x	value of an independent variable
$\bar{x}$	estimate of population mean or sample mean
$\bar{\bar{x}}$	mean of means
X	$= (x - \bar{X})$
z	$= \dfrac{x - \mu}{\sigma}$
μ	true mean
σ	true standard deviation
σ^2	true variance
ν	number of degrees of freedom

BASIC
STATISTICAL
METHODS
for Engineers and Scientists

chapter 1

Introduction

It is a truism to say that an improvement in the knowledge of the world around us requires an ever-increasing use of statistical methods and inferences. Almost everyone needs some knowledge of statistics. However, because of the width and depth of the subject, we have to select the field of knowledge and of methods relevant to a particular purpose. This book is primarily concerned with basic applications in engineering and in science, although much of the knowledge of basic applied statistics is of use to workers and students in other fields of study.

Statistics is concerned with two basic types of problems: *descriptive problems* and inference problems. The former include presentation of sets of observations in such a manner that they can be comprehended and interpreted. The numerical characteristics used to describe the set are called statistics.[1] *Inference problems* are those that involve inductive generalizations, for example, from a sample actually tested to the whole from which the sample was drawn. Statistical inference enables us to obtain the maximum amount of accurate information from a given effort of testing; in other words, the use of statistics makes testing more efficient.

In the fields of engineering and experimental sciences the use of statistics is almost invariably required in routine testing in the laboratory, in research work, and in production and construction.

In the laboratory, we may want to know whether our testing is "precise," or whether the variability of our results is greater than expected, or greater than in some other test.

In research, we may want to know whether a change in an ingredient affects the properties of the resulting material; to compare the efficiency of processes or of testing machines; to determine whether the results fit a suspected or postulated form; or to design an experiment which will enable us to separate out the variation due to different causes.

The latter problem also arises in production, as the knowledge of variation in observations caused by a certain factor enables us to decide whether it is economic to control this factor more closely. We may want to know the probability of obtaining a strength above or below a certain value; to check whether the production has altered so as to change this probability; to determine the proportion of items that have a certain attribute; or to

---

[1] Singular: a statistic.

know the size of the sample that we have to use in order that our conclusions will have a specified reliability.

There are two basic types of variables with which we are concerned: *continuous variables*, which may differ by infinitesimal amounts, and *discrete variables*, which can have only specified values but not intermediate values between the specified values. These concepts are familiar from a study of mathematics and are of interest as the two types of variables generally follow different distributions. By *distribution* we mean the frequency with which different observed values occur.

The "different values" occur in two ways. We may measure a certain property, e.g., a dimension of *one* particular thing, a number of times. Because of errors in measurement we shall not record exactly the same value every time. The second case occurs when we manufacture items all of which are to have a certain property, e.g., a dimension, the same. Because of variations in the manufacture, as well as errors in measurement, the recorded values vary. In either case, if we take a number of observations, we obtain results that vary among themselves, and it is one of the main functions of statistics to evaluate information of this type so that we can estimate the "best" value of the quantity being measured *and* assess the precision of our estimate.

The distribution of discrete variables is of interest primarily in problems involving items which have or have not a certain attribute: balls which are black or not black, manufactured items which are defective or not defective, specimens which have or have not a strength in excess of an expected value, and so on.

It may be relevant to mention that for the purpose of statistical analysis the discrete and continuous variables are not irrevocably separated from one another. If values of a variable which is continuously distributed are grouped in intervals and further treated in the grouped form, the problem becomes essentially one of discrete variables. Conversely, when a discrete variable consists of a large number of classes and is determined a large number of times, its distribution approximates that of a continuous variable, and the use of such an approximation is often convenient.

In statistical analysis we refer to the quantity which varies as the *variate*: it may be the original variable or a derived quantity such as the mean of samples,[2] their standard deviation,[3] and so on.

In a great many practical problems we cannot test or observe all of the items involved, and therefore have to resort to sampling. We measure then the properties of a sample for the purpose of estimating the properties of all the items from which the sample was drawn. Inference from samples is of tremendous value in many fields, varying from assessing whether a con-

---

[2] See Chapter 3.
[3] See Chapter 4.

signment of goods is up to specification, to the prediction of election results. Experience with the latter type of problem makes us realize that not only must the sample be properly taken so as to be representative of the underlying population, but also that our conclusion is only *probably* correct; certainty on the basis of sampling is not possible.

This is so because samples from the same population or collection of items vary among themselves, and variation is inherent in all natural phenomena and in all manufacturing operations. For this reason, all statistical inference is presented in terms of probability statements.

Although the greater part of this book is concerned with the use of statistics in extracting information from the results of experiments that have already been carried out, we must not forget the importance of statistics in planning experiments. With an appropriate program we can obtain more information from a given experimental effort than if the tests are made in a haphazard manner and the use of statistics is brought in only *a posteriori*. For this reason, we should view statistics not merely as an aid in the interpretation of experimental results but as an integral part of the design of experiments.

chapter 2

Frequency Distribution

We mentioned in Chapter 1 the variability of engineering and scientific measurements arising from inaccuracies known as errors. Errors are dealt with more fully in Chapter 9, and at this stage we are concerned only with the fact that if we measure something repeatedly we obtain different observations or results, even if our determination of the measured value is made under as closely similar conditions as possible. This is due to variation, however small, in temperature, pressure, potential, instrument setting, etc. By a similar argument it can be seen that there are differences between supposedly similar items manufactured by the same process. If we measure some property of the various items of the same type, we obtain a collection of data, but without an intelligent treatment, interpretation of such data is well-nigh impossible.

We should stress that we have ignored the possibility of a mistake in our measurements and are concerned only with a number of "equally good" observations that are truly representative of the measured quantity.

TABULATION OF DATA

Imagine, then, that we have a collection of measurements, each represented by a number, which gives us information about the quantity being determined. Some of the numbers occur only once; others are repeated several times. If we write down the results in the order in which they occur, they are said to be in the form of *ungrouped data*. This form enables us to study the sequence of the values, e.g., of "high" or "low" values, and, hence, possibly to discover some of the causes of variation. However, arithmetical processing of ungrouped data is cumbersome, and we usually resort to tabulation. A convenient form is to write the numbers in an increasing order of magnitude, i.e., in *rank* order; such a form is sometimes called *ungrouped frequency distribution*.

As an example, let us consider the results of tests on the transverse strength of 270 bricks from one works. Table 2-1 gives the ungrouped data as they were obtained in the order of testing, and Table 2-2 shows the same data ranked in an increasing order, but even this form is rather difficult to take in at a glance.

FREQUENCY GROUPING

For this reason, if there are more than about 40 observations, a more compact representation is advantageous. This is obtained by arranging

TABLE 2-1
TRANSVERSE STRENGTH OF 270 BRICKS FROM ONE SOURCE, PSI*

860	1,320	820	1,040	1,000	1,010	1,190	1,180	1,080	1,100	1,130
920	1,100	1,250	1,480	1,150	740	1,080	860	1,000	810	1,000
1,200	820	1,100	890	270	1,070	830	1,380	960	1,360	730
850	920	940	1,310	1,330	1,020	1,390	830	820	980	1,330
920	1,070	1,630	670	1,150	1,170	920	1,120	1,170	1,160	1,090
1,090	700	910	1,170	800	960	1,020	1,090	2,010	890	930
830	880	870	1,340	840	1,180	740	880	790	1,100	1,260
1,040	1,080	1,040	980	1,240	800	860	1,010	1,130	970	1,140
1,510	1,060	840	940	1,110	1,240	1,290	870	1,260	1,050	900
740	1,230	1,020	1,060	990	1,020	820	1,020	860	850	890
1,150	860	1,100	840	1,060	1,030	990	1,100	1,080	1,080	970
1,000	720	800	1,170	970	690	1,030	890	700	880	1,150
1,140	1,080	990	570	790	1,070	820	580	820	1,060	980
1,030	960	870	800	1,040	820	1,180	1,350	1,180	950	1,100
700	860	660	1,180	780	1,230	950	900	760	1,380	900
920	1,100	1,080	980	760	830	1,220	1,100	1,090	1,380	1,270
860	990	890	940	910	1,110	1,020	1,380	1,010	1,030	950
950	880	970	1,000	990	830	850	630	710	900	890
1,020	750	1,070	920	870	1,010	1,230	780	1,000	1,150	1,360
1,300	970	800	650	1,180	860	1,150	1,400	880	730	830
890	1,030	1,060	1,610	1,190	1,400	850	1,010	1,010	1,240	
1,070	970	960	1,180	1,050	910	1,110	780	780	1,190	
910	1,100	870	980	730	800	800	1,140	940	980	
870	970	910	830	1,030	1,050	710	890	1,010	1,120	
810	1,070	1,100	460	860	1,070	880	1,240	940	860	

*Report of Committee on Manual on Presentation of Data, *Proc. A.S.T.M.*, vol. 33 (1933), Part 1, p. 454.

the results into *class intervals*, usually of equal width, and recording the number of items in each interval, this number being called the *class frequency*. For example, we can choose a class width of 150 psi, with the midpoint of the lowest interval at 300 psi. Such a choice is quite arbitrary, but it is usually convenient to have 10 to 25 intervals. If too many class intervals are used, the class frequencies are low and the saving in computational effort is small. Conversely, with too few class intervals the true character of the distribution may be obscured and information may be lost.

It is generally preferable to choose class intervals in such a way that no result falls on the *class boundary*. Since in the present case the results are given to the nearest 1 psi, the class intervals may be chosen as 225–374, 375–524, etc. For simplicity, class intervals such as 225–375, 375–525, 525–675 are sometimes written down, it being understood that the upper boundary is exclusive. Other ways of dealing with the boundary between class intervals exist, but no fundamental point is involved; what is essential is that there is no gap and no overlap between classes. In the numerical examples given in the book, the class boundaries are in all cases assumed to be such that the interval to either side contains one-half of the values falling on the boundary. This method has the advantage of leading to simple numerical values, desirable in a textbook.

TABLE 2-2

DATA OF TABLE 2-1 ARRANGED IN RANK (ASCENDING) ORDER

270	780	830	870	920	970	1,020	1,070	1,100	1,180	1,310
460	780	830	880	920	980	1,020	1,070	1,100	1,180	1,320
570	780	830	880	920	980	1,020	1,070	1,100	1,180	1,330
580	790	840	880	920	980	1,020	1,070	1,100	1,180	1,330
630	790	840	880	920	980	1,020	1,070	1,110	1,180	1,340
650	800	840	880	930	980	1,020	1,070	1,110	1,180	1,350
660	800	850	880	940	980	1,020	1,070	1,110	1,180	1,360
670	800	850	890	940	990	1,030	1,080	1,120	1,190	1,360
690	800	850	890	940	990	1,030	1,080	1,120	1,190	1,380
700	800	850	890	940	990	1,030	1,080	1,130	1,190	1,380
700	800	860	890	940	990	1,030	1,080	1,130	1,200	1,380
700	800	860	890	950	990	1,030	1,080	1,140	1,220	1,380
710	810	860	890	950	1,000	1,030	1,080	1,140	1,230	1,390
710	810	860	890	950	1,000	1,040	1,080	1,140	1,230	1,400
720	820	860	890	950	1,000	1,040	1,090	1,150	1,230	1,400
730	820	860	900	960	1,000	1,040	1,090	1,150	1,240	1,480
730	820	860	900	960	1,000	1,040	1,090	1,150	1,240	1,510
730	820	860	900	960	1,000	1,050	1,090	1,150	1,240	1,610
740	820	860	900	960	1,010	1,050	1,100	1,150	1,240	1,630
740	820	860	910	970	1,010	1,050	1,100	1,150	1,250	2,010
740	820	870	910	970	1,010	1,060	1,100	1,160	1,260	
750	830	870	910	970	1,010	1,060	1,100	1,170	1,260	
760	830	870	910	970	1,010	1,060	1,100	1,170	1,270	
760	830	870	910	970	1,010	1,060	1,100	1,170	1,290	
780	830	870	920	970	1,010	1,060	1,100	1,170	1,300	

Arrangement of observations in class intervals, with the class frequencies tallied, produces a *grouped frequency distribution*. The concept of frequency distribution is of utmost importance. Table 2-3 gives the grouped frequency distribution for the data of Table 2-1. The advantages of this presentation are clear: we can see whether values near the extremes occur

TABLE 2-3

GROUPED FREQUENCY TABLE FOR DATA OF TABLE 2-1

Class interval	Class midpoint x_i	Class frequency f_i	Cumulative frequency F	Relative cumulative frequency F/n	$f_i x_i$
225–375	300	1	1	0.00370	300
375–525	450	1	2	0.00741	450
525–675	600	6	8	0.0296	3,600
675–825	750	38	46	0.170	28,500
825–975	900	80	126	0.467	72,000
975–1,125	1,050	83	209	0.774	87,150
1,125–1,275	1,200	39	248	0.918	46,800
1,275–1,425	1,350	17	265	0.981	22,950
1,425–1,575	1,500	2	267	0.989	3,000
1,575–1,725	1,650	2	269	0.996	3,300
1,725–1,875	1,800	0	269	0.996	0
1,875–2,025	1,950	1	270	1.000	1,950
Totals		$\Sigma f_i = 270 = n$			$\Sigma f_i x_i = 270,000$

frequently or whether the observations cluster near some central value, and specifically which class intervals contain the most values.

If instead of actual frequency we consider the frequency of each interval divided by the total number of observations, we obtain results in terms of relative frequency; we then deal with a *relative-frequency distribution*.

CUMULATIVE FREQUENCY

Furthermore, we may be interested (to continue with our example) in the number of bricks whose strength is higher or lower than a specified value. This is given by the *cumulative frequency F* column of Table 2-3. The "lower than" F is a sum of the frequencies of all class intervals below the specified value. For example, $1 + 1 + 6 + 38 = 46$ bricks have a strength lower than 825 psi. A "not lower than" F is similarly obtained by summing frequencies of intervals from the highest; for example, $1 + 0 + 2 + 2 = 5$ bricks have a strength not lower than 1,425 psi. It is not possible to say how many bricks have a strength higher than 1,425 psi because bricks whose strength is exactly 1,425 psi are included in the interval 1,425–1,575 psi.

In many cases the proportion of results rather than their number is of interest; to obtain this the cumulative frequency is simply divided by the total number of results n, the quotient being known as relative or *fractional cumulative frequencies*. The calculated values are given in Table 2-3, and it can be seen, for example, that the proportion of bricks whose strength is lower than 825 psi is $46/270 = 0.17$.

GRAPHICAL REPRESENTATION

A grouped frequency distribution may be represented diagrammatically in several ways. The most common of these is the *histogram*. Here, the class intervals are set out on a horizontal axis, and the frequency in a given interval is measured in the vertical direction and marked by means of a horizontal line across the width of the class interval; the scale chosen is quite arbitrary. Figure 2-1 shows a histogram for the data of Table 2-3. Strictly speaking, it is the area of each rectangle that represents the frequency in that interval, and the total area under the histogram represents the total number of results to an appropriate scale, but when the width of all class intervals is the same, the heights and areas are proportional to one another. However, when the class intervals are not all of the same width (and this should be avoided whenever possible), the ordinates should be plotted so that the area of each rectangle is proportional to the class frequency. Thus the ordinate no longer represents the frequency but a ratio of frequency to the class width, i.e., density. This concept is of importance and will be encountered again in Chapter 11.

The choice of the class width is governed by the same considerations as in the case of grouping for computational purposes only. If too many intervals are used, the histogram becomes irregular, and no clear pattern of frequency distribution can be seen. This is illustrated in Fig. 2-2a; by

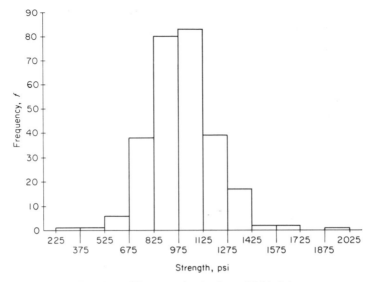

F<small>IG</small>. 2-1.   Histogram for the data of Table 2-3.

contrast, Fig. 2-2*b* shows a histogram for the same data but with a class width twice that in case (*a*).

Sometimes the frequency within a class interval is plotted as a point whose abscissa is that of the class midpoint. If adjacent points are connected, a *frequency polygon* is obtained, as shown in Fig. 2-3 for the data of Fig. 2-1. When plotting a frequency polygon, it is usual to indicate the values of the class midpoints rather than class boundaries as in the case of a histogram. The line between the points has no significance, and intermediate values must not be read off the line. Frequency polygons are particularly applicable to observations on discrete variables, especially when the class width corresponds to the smallest increment in the variable— as, for example, in plotting the number of accidents with a class width of one. With continuous variables, frequency polygons are useful when we want to compare visually two or more frequency distributions. Superimposed frequency polygons give a clearer picture than histograms.

If we are interested in proportions of results within various class intervals, we plot the relative frequency—i.e., frequency divided by the total number of results. *Percentage frequency*, which is simply relative frequency multiplied by 100, is particularly convenient. The difference between histograms showing the frequency and those showing the relative or percentage frequency lies in the scale of the ordinates only; the form of the diagram is the same in either case.

If the total number of results is increased indefinitely so that the class width can be correspondingly decreased, the histogram becomes trans-

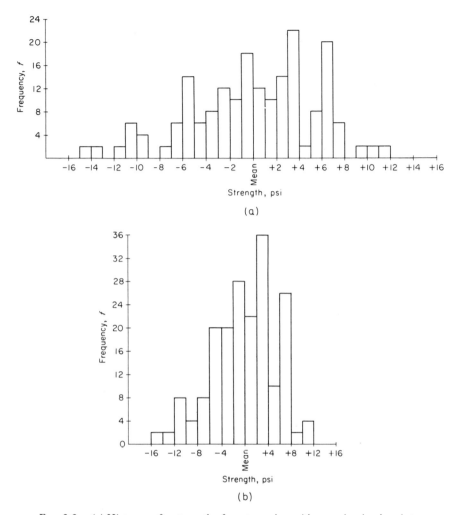

Fig. 2-2. (a) Histogram for strength of mortar cubes with grouping in class intervals of too small a width. (b) Histogram for the same data as (a) but with a class width of twice the size.

formed, in the limiting case, into a *frequency distribution curve*. The ordinate should then properly be regarded to represent the frequency density.

Cumulative frequency can also be represented graphically. The class intervals are set out horizontally as before, and the cumulative frequency is plotted as the ordinate at the right-hand end of each interval. This ordinate thus represents the area to the left of the corresponding ordinate in a histogram. The cumulative frequency curve is also called an *ogive*.[1]

---

[1] Pronounced $\bar{o}$ - $j\bar{i}v'$.

Frequency Distribution

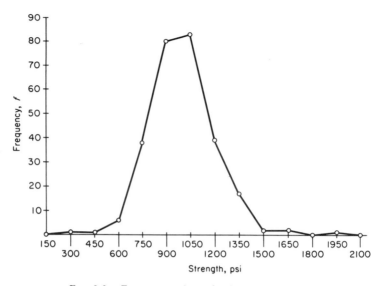

Fɪɢ. 2-3. Frequency polygon for the data of Fig. 2-1

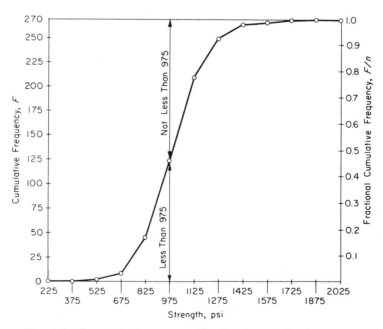

Fɪɢ. 2-4. Cumulative frequency and fractional cumulative frequency curve for the data of Table 2-3.

Fig. 2-4 shows the "less than" curve for the data of Table 2-3, the ordinates giving both the cumulative frequency and the fractional cumulative frequency. The number or the fraction of results below or above any strength can easily be read off such a diagram, but care is required in distinguishing between fractions "less than" and "not greater than" a specified value. The cumulative frequency curve for the so-called normal distribution is considered in Chapter 10.

SOLVED PROBLEM

2-1. In a test on 35 glue-laminated beams the following values of the spring constant (in kips/in.) were found:

Spring Constant × 100

6.72	6.77	6.82	6.70	6.78	6.70	6.62
6.75	6.66	6.66	6.64	6.76	6.73	6.80
6.72	6.76	6.76	6.68	6.66	6.62	6.72
6.76	6.70	6.78	6.76	6.67	6.70	6.72
6.74	6.81	6.79	6.78	6.66	6.76	6.72

(*a*)   Obtain a frequency table;
(*b*)   Draw a histogram and a frequency polygon;
(*c*)   Draw a cumulative frequency diagram;
(*d*)   Estimate the fraction of beams that will have a constant of less than 6.71 × 100 kip/in.   Estimate also the spring constant which is not exceeded by 80 percent of the beams tested.

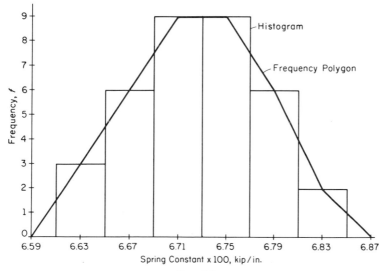

Fig. 2-5

Solution:

(a)   We shall assign the observations to 6 classes. The lowest and highest
      values in the table are 6.62 and 6.82. The difference is 0.20, which gives,
      when divided by 6, approximately 0.04. We shall, therefore, adopt 0.04 as
      class width, the lowest boundary being 6.61

Class interval	Frequency f_i	Cumulative frequency F
6.61–6.65	3	3
6.65–6.69	6	9
6.69–6.73	9	18
6.73–6.77	9	27
6.77–6.81	6	33
6.81–6.85	2	35
Total.......	$\Sigma f_i = 35$	

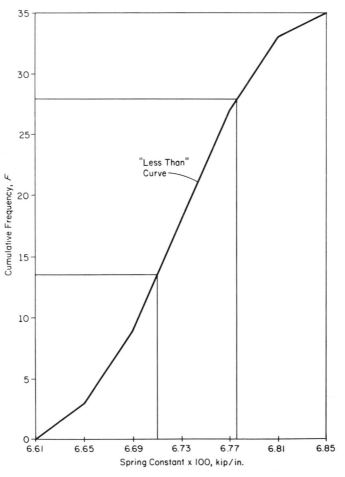

Fig. 2-6

(b)   The histogram and the frequency polygon are shown in Fig. 2-5.

(c)   The cumulative frequency diagram is shown in Fig. 2-6.

(d)   From the cumulative frequency diagram it is estimated that 13 beams have a constant of less than 6.71 × 100 kip/in., which corresponds to a fractional cumulative frequency of 13/35 = 0.37. Eighty percent of the beams (28 beams) are estimated to have a spring constant of less than 6.776 × 100 kip/in.

PROBLEMS

2-1.   The annual precipitation (in inches) at some city is as follows:

Year	Precipitation	Year	Precipitation	Year	Precipitation
1904	19.5	1923	18.8	1942	21.0
1905	10.9	1924	9.3	1943	13.5
1906	12.6	1925	15.9	1944	14.0
1907	10.4	1926	13.6	1945	13.3
1908	14.1	1927	17.0	1946	16.2
1909	15.9	1928	12.9	1947	13.6
1910	11.1	1929	9.0	1948	10.2
1911	19.4	1930	11.5	1949	15.5
1912	16.7	1931	11.6	1950	16.3
1913	13.5	1932	10.1	1951	16.4
1914	12.7	1933	9.8	1952	10.7
1915	10.5	1934	9.9	1953	13.4
1916	17.4	1935	17.8	1954	20.4
1917	10.3	1936	11.3	1955	15.4
1918	12.7	1937	10.7	1956	13.7
1919	13.4	1938	18.0	1957	10.1
1920	15.2	1939	15.7	1958	11.7
1921	21.0	1940	12.9	1959	13.4
1922	11.4	1941	10.3	1960	10.2

(a)   Arrange the data in (ascending) rank order.

(b)   Prepare a frequency table. Take a class width of 1.0 in. and commence with the lower boundary of the first class interval of 9.0 in.

(c)   Draw a histogram, a frequency polygon, and a cumulative frequency diagram.

(d)   What is the number of years in which the annual precipitation exceeded 14.5 in. and the number of years in which the annual precipitation was lower than 11.0 in.?

2-2.   The following marks were obtained in an examination taken by 100 students:

Mark	0–30	31–40	41–45	46–50	51–55	56–65	66–75	76–80	81–90	91–100
No. of students	2	10	7	8	25	18	12	10	5	3

(a)   Draw a histogram for the above data.

(b)   Draw a cumulative frequency diagram, and hence estimate the mark exceeded by the top 25 percent of students.

(c)   Suggest a passing mark if 15 percent of the students are to fail.

2-3.   The frequency distribution of 500 radio tubes tested at a certain company is as follows:

Lifetime (hours)	400–499	500–599	600–699	700–799	800–899	900–999	1000–1099	1100–1199
Number of tubes	25	65	79	108	92	76	34	21

(a)   Construct a histogram, a frequency polygon, and a cumulative frequency diagram.
(b)   Find the percentage of tubes whose lifetimes do not exceed 700 hours.
(c)   Find the percentage of tubes whose lifetimes are at least 600 but not more than 1000 hours.

2-4.   The moisture content in percent of 44 samples of clay was measured as follows:
10.3, 10.7, 9.2, 11.4, 11.5, 8.4, 10.3, 10.2, 9.8, 10.2, 11.4, 10.4, 11.6, 10.3, 11.4, 10.3, 7.8, 8.7, 11.7, 9.3, 9.8, 11.4, 10.4, 9.3, 10.4, 11.2, 10.6, 9.8, 10.1, 13.1, 10.5, 12.2, 9.6, 7.0, 12.3, 12.3, 12.3, 9.7, 10.7, 11.5, 10.6, 13.0, 13.0, 9.0.

(a)   Compute a grouped frequency distribution for these results.
(b)   Draw a histogram.
(c)   Draw a frequency polygon and cumulative frequency diagram.

chapter 3

Characteristics of Distributions: Central Tendency

Chapter 2 explained how to arrange a collection of observations in a frequency distribution form. We shall now proceed with statistical analysis in order to learn how to present information about the distribution in a clear and concise form.

There are two obvious features of the data that can be characterized in a simple form and yet give a very meaningful description of a set of observations: *central tendency* and *dispersion*. The central tendency is measured by averages; these describe the point about which the various observed values cluster. The measure of dispersion is concerned with scatter about the average, and is dealt with in Chapter 4.

AVERAGES

Averages are commonly used in everyday life to give a *typical* representation of a group as a whole, possibly as a basis for comparison with other groups. In many cases the data in hand refer to a sample drawn from a larger body of data—for example, we may take a number of rock specimens from some stratum and measure their density. The tested specimens are referred to collectively as a *sample*, and the whole body of rock as the parent *population*. We measure the average density of the sample for the purpose of obtaining information about the average density of the population. This type of problem is dealt with in Chapter 6.

It may be relevant to note that if we take repeated measurements of a quantity, the average does not represent a "true" value of the quantity. In many cases the term "true value" has no meaning (e.g., the time taken by jet planes to fly between New York and San Francisco); in other cases, we may never be able to determine the true value but can determine only the most probable value (e.g., the difference in level between two points on the ground).

There are several types of averages, which will now be discussed; the appropriate one to use depends on the problem in hand.

ARITHMETIC MEAN

This is the most common type of average, often referred to simply as the "average" or "mean." The latter term will be used here.

Mean is a value such that the sum of deviations of observations from it is zero, and is thus the sum of the observations divided by their number,:

$$\bar{x} = \frac{1}{n} \sum_{i=1}^{n} x_i \tag{3-1}$$

where x_i = an observation or measurement

n = total number of observations

$\bar{x}$ = mean

The concept of mean is so well known that no further discussion is needed, but a simple example will be given to illustrate some shortcuts in computation.

Example. The solids content of water, in parts per million (ppm), was measured on eleven samples, the following results being obtained:

4,520, 4,570, 4,520, 4,490, 4,540, 4,570, 4,500, 4,520, 4,520, 4,500, 4,590

Hence,

$$\text{Mean} = \bar{x} = \frac{\Sigma \text{ above values}}{11} = 4,530.9 \text{ ppm}$$

When the frequency of some of the observations is greater than 1, computation may be simplified by setting the data in a tabular form and using frequency grouping. If f_i is the frequency of any value x_i, then the mean can be written as

$$\bar{x} = \frac{\Sigma f_i x_i}{\Sigma f_i} \tag{3-2}$$

A further saving in effort is effected by reducing all the observations by a constant value, and possibly also by dividing them by a factor such as 10. This transformation of the original variable is known as *coding*. In our case we can thus subtract 4,400 (column 2) and divide by 10 (column 3).

(1)	(2)	(3)	(4)	(5)
Solids content ppm x_i	$(-4,400)$	$(\div 10)$ x_i'	Frequency f_i	$x_i' f_i$
4,490	90	9	1	9
4,500	100	10	2	20
4,520	120	12	4	48
4,540	140	14	1	14
4,570	170	17	2	34
4,590	190	19	1	19
Totals			$\Sigma f_i = 11$	$\Sigma x_i' f_i = 144$

Hence from Eq. 3-2,

$$\bar{x}' = \frac{144}{11} = 13.09$$

and $\bar{x} = 10\bar{x}' + 4,400 = 4,530.9$ ppm, as before.

When dealing with a large number of observations, or a large sample, the computation of the mean can be shortened considerably, with only a small loss of accuracy, by using the class-interval method explained in Chapter 2. Instead of considering each individual observation, we treat all observations within a class interval as a group, and assume that in any class the observations are uniformly distributed throughout the interval so that the class frequency may be assumed to be concentrated at the class midpoint x_i'. The procedure is then as follows:

1. Take the first class midpoint x_0 as an arbitrary origin for the purpose of calculating the fictitious mean.

2. Calculate deviations X_i' from this origin, expressed in terms of the class width w, that is, $X_i' = \dfrac{x_i' - x_0}{w}$

3. Find the product of class frequency f_i and X_i'.

4. Obtain the fictitious mean $\bar{X}' = \dfrac{\Sigma f_i X_i'}{\Sigma f_i}$

5. Convert $\bar{X}'$ to the true mean $\bar{x}$:

$\bar{x} = $ arbitrary origin $+$ (fictitious mean) $\times$ (class width)

That is,

$$\bar{x} = x_0 + \frac{\Sigma f_i X_i'}{\Sigma f_i} \times w = x_0 + \bar{X}'w \tag{3-3}$$

As an example, the short method of computing the mean will be used for the data of Table 2-1. The class width, as in Table 2-3, is $w = 150$, and the origin is taken at $x_0 = 300$ psi. From Table 3-1 the fictitious mean (in terms of class width) is

$$\bar{X}' = \frac{\Sigma f_i X_i'}{\Sigma f_i} = \frac{1,260}{270} = 4.666$$

Using Eq. 3-3, the true mean is

$$\bar{x} = 300 + 4.666 \times 150$$
$$= 1,000.00 \text{ psi}$$

The exact mean of the measurements in Table 2-1 is 999.81 psi. For many purposes the difference between the two is not significant.

The value that we have found is the mean of the values comprising our sample of bricks, but if we took another sample from the same source, it would, in all likelihood, have a different mean. Thus, so far as the population of all bricks manufactured by the given works is concerned, the mean

TABLE 3-1

CALCULATION OF THE MEAN FOR DATA OF TABLE 2-3
USING THE CLASS-INTERVAL METHOD

Class midpoint	Class frequency f_i	Deviation from origin in terms of class width X_i'	$f_i X_i'$	$f_i X_i'^2$
300	1	0	0	0
450	1	1	1	1
600	6	2	12	24
750	38	3	114	342
900	80	4	320	1,280
1,050	83	5	415	2,075
1,200	39	6	234	1,404
1,350	17	7	119	833
1,500	2	8	16	128
1,650	2	9	18	162
1,800	0	10	0	0
1,950	1	11	11	121
Totals	$\Sigma f_i = 270$		$\Sigma f_i X_i' = 1,260$	$\Sigma f_i X_i'^2 = 6,370$

as determined from samples is a variable quantity, but much less variable than the strength of the individual bricks. This applies, of course, to measurements in all problems of this type. In general terms, we can state that statistics derived from a random sample are also random variables.

As we saw earlier, the arithmetic mean is the average that is most commonly used, but it is not the only one of importance, and we shall now consider the other averages.

MEDIAN

The median of a set of observations is the middle observation when the observations are ranked or arranged in order of magnitude. The term middle observation refers to the distance from the extremes and not to the numerical value. The median is sometimes defined as an observation above and below which there is an equal number of observations, but this definition may not be satisfactory when observations repeat themselves at the median. It is therefore preferable to define the median as a value which is neither greater than nor smaller than the value of one-half the number of the observations. Thus a median of 10, 12, 16, 16, 18 is 16.

Since the area of a histogram is proportional to the number of observations, it follows from the above definition that the median divides a histogram (or a frequency polygon or curve) into two equal areas.

If the number of observations is even, the median is taken as one-half the sum of the two "middle" values. For example, the median of 17, 21, 22, 22, 26, 31, 31, 34 is $(22 + 26)/2 = 24$.

Because the median is a positional value (in contrast with the arithmetic character of the mean), it is less affected by extreme values within the group than the mean. This property of the median makes it in some cases a useful measure of the central tendency. For example, a median of 2, 3, 6, 8, 9, 9, 12 is 8. If the extreme values change so that the set is now 3, 3, 6, 8, 9, 9, 18, the median is still 8 but the mean has increased from 7 to 8.

We can now find the median value for the data on the solids content of water, given previously. Arranging the results in ascending order, we have 4,490, 4,500, 4,500, 4,520, 4,520, 4,520, 4,520, 4,540, 4,570, 4,570, 4,590, and the median value is 4,520 ppm.

MODE

Mode is the value of the observation which occurs most frequently if the variable is discrete, or the class interval (often quoted as a class mid-point) which has the highest frequency if the distribution is continuous. The mode thus represents a peak value in a frequency distribution. Like the median, the mode is less affected by extreme values than the mean.

In the example concerning the solids content of water, the value of 4,520 has the highest frequency, namely 4, and is, therefore, the modal value. We have thus a mode and a median of 4,520, and a mean of 4,531 ppm.

Some distributions have more than one mode but in experimental work this is rare, although bimodal distribution is encountered in microscope counts and particle-size gradings. In many other cases the appearance of a bimodal distribution means that the data contain values from two different distributions. For example, if two machines manufacturing an item are set at different averages sufficiently far apart and all the items are pooled, the resulting frequency distribution will be bimodal.

SKEWNESS

We can now view the three measures of central tendency: mean, median, and mode on a general frequency distribution curve, shown in Fig. 3-1. The mode is the value corresponding to the highest point on the curve; the median divides the area under the curve into two halves; and the mean passes through the centroid of the area. (The latter arises from the fact that the sum of deviations of all observations from the mean is zero.) The median lies between or coincides with the mean and the mode.

When the three averages do not coincide, the frequency distribution curve is said to be *skew* or *skewed*. It is skewed to the right when the median is to the right of the mode, that is, when the tail to the right (the direction of increasing values) is longer than the tail to the left. Such a curve is also said to be *positively skewed*.

There is no accepted method of measuring skewness. To compare the

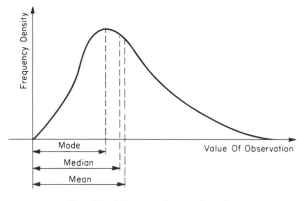

FIG. 3-1. Mean, median, and mode.

skewness of different distributions the ratio

$$\frac{\text{Mean} - \text{mode}}{\text{Standard deviation}}$$

may be used. The term in the denominator, standard deviation (see Chapter 4), makes a comparison of distributions with different widths of scatter possible.

For moderately skewed distributions there is an approximate relation between the various averages:

$$\text{Mean} - \text{mode} = 3(\text{mean} - \text{median}) \qquad (3\text{-}4)$$

It is interesting to note that in skew distributions which are sharply peaked, the median is often a particularly useful measure of central tendency. For example, if we are interested in the distribution of periods of time at which atoms of a radioactive element have disintegrated, the median represents the time at which half the atoms have disintegrated, and is a common measure of radioactivity.

Skewness arises usually from natural causes and is characteristic of many distributions, such as those dealt with in Chapters 7 and 8, and also of some continuous distributions. For example, the frequency of the occurrence of a very large defect in a material (e.g., a blowhole) is smaller than that of a very small defect. Thus the frequency curve for defects of various sizes is skewed to the left. However, skewness can also be caused by selection. For example, in testing concrete specimens the very poorly made ones may well be discarded prior to testing, with the result that a frequency curve for the strength of the concrete specimens would be skewed to the right. This behavior has, in fact, been observed in some tests.

A great many random variables are, of course, distributed symmetrically, i.e., the departure of observations from the mean by any given amount occurs with a sensibly equal frequency in the up and down directions. Such a distribution is simply said to be *symmetrical*, and the mean, mode, and median all coincide.

QUANTILES

In a manner similar to that of the median, which divides a set of observations so that 50 percent of them fall above and 50 percent below the median, we can introduce other points, which divide the observations into a number of equal parts, known as *quantiles*. An example of commonly used quantiles are *quartiles* which divide the set into four equal parts; e.g., the upper quartile is the value above which 25 percent of the set falls. The *interquartile range* contains the middle 50 percent of the set, with 25 percent falling above and 25 percent below the range, and is sometimes used as a measure of dispersion. A *decile* divides the set of observations into ten groups, the lowest decile, for example, being a value below which 10 percent of the set falls. Other quantiles are described as *percentiles*, e.g., a 5 percentile.

GEOMETRIC MEAN

There is one more type of average which is of interest in engineering calculations. This is the geometric mean, defined as the nth root of the product of n observations. Thus, the geometric mean $\bar{x}_g$, of n observations $x_1, x_2, \ldots, x_n$ is

$$\bar{x}_g = \sqrt[n]{x_1 \times x_2 \times \cdots \times x_n} \tag{3-5}$$

This average is used when dealing with observations each of which bears an approximately constant ratio to the preceding one, e.g., in averaging rates of growth (increase or decrease) of a statistical population, as illustrated in the following example.

Example. The number of degrees *cum laude* awarded at a university during six consecutive years is given below. What is the average percentage increase in the number of such degrees per annum?

Year	Number of degrees	Ratio to previous year's value
1959	5	—
1960	6	1.20
1961	9	1.50
1962	15	1.67
1963	30	2.00
1964	50	1.67

To find the answer we calculate the geometric mean of the ratios given in the last column. This is

$$\sqrt[5]{1.2 \times 1.5 \times 1.67 \times 2.0 \times 1.67} = 1.585$$

i.e., an average increase per year of 58.5 percent.

It might be asked why an arithmetic mean cannot be used. This is $\frac{1}{5}(1.2 + 1.5 + 1.67 + 2.0 + 1.67) = 1.61$ or an increase of 61 percent, which is higher than that given by the geometric mean; the arithmetic mean is always higher than the geometric mean. The bias in the answer given by the arithmetic mean arises from the influence of the absolute magnitude of the ratios. For example, doubling a value represents a ratio of 2, while halving means a ratio of $\frac{1}{2}$. Thus if we consider a value of 100 which falls to 50 and subsequently rises to 100, the ratios are $\frac{1}{2}$ and 2, respectively. The geometric mean is $\sqrt{\frac{1}{2} \times 2} = 1$, and this is the average rate of increase. This answer is intuitively correct as the overall change is zero. However, the arithmetic mean of the ratios is $\frac{1}{2}(\frac{1}{2} + 2) = 1.25$. If the ratios were 3 and $\frac{1}{3}$, the geometric mean would still be 1 but the arithmetic mean would be $1\frac{2}{3}$.

The use of the geometric mean can be avoided by transforming the original variate x into log x: the arithmetic mean of the new variate will then give the right answer since from Eq. 3-5:

$$\log \bar{x}_g = \frac{\Sigma (\log x_i)}{n}$$

SOLVED PROBLEMS

3-1. Three hundred and three cement briquettes were made with a given cement and gave the following tensile strengths at the age of seven days:

Strength interval psi	200–230	230–260	260–290	290–320	320–350	350–380	380–410	410–440	440–470	470–500
Number of briquettes	7	30	50	77	53	40	35	6	3	2

(*a*) Complete the frequency table;
(*b*) Draw the histogram and frequency polygon;
(*c*) Draw the cumulative-frequency diagram;
(*d*) Calculate the mean tensile strength and indicate this on the histogram.

Class interval	Class midpoint	Class frequency f_i	Cumulative frequency F	Deviation from origin in terms of class width X_i'	$f_i X_i'$	$f_i X_i'^2$
200–230	215	7	7	0	0	0
230–260	245	30	37	1	30	30
260–290	275	50	87	2	100	200
290–320	305	77	164	3	231	696
320–350	335	53	217	4	212	848
350–380	365	40	257	5	200	1,000
380–410	395	35	292	6	210	1,260
410–440	425	6	298	7	42	294
440–470	455	3	301	8	24	192
470–500	485	2	303	9	18	162
Totals					$\Sigma f_i X_i' = 1,067$	$\Sigma f_i X_i'^2 = 4,679$

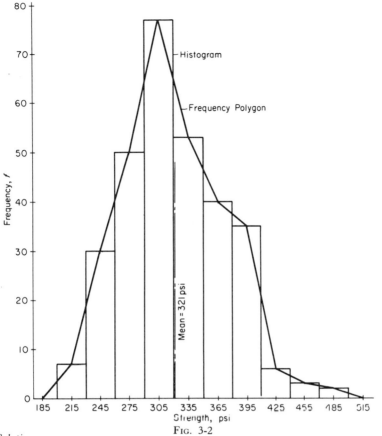

Fig. 3-2

Solution:

(a) In view of the form in which the data are presented we shall adopt a class width of 30 psi, with the first class midpoint at 215 psi. In tabular form:

(b) The histogram and frequency polygon are shown in Fig. 3-2.

(c) The cumulative-frequency diagram is shown in Fig. 3-3.

(d) From the Table in (a):

$$\text{Mean from first class midpoint in terms of class width} = \frac{1{,}067}{303} = 3.52$$

$$\text{Mean} = 215 + 3.52 \times 30 = 321 \text{ psi}$$

The mean tensile strength of the briquettes is marked in Fig. 3-2.

3-2. Mid-block passenger-car spot speeds under urban conditions were found to be:[1]

Speed interval, mph	5–10	10–15	15–20	20–25	25–30	30–35	35–40	40–45	45–50	50–55	55–60
Number of vehicles	0	1	34	146	178	130	31	16	3	2	0

[1] Data from T. M. Matson, W. S. Smith, and F. W. Hurd, *Traffic Engineering* (New York: McGraw Hill Book Company, Inc., 1941) p. 50.

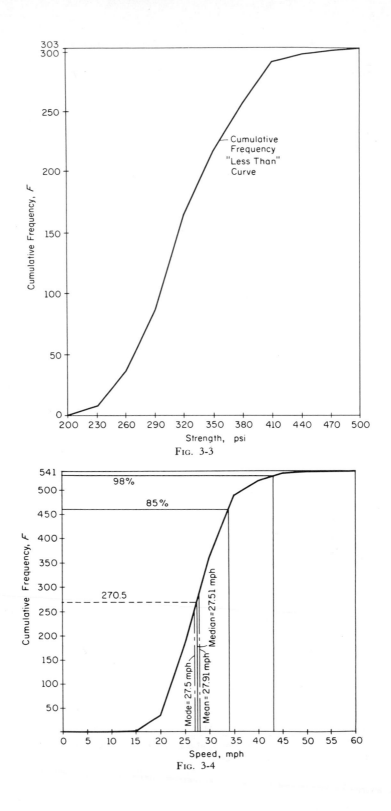

Fig. 3-3

Fig. 3-4

(a) Complete the frequency table;
(b) Draw the cumulative-frequency diagram;
(c) Find the mode, median, and the mean speed;
(d) If the 85 and 98 percentiles are employed in speed regulation and design respectively, calculate the speed limit and the design speed for the locality.

Solution:

(a) Take the origin at the first class midpoint, i.e., at 7.5 mph. With a class width $w = 5$ mph we tabulate the data as follows:

Class interval	Class midpoint	Class frequency f_i	Cumulative frequency F	Deviation from origin in terms of class width X_i'	$f_i X_i'$	$f_i X_i^2$
5–10	7.5	0	0	0	0	0
10–15	12.5	1	1	1	1	1
15–20	17.5	34	35	2	68	136
20–25	22.5	146	181	3	438	1,314
25–30	27.5	178	359	4	712	2,848
30–35	32.5	130	489	5	650	3,250
35–40	37.5	31	520	6	186	1,116
40–45	42.5	16	536	7	112	784
45–50	47.5	3	539	8	24	192
50–55	52.5	2	541	9	18	162
55–60	57.5	0	541	10	0	0
Totals		$\Sigma f_i = 541$			$\Sigma f_i X_i' = 2,209$	$\Sigma f_i X_i^2 = 9,803$

(b) The cumulative-frequency diagram is shown in Fig. 3-4.

(c) By inspection of the Table in (a) the mode = 27.5 mph. The median divides the histogram into 2 equal areas.

Now, one-half the area of the histogram = $(w \times 541)/2 = 270.5 \times w$. The median will fall to the right of the class interval with the highest cumulative frequency below 270.5, that is, to the right of the 20–25 mph class interval. Hence

$$181 \times w + 178 \times x = \frac{541 \times w}{2}$$

or

$$x = \frac{89.5}{178} \times w = \frac{89.5}{178} \times 5$$

$$= 2.51 \text{ mph to the right of 25 mph}$$

Therefore

$$\text{Median} = 25 + 2.51 = 27.51 \text{ mph}$$

$$\text{Mean} = 7.5 + \frac{2209}{541} \times 5 = 27.91 \text{ mph}$$

(d) 98 percent of 541 cars = 530 cars, and 85 percent of 541 cars = 460 cars.

From the cumulative-frequency diagram the speed not exceeded by 530 cars is 42 to 43 mph; i.e., the design speed is, say, 43 mph. For 460 cars the corresponding speed is 34 mph—i.e., the speed limit for the locality is 34 mph.

PROBLEMS

3-1.   The following was the number of vehicles passing a certain point on different days:

1310,   1207,   760,   983,   260,   618,   1262,   1152,   598,   1218,   1391.

Determine the mean, median, and mode for the above values.

3-2.   The diameters in inches of a sample of 50 ball bearings manufactured by one company are as follows:

0.529	0.538	0.532	0.529	0.535
0.536	0.534	0.542	0.537	0.530
0.538	0.536	0.536	0.536	0.526
0.525	0.524	0.543	0.530	0.539
0.542	0.528	0.546	0.532	0.534
0.535	0.539	0.527	0.544	0.527
0.535	0.534	0.540	0.540	0.536
0.532	0.535	0.535	0.535	0.528
0.541	0.531	0.540	0.532	0.535
0.533	0.535	0.537	0.537	0.545

(*a*)   Prepare a frequency table.

(*b*)   Draw a histogram, a frequency polygon, and a cumulative frequency diagram.

(*c*)   Calculate the mean diameter from the grouped data in the frequency table, and indicate the mean on the histogram.

3-3.   Calculate the mean of data for the annual precipitation given in Prob. 2-1 from (*a*) the ungrouped data, and (*b*) the frequency table.

Calculate and then comment on the percentage error between the values of the mean found from (*a*) and (*b*) above.

3-4.   Calculate the mean, median, and mode for the data given in Prob. 2-2.

3-5.   The number of students entering engineering increased in 5 years from 3,000 to 4,880. Calculate the average annual rate of increase.

3-6.   For the data of Prob. 2-4 find the mean, mode, and median. Also find the mean using a grouped frequency table.

chapter 4

Characteristics of Distributions: Dispersion

In the preceding chapter we considered the central tendency of sets of observations and the calculation of averages. The average is a single value that typifies the whole group but does not generally give adequate information about the distribution of observations within the group. To choose a simple example,

Mean of 99.9 cm, 100.0 cm, and 100.1 cm is 100.0 cm

Mean of 99.0 cm, 100.0 cm, and 101.0 cm is also 100.0 cm

but it is clear that the two sets of observations differ appreciably in the scatter of the values about their mean. And yet the scatter may be of considerable importance. Let us assume, for example, that tests show the mean strength of a structural material to be 30,000 psi, but it is only the knowledge of scatter of the results that will tell us the proportion of specimens whose strength is, say, below 20,000 psi, the latter value being critical for safety.

There are several measures of scatter or dispersion, and these will now be considered.

VARIANCE

If our set of values (a finite population) consists of n observations x_i, whose mean is μ, we can write for each observation the *deviation* $(x_i - \mu)$, known also as the *residual*. The mean square deviation is known as variance, which is given by:

$$\sigma^2 = \frac{\sum_{i=1}^{n} (x_i - \mu)^2}{n} \qquad (4\text{-}1)$$

For reasons to be discussed later it is important to remember that the deviations must be calculated from the true mean of the set of values.

STANDARD DEVIATION

While variance is a fundamental measure of dispersion, it is not a convenient practical measure as its units are the square of the units of the variate.[1] Furthermore, many numerical characteristics of distributions are expressed directly in terms of the square root of variance. It is therefore preferable to give this square root the name *standard deviation* σ. Standard deviation is thus the root-mean-square (rms) deviation, and is always positive. Its units are the same as those of the variate. The standard deviation is thus

$$\sigma = \sqrt{\frac{\sum\limits_{i=1}^{n} (x_i - \mu)^2}{n}} \tag{4-2}$$

For the simple case of the groups of observations given at the beginning of this chapter, the values of the standard deviation in the two cases are respectively:

$$\sigma_1 = \sqrt{\frac{(0.1)^2 + (0.1)^2}{3}} = \sqrt{0.0067} = 0.08 \text{ cm}$$

and

$$\sigma_2 = \sqrt{\frac{1^2 + 1^2}{3}} = \sqrt{\frac{2}{3}} = 0.8 \text{ cm}$$

Equation 4-2 is applicable when we are interested in the mean of a set of n items (specimens or observations), all of which have been determined; μ is then the true mean. In many cases, however, we actually test only a limited number of specimens out of a *population* (or a *universe*, the two terms being synonymous) of all those that could be tested. The same applies to taking a limited number of observations (e.g., temperature at intervals of time) when we are really interested in all the observations that could be made (in this case, an infinite number of determinations of temperature during the given time interval). Under such circumstances, the true or population mean μ is unknown, and we have only the mean of the actual observations $\bar{x}$, that is, the sample mean. We calculate the deviations from $\bar{x}$ and not from μ, and therefore put $(n - 1)$ instead of n in the denominator of the expression for the estimate of σ; the estimate is denoted by s to distinguish it from the true standard deviation σ. The reason for this correction of $\sqrt{n/(n - 1)}$, known as *Bessel's correction*,[2] is that the sum of squares of deviations has a minimum value when taken about the sample mean $\bar{x}$, and is therefore smaller than it would be if taken about the population mean (which is presumably different from $\bar{x}$). Thus, the estimate

---

[1] The quantity which varies and is being studied.
[2] Strictly speaking, Bessel's correction is applied to variance, and is equal to $n/(n - 1)$.

of σ is

$$s = \sqrt{\frac{\sum_{i=1}^{n}(x_i - \bar{x})^2}{n - 1}} \qquad (4\text{-}3)$$

Appendix A gives a proof of the above equation. Bessel's correction can, of course, be neglected when n is large.

It is important to appreciate the difference between Eq. 4-2 and 4-3, and to use the correct one, depending on whether we are interested in the standard deviation of the observations in hand (considered as a finite population) or in an estimate of the standard deviation of the population.

At this stage it may be convenient to introduce the concept of the number of *degrees of freedom*. This is the number of *independent* observations that can be hypothesized. In the case of the estimate of variance from a sample of size n only $(n - 1)$ values can be assigned arbitrarily; the nth value must be such that the mean of all values is $\bar{x}$. Thus, $(n - 1)$ is the number of degrees of freedom of the variance s^2.

On the other hand, if the true mean is known, every observation can be arbitrarily assigned, and in such a case the number of degrees of freedom is equal to the number of observations n.

The concept of degrees of freedom, which is of some difficulty, is discussed further in Chapter 12.

From Eq. 4-3 we can see that if only one observation is made, nothing can be said about its precision. Assume that the observation is x_1. Then the best estimate of the population mean is given by $\bar{x} = x_1$. Hence

$$s^2 = \frac{(\bar{x} - x_1)^2}{n - 1} = \frac{0}{0}$$

and the estimate of the population standard deviation is therefore indeterminate.

The calculation of the standard deviation by Eqs. 4-2 and 4-3 is laborious, especially when the mean involves more significant places than the variate and thus introduces fractional values. It is therefore more convenient to use another form of Eq. 4-2, namely:

$$\sigma = \sqrt{\frac{\sum x_i^2}{n} - \mu^2} = \frac{1}{n}\sqrt{n\sum x_i^2 - (\sum x_i)^2} \qquad (4\text{-}4)$$

Here σ^2 denotes the variance of the set of n items and we require s^2, the unbiased estimate of the population from which the n items are drawn.

It may be noted that we have now omitted the symbols indicating that the summation proceeds from $i = 1$ to $i = n$, as such a notation is cumbersome. We must remember, however, that these are the limits of our summation unless otherwise indicated. Equation 4-4 arises from the algebraic identity (working in terms of $\bar{x}$):

$$\sum(x_i - \bar{x})^2 = \sum x_i^2 - 2\bar{x}\sum x_i + n\bar{x}^2$$

But

$$\bar{x} = \frac{\Sigma x_i}{n} \quad \text{(by definition)}$$

Therefore

$$2\bar{x}\,\Sigma x_i = 2\bar{x}n\bar{x} = 2n\bar{x}^2$$

Hence

$$\Sigma(x_i - \bar{x})^2 = \Sigma x_i^2 - n\bar{x}^2$$

or

$$\Sigma(x_i - \bar{x})^2 = \Sigma x_i^2 - \frac{(\Sigma x_i)^2}{n}$$

The advantage of Eq. 4-4 is that we do not need to find the deviations $(x_i - \bar{x})$. The squares of the variate x_i^2 can be obtained rapidly from tables or by means of a calculating machine. The fundamental difference between Σx_i^2 and $(\Sigma x_i)^2$ must not be overlooked.

To obtain s, Bessel's correction is applied:

$$s = \sigma \sqrt{\frac{n}{n-1}} \tag{4-5}$$

SIMPLIFIED COMPUTATION OF STANDARD DEVIATION

Computations can be simplified without any loss in accuracy by a suitable reduction of data. Two rules are useful:

(a)   If a constant number is added to or subtracted from a set of numerical variates, their mean will increase or decrease by the same constant number, the standard deviation remaining unaffected.

(b)   If a set of numerical variates is multiplied or divided by a constant number, their mean and standard deviation are multiplied or divided by the same constant number.

Example. Let us consider the data on the strength of bricks, given in Table 2-2. To compute the standard deviation by Eq. 4-2, we first require the mean; this was quoted previously to be $\bar{x} = 999.8$ psi. We now compute the deviations $(x_i - \bar{x})$ and find their squares; a tabular form is convenient:

Observation	x_i	$\lvert x_i - \bar{x}\rvert$ [†]	$(x_i - \bar{x})^2$
1	270	729.8	532,608.04
2	460	539.8	291,384.04
3	570	429.8	184,728.04
.	.	.	.
.	.	.	.
.	.	.	.
269	1,630	630.2	397,152.04
270	2,010	1,010.2	1,020,504.04
$n = 270$		$\Sigma(x_i - \bar{x})^2 = 10,956,079.98$	

[†] The absolute value of the deviation is entered, since its sign is immaterial.

Thus, from Eq. 4-2

$$\sigma = \sqrt{\frac{10,956,080}{270}} = 201.44 \text{ psi}$$

Let us now find the solution using Eq. 4-4. We tabulate:

Observation	x_i	x_i^2
1	270	72,900
2	460	211,600
3	570	324,900
.	.	.
.	.	.
.	.	.
269	1,630	2,656,900
270	2,010	4,040,100
$n = 270$	$\Sigma\, x_i = 269,950$	$\Sigma\, x_i^2 = 280,855,900$

Thus

$$\Sigma\, x_i = \qquad\quad 269,950$$
$$(\Sigma\, x_i)^2 = 72,873,002,500$$

and

$$\Sigma\, x_i^2 = \qquad 280,855,900$$

Hence,

$$\sigma - \frac{1}{270} \times \sqrt{270 \times 280,855,900 - 72,873,002,500}$$

$$= 201.44 \text{ psi, as before}$$

We can now use the simplifications of rules (*a*) and (*b*). Since all values end in zero we can easily divide them by 10. To reduce the numerical values further, we can subtract 27 from all the values. (It is generally preferable to avoid negative values, such as would result from subtracting, say, 70 but there is nothing incorrect in doing so.) We can tabulate the computation as follows:

Observation	$X_i' = x_i/10 - 27$	$X_i'^2$
1	0	0
2	19	361
3	30	900
.	.	.
.	.	.
.	.	.
269	136	18,496
270	174	30,276
$n = 270$	$\Sigma X_i' = 19,705$	$\Sigma\, X_i'^2 = 1,547,659$

Thus $(\Sigma\, X_i')^2 = 388,287,025$

Hence, in terms of X'

$$\sigma_{X'} = \frac{1}{270} \times \sqrt{270 \times 1,547,659 - 388,287,025}$$

$$= 20.144$$

To allow for the division by 10 we have to multiply $\sigma_{X'}$ by 10; hence,

$$\sigma = 10 \times 20.144$$

$$= 201.44 \text{ psi, as before}$$

The decision on the amount of simplification is a matter for individual preference, but the advantage of Eq. 4-4 over Eq. 4-2 is great, especially when a calculating machine is used.

With data in a grouped-frequency form, a shorter, though approximate, computation of the standard deviation can be made. We assume that each observation is replaced by an observation at the class midpoint, so that

$$\sigma = \sqrt{\frac{\Sigma\, f_i (x_i' - \bar{x})^2}{n}} \tag{4-6}$$

where f_i is the frequency in the class interval and x_i' is the class midpoint. Following Eq. 4-4, the expression becomes

$$\sigma = \sqrt{\frac{\Sigma\, f_i x_i'^2 - \dfrac{(\Sigma\, f_i x_i')^2}{n}}{n}} \tag{4-7}$$

We can further replace x_i' by $X_i' = $ deviation from an arbitrary origin, measured in terms of class width w. Then

$$\sigma = w \sqrt{\frac{\Sigma\, f_i X_i'^2 - \dfrac{(\Sigma\, f_i X_i')^2}{n}}{n}} \tag{4-8}$$

As an example, let us apply this method of calculation of the standard deviation to the data of Table 3-1. Then

$$\sigma = w \sqrt{\frac{6,370 - \dfrac{(1,260)^2}{270}}{270}} = 1.347 w$$

Since the class width $w = 150$,

$$\sigma = 1.347 \times 150 = 202.05 \text{ psi}$$

The difference between this value and the accurate value of σ from Eq. 4-4 is small and for most purposes not significant.

MEAN DEVIATION

In some cases, instead of standard deviation, mean (absolute) deviation d_m is used; this is the mean of the absolute values of deviations:

$$d_m = \frac{\Sigma \mid x_i - \bar{x} \mid}{n} \tag{4-9}$$

The use of absolute values is necessary because the algebraic sum of deviations from the mean is, by definition of the mean, always equal to zero.

The usefulness of the mean deviation in statistical calculations is small, and practically no statistical methods of analysis involve its use. However, in the case of normal distribution there is a simple relation between the mean deviation and standard deviation; this is discussed in Chapter 10.

COEFFICIENT OF VARIATION

As mentioned before, the standard deviation is expressed in the same units as the original variate x_i, but for many purposes it is convenient to express the dispersion of results on a percentage basis, i.e., in relative rather than absolute terms. To achieve this we take the ratio of the standard deviation to the mean, and define the coefficient of variation V as:

$$V = \frac{\sigma}{\bar{x}} \times 100 \tag{4-10}$$

It is a dimensionless quantity.

For the observations on the strength of bricks used in the preceding example, the coefficient of variation is

$$V = \frac{201.4}{1000} \times 100 = 20.14 \text{ percent}$$

While the coefficient of variation is extremely useful in giving a value which is independent of the units employed, it may sometimes be meaningless. This is the case when the origin of measurement is not uniquely fixed; for example, if we measure temperature and find the mean to be 10°C and the standard deviation 1°C, we could report the coefficient of variation as $(1/10) \times 100 = 10$ percent. If, however, the measurements were converted to degrees Fahrenheit, we would have a mean of 50°F and a standard deviation of 1.8°F. One could thus report a coefficient of variation of $(1.8/50) \times 100 = 3.6$ percent. The absurdity of these calculations is obvious, and we would have done well to have reported our results in terms of standard deviation.

RANGE

Range is a simple measure of dispersion, very rapid to compute as it is merely the difference between the highest and the lowest observations.

However, because of this dependence on two values only, range is a rather crude measure of dispersion, and is an efficient statistic[3] when we deal with small samples only.

It is important to note that the larger the number of observations in a sample the more likely it is that values remote from the mean will be encountered. Thus range increases with the sample size. If this is not remembered and the ranges of samples of different sizes are compared indiscriminately, misleading results are obtained.

The range and the standard deviation are related to one another, so that for any given number of observations n, an estimate of the standard deviation s of the underlying population can be obtained from the mean value of sample range $\bar{R}$:

$$s = \bar{R} \times d \qquad (4\text{-}11)$$

This expression is valid when the variate is normally distributed,[4] and the estimate s becomes less accurate the more the distribution departs from normality.

The values of d are given in Table A-1. It may be observed that for n between 3 and 12, d varies approximately as $1/\sqrt{n}$.

We must remember that the estimate of the standard deviation given by Eq. 4-11 is no more than an approximation and should be used only when the average range $\bar{R}$ is obtained from a reasonably large number of samples

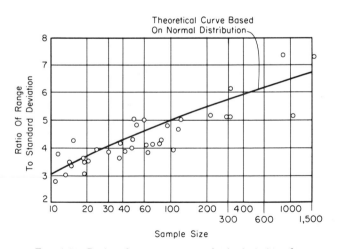

Fig. 4-1. Ratio of range to standard deviation for samples of different sizes; tests on concrete compression cubes. (From P. J. F. Wright, "Variations in the Strength of Portland Cement," *Magazine of Concrete Research*, Vol. 10, no. 30, November 1958, pp. 123–132.)

---

[3] A value which characterizes the data.

[4] For a definition of the normal distribution, see Chapter 9.

(say, not less than 10) all of the same size. For the same total number of observations the estimate is considerably more accurate when the samples are many and small, rather than few and large.

If a large number of observations has been made without subdivision into samples, a breakdown of the observations into equal subgroups can be achieved by random sampling. The range R of each subgroup is then calculated, and, hence, the mean value of range $\bar{R}$. This is then multiplied by the coefficient d from Table A-1, corresponding to the number of observations in a subgroup, and hence an estimate of the standard deviation is obtained. This procedure is illustrated by the following example.

Example. The modulus of rupture (in psi) was determined on 52 concrete test beams. By random selection the observations were arranged in 13 subgroups, as shown below.

Subgroup	Observations, psi	Range R
1	565—580—585—542	43
2	525—588—570—575	63
3	593—607—653—545	108
4	583—582—500—588	88
5	620—599—575—578	45
6	683—627—600—643	83
7	590—575—655—592	80
8	652—627—578—588	74
9	593—597—528—600	72
10	575—588—590—566	24
11	573—572—588—555	33
12	603—568—617—573	49
13	632—582—595—577	55
Total		$\Sigma R = 817$

From K. E. C. Nielsen, "Calculation of Statistical Data," *Beton-Teknik* (Copenhagen), vol. 3, No. 24, 1958, p. 170.

The value of range for each subgroup is shown in the right-hand column. Hence, the mean value of range is

$$\bar{R} = \frac{817}{13} = 62.8$$

For $n = 4$, Table A-1 gives $d = 0.4857$. Using Eq. 4-11, the standard deviation is estimated to be $s = 62.8 \times 0.4857 = 30.5$ psi.

A direct calculation of s using Eq. 4-3 gives $s = 33.4$ psi. The difference may for some purposes not be important, while the saving in computational effort is considerable. A comparison of experimental results with the theoretical relation between range and standard deviation is shown in Fig. 4-1 for tests on the compressive strength of concrete. (It has been shown that the compressive strength of concrete sensibly follows a normal distribution.[5])

[5] A. M. Neville, "Some Aspects of the Strength of Concrete," *Civil Engineering* (London), vol. 54 (Oct.–Dec., 1959).

SOLVED PROBLEMS

4-1. To obtain the shrinkage limit of a particular clay, the moisture content in percent of dry weight was determined on 20 specimens with the following results:

$$
\begin{array}{cccccccccc}
15.2 & 16.7 & 15.8 & 14.6 & 18.1 & 17.2 & 18.0 & 15.9 & 16.1 & 16.9 \\
14.8 & 17.6 & 18.2 & 16.9 & 17.3 & 16.5 & 15.6 & 16.7 & 15.8 & 18.2
\end{array}
$$

(a) Calculate the mean and standard deviation by the long method.
(b) Calculate the mean and standard deviation using an arbitrary origin.
Solution:

(a) Mean $= \bar{x} = \dfrac{\Sigma x}{n}$

$$
= \frac{15.2 + 16.7 + \cdots + 16.9 + 14.8 + 17.6 + \cdots + 18.2}{20}
$$

$$
= \frac{332.1}{20}
$$

$$
= 16.605
$$

The standard deviation of the population of clay samples is estimated by

$$
s = \sqrt{\frac{\Sigma x^2 - \dfrac{(\Sigma x)^2}{n}}{n - 1}}
$$

Now

$$
\Sigma x^2 = 15.2^2 + 16.7^2 + \cdots + 18.2^2 = 5{,}538.13
$$

and

$$
(\Sigma x)^2 = (332.1)^2 = 110{,}290.41
$$

Hence

$$
s = \sqrt{\frac{5{,}538.13 - \dfrac{110{,}290.41}{20}}{19}}
$$

$$
= \sqrt{\frac{23.61}{19}}
$$

$$
= 1.11
$$

(b) Let the arbitrary origin $= 16$. Then, in tabular form:

x_i	Deviation from arbitrary origin X_i'		$X_i'^2$
	Negative	Positive	
15.2	0.8		0.64
16.7		0.7	0.49
15.8	0.2		0.04
14.6	1.4		1.96
18.1		2.1	4.41
17.2		1.2	1.44

continued

x_i	Deviation from arbitrary origin X_i'		$X_i'^2$
	Negative	Positive	
18.0		2.0	4.00
15.9	0.1		0.01
16.1		0.1	0.01
16.9		0.9	0.81
14.8	1.2		1.44
17.6		1.6	2.56
18.2		2.2	4.84
16.9		0.9	0.81
17.3		1.3	1.69
16.5		0.5	0.25
15.6	0.4		0.16
16.7		0.7	0.49
15.8	0.2		0.04
18.2		2.2	4.84
Totals	$\Sigma X_i' = -4.3$	$+$ $\quad$ $16.4 = 12.1$	$\Sigma X_i'^2 = 30.93$

Therefore

$$\text{Mean} = \bar{x} = 16 + \frac{\Sigma X_i'}{n}$$

$$= 16 + \frac{12.1}{20}$$

$$= 16.605$$

$$\text{Standard deviation} = s = \sqrt{\frac{\Sigma X'^2 - \frac{(\Sigma X')^2}{n}}{n-1}} = \sqrt{\frac{30.93 - \frac{(12.1)^2}{20}}{19}}$$

$$= \sqrt{1.243}$$

$$s = 1.11$$

4-2. Calculate the range and the standard deviation of the data given in Solved Problem 3-1. If the permissible tensile stress allowed in design is equal to the mean less 2.33 times the standard deviation, calculate this allowable stress and indicate whether any of the 303 briquettes fell below this stress. If this criterion for allowable stress is used, show that when the coefficient of variation $V = 10$ percent the maximum allowable design tensile stress $= 0.77 \times$ mean stress.

Solution:

Range $= 500 - 200 = 300$ psi. For grouped data

$$s = w \sqrt{\frac{\Sigma f_i X_i'^2 - \frac{(\Sigma f_i X_i')^2}{n}}{n-1}}$$

From the values in the table for Solved Problem 3-1, we have:

$$s = w \sqrt{\frac{4{,}679 - \frac{(1{,}067)^2}{303}}{302}} = 1.75 \times \text{class width}$$

$$= 1.75 \times 30 = 52.5 \text{ psi}$$

Allowable tensile stress in design $= 321 - 2.33 \times 52.5 = 199$ psi. Inspection of the above mentioned table will show that no briquette had a tensile strength below 199 psi.

Now the maximum allowable design tensile stress $= \bar{x} - 2.33s$. But

$$V = \frac{s}{\bar{x}}$$

Thus

$$s = V\bar{x}$$

Hence maximum allowable design tensile stress

$$= \bar{x} - 2.33 V\bar{x}$$
$$= (1 - 2.33 \times 0.10)\bar{x}$$
$$= 0.77\bar{x} \text{ (approximately)}, \quad \text{for} \quad V = 0.10$$

PROBLEMS

4-1. The following measurements (in lb) were obtained from a test on the tensile strength of rubber samples:

1,419	1,410	1,410
1,403	1,396	1,389
1,400	1,380	1,422

Calculate the mean and the estimated standard deviation of the tensile strength of the rubber from which the samples were drawn. What is the range?

4-2. Determine the variance, standard deviation, and coefficient of variation of the distribution in Prob. 3-1. Can you estimate the standard deviation from the range in this case? State the reason.

4-3. Determine the range of the data in Prob. 3-2. Also find the standard deviation of the diameters of the ball bearings from (*a*) the ungrouped data, and (*b*) the frequency table.

What is the coefficient of variation in each case?

By random selection, arrange the data in 10 subgroups, and hence estimate the standard deviation from the mean range. Compare this value with the values obtained in (*a*) and (*b*).

4-4. Calculate the estimate of the standard deviation of the population of radio tubes in Prob. 2-3. Determine the variance and the coefficient of variation of the tubes.

4-5. In order to determine the hardness of concrete in a shell roof the roof area was divided into 64 equal parts.[6] The average of 10 measurements of hardness (sclerometer readings) in each part is given on page 39 for all 64 parts.

---

[6] "Détermination de la Dispersion des Valeurs de la Résistance du Béton en Place au Moyen du Scléromètre," *Bulletin du Ciment*, No. 10 (Switzerland, Oct. 1962).

	1	2	3	4	5	6	7	8
A	49.7	52.2	55.9	57.4	59.5	56.5	55.4	55.2
B	52.0	56.2	56.2	56.8	54.8	55.6	53.5	51.2
C	58.1	52.3	55.4	49.6	51.2	50.6	51.0	50.9
D	53.8	56.6	54.1	55.7	54.2	53.4	50.9	54.6
E	53.0	54.6	55.3	54.3	56.8	50.6	55.7	55.2
F	57.7	55.6	52.7	53.8	53.7	56.4	53.5	52.3
G	52.4	55.2	51.4	49.4	50.5	56.3	52.4	55.2
H	54.9	52.3	53.9	55.4	51.6	57.1	52.4	59.4

The individual values of hardness readings in 8 parts were as follows:

Point	Individual values of hardness										Mean value	Standard deviation
A 1	48	52	50	45	45	44	49	54	55	55	49.7	4.21
B 1	56	54	52	51	52	52	52	50	50	51	52.0	1.82
C 1	55	61	61	57	56	56	57	60	60	58	58.1	2.23
D 1	54	56	57	58	55	54	52	50	50	52	53.8	2.78
E 1	52	50	48	57	50	53	59	58	49	54	53.0	3.92
F 1	61	59	56	57	57	57	55	58	58	59	57.7	1.70
G 1	55	53	56	51	52	53	51	50	55	48	52.4	2.50
H 1	52	56	52	58	59	60	54	55	51	52	54.9	3.25

(*a*) Find the root-mean-square value of the standard deviation in the eight parts (No. 1). Hence estimate the testing error (the rms value divided by the square root of the number of values, namely 8). [HINT: The individual readings need not be used.]

(*b*) Find the standard deviation of the hardness readings for the entire roof, exclusive of the testing error (the square root of the difference between the variance of the 64 average values and the square of the testing error).

4-6. On a construction job it was required to make concrete with a specified minimum compressive strength of 2,500 psi. The minimum was understood to be a value exceeded by not less than 96 percent of test results. The values of strength of 50 test cubes are given below.[7]

Calculate the mean strength, range, mean deviation, standard deviation, and coefficient of variation. Find whether the specification requirements are satisfied.

Cube' No.	Strength, psi		Cube No.	Strength, psi
1	3,240		4	3,410
2	2,640		5	2,870
3	3,590		6	3,920

(continued)

[7] Cement and Concrete Association: Technical Memorandum No. 8. (London, April 1960).

Cube No.	Strength, psi	Cube No.	Strength, psi
7	3,750	29	3,400
8	4,230	30	2,620
9	3,500	31	3,400
10	3,530	32	3,330
11	3,150	33	3,430
12	3,400	34	3,680
13	3,380	35	3,220
14	4,110	36	2,580
15	3,400	37	4,060
16	2,900	38	4,180
17	3,780	39	3,200
18	2,200	40	2,910
19	2,900	41	3,020
20	3,300	42	3,330
21	4,640	43	4,090
22	3,720	44	3,330
23	3,020	45	4,410
24	3,360	46	3,640
25	3,900	47	3,590
26	3,300	48	2,880
27	3,200	49	2,640
28	3,080	50	3,640

4-7. The following are the strengths of concrete specimens,[8] made two at a time over a period of two months on a construction site:

Test No.	28-day strength, psi		Test No.	28-day strength, psi	
	Cylinder No. 1	Cylinder No. 2		Cylinder No. 1	Cylinder No. 2
1	3,600	3,190	16	3,150	2,960
2	3,560	3,550	17	2,930	2,700
3	3,420	3,670	18	3,610	3,210
4	2,920	3,300	19	4,440	4,000
5	3,330	3,190	20	3,870	3,770
6	3,750	3,400	21	4,390	3,600
7	4,030	3,920	22	3,560	3,790
8	4,010	3,540	23	3,040	3,400
9	3,690	3,650	24	3,410	3,500
10	2,830	3,120	25	2,780	3,180
11	2,950	3,450	26	3,090	3,300
12	3,040	3,200	27	3,210	3,310
13	3,210	2,900	28	3,490	3,300
14	3,810	3,190	29	2,890	3,040
15	3,950	3,730	30	3,810	3,500

(continued)

[8]"Evaluation of Compression Test Results of Field Concrete," *Journal of American Concrete Institute*, Vol. 52 (Nov. 1955), p. 255.

	28-day strength, psi				28-day strength, psi	
Test No.	Cylinder No. 1	Cylinder No. 2	Test No.	Cylinder No. 1	Cylinder No. 2
31	3,830	3,800	39	3,370	3,600
32	4,590	4,370	40	4,210	3,860
33	3,600	3,700	41	3,800	3,200
			42	3,000	3,050
34	3,510	3,260	43	3,530	3,340
35	3,350	3,840			
36	3,020	3,480	44	3,950	3,250
37	3,150	2,940	45	3,590	3,440
38	2,510	2,820	46	3,910	3,760

Find the mean strength, standard deviation, and coefficient of variation, working in terms of mean test values.

4-8. For the data of Prob. 4-7, estimate the standard deviation from the mean range.

4-9. For the data of Prob. 4-7, determine the value of strength exceeded by 90 percent of tests (a "test" is the average of two specimens).

chapter 5

Permutations, Combinations, and Probability

The purpose of this chapter is to present briefly information on some simple concepts extensively used in statistical computations. The first two topics are undoubtedly familiar to the majority of readers, but for the sake of presenting a complete picture brief notes on permutations and combinations will be given.

PERMUTATIONS

The number of permutations of n different items is the number of different arrangements in which these items can be placed. We can take all n items every time, or r $(r < n)$ items at a time. Not only their identity but also the order in which the items are arranged is significant.

We write the number of permutations as $_nP_r$, n being the number of items available, and r the number chosen at a time. Thus if all items are chosen every time, the number of permutations is $_nP_n$.

In the general case we have r places to fill with n items to choose from, so that

the first place can be filled in n ways,

the second place can be filled in $n - 1$ ways,

the third place can be filled in $n - 2$ ways,

$$\cdot \qquad \cdot \qquad \cdot \qquad \cdot \qquad \cdot \qquad \cdot$$
$$\cdot \qquad \cdot \qquad \cdot \qquad \cdot \qquad \cdot \qquad \cdot$$
$$\cdot \qquad \cdot \qquad \cdot \qquad \cdot \qquad \cdot \qquad \cdot$$

the rth place can be filled in $n - r + 1$ ways.

We now apply a fundamental principle which states that if one selection can be made in p ways and if, after this selection has been made, the second selection can be made in q ways, the two selections together can be made in pq ways. Using this principle in succession, the number of permutations is

$$_nP_r = n(n-1)(n-2) \cdots (n-r+1)$$

$$= \frac{n!}{(n-r)!} \tag{5-1}$$

in which $n!$ is the symbol for factorial $n = 1 \times 2 \times 3 \times \cdots (n-1)n$. When $r = n$,

$$_nP_n = n! \tag{5-2}$$

since by definition $0! = 1$.

Example. How many three-digit numbers can be formed from the numbers 1, 2, 3, 4, 5 if each number can be repeated?

The first place can be filled in 5 ways; the second place can also be filled in 5 ways; and so can the third place. Hence we can form

$$5 \times 5 \times 5 = 125 \text{ different numbers}$$

Example. How many four-digit numbers can be formed from the numbers 1 to 9? There is no provision for repeating any number. We can thus use the standard expression with $n = 9$ and $r = 4$:

$$_nP_r = \frac{n!}{(n-r)!} = \frac{9!}{5!} = 9 \times 8 \times 7 \times 6 = 3,024 \text{ numbers}$$

Example. A product is coded by three letters and two numbers, the letters preceding the numbers. Only the letters A and B and the numbers 1 to 6 can be used. How many different code "numbers" are possible?

Consider the letters:

Each can appear as A or B, that is, in 2 ways

Therefore,

3 letters can be arranged in $2 \times 2 \times 2 = 8$ ways

Consider the numbers:

Each can appear as 1 or 2 or ... 6, that is, in 6 ways

Therefore,

2 numbers can be arranged in $6 \times 6 = 36$ ways

Thus the total number of code "numbers" is $8 \times 36 = 288$.

Consider now the permutation of n items taken all at a time, when the n items consist of r_1 alike, r_2 alike, ..., r_k alike, so that $r_1 + r_2 + \cdots + r_k = n$. The number of permutations is then

$$P = \frac{n!}{r_1! r_2! \ldots r_k!} \tag{5-3}$$

Example. How many different patterns (in a single row) can be made with 3 yellow tabs, 2 red ones, and 7 green ones?
We have

$$n = 3 + 2 + 7 = 12$$

From Eq. 5-3,

$$P = \frac{12!}{3! \times 2! \times 7!} = 7,920$$

COMBINATIONS

The number of combinations of n different items is the number of different selections of r items each, without reference to the order or arrangement of the items in the group.   This disregard of arrangement distinguishes combinations from permutations.

The reason that r items can be arranged in $r!$ ways is that:

the first place can be filled in r ways,
the second place can be filled in $r - 1$ ways,
the third place can be filled in $r - 2$ ways,

.   .   .   .   .

.   .   .   .   .

.   .   .   .   .

the last can be filled in 1 way,

so that r places can be filled in $r(r - 1)(r - 2) \ldots 1 = r!$ ways.

Thus, the number of combinations of r items from n items, denoted by $_nC_r$ or $\binom{n}{r}$, is $r!$ times smaller than the number of permutations. Hence,

$$_nC_r = \frac{_nP_r}{r!} = \frac{n!}{(n - r)!\,r!} \tag{5-4}$$

It follows from symmetry that

$$_nC_r = {_nC_{n-r}} \tag{5-5}$$

The use of this identity may save time in computations.

Example. In how may ways can a team of 9 be selected from 12 people?

This is evidently a problem of selection and not of arrangement, as the assignment of positions is not considered. We use, therefore, Eq. 5-4 with $n = 12$ and $r = 9$

$$_nC_r = \frac{n!}{r!\,(n - r)!} = \frac{12!}{9! \times 3!} = \frac{12 \times 11 \times 10}{2 \times 3} = 220$$

Example. From 5 men and 4 women, in how many ways can we select a group of 3 men and 2 women?

(*a*) We can select 3 men from 5 men in $_5C_3$ ways.

(*b*) We can select 2 women from 4 women in $_4C_2$ ways.

By the fundamental principle of selections we can do (*a*) and (*b*) in $_5C_3 \times _4C_2$ ways. Thus the number of possible selections is

$$\frac{5 \times 4}{2} \times \frac{4 \times 3}{2} = 60$$

Example. From 6 men and 5 women, how many committees of 8 members can be formed when each committee is to contain at least 3 women?

The conditions of the problem are satisfied if a committee contains

5 men and 3 women	selected in $_6C_5 \times _5C_3$ ways
4 men and 4 women	selected in $_6C_4 \times _5C_4$ ways
3 men and 5 women	selected in $_6C_3 \times _5C_5$ ways

The number of possible committees is thus:

$$_6C_5 \times _5C_3 + _6C_4 \times _5C_4 + _6C_3 \times _5C_5 = 155$$

It frequently happens that a problem involves both a selection and an arrangement with a limitation upon either or both. A safe procedure is to deal first with the selections (combinations) and then with the arrangements (permutations).

Example. How many lineups are possible in choosing a hockey team composed of 4 seniors and 2 juniors from 8 seniors and 7 juniors if any man can be used in any position?

4 seniors can be selected in $_8C_4$ ways

2 juniors can be selected in $_7C_2$ ways

Hence a team of players can be selected in $_8C_4 \times _7C_2$ ways. Any one set of 6 men can be arranged in 6! ways. Thus, the total number of possible lineups is $_8C_4 \times _7C_2 \times 6! = 1,058,400$.

Example. Suppose that in the last example any chosen team had to include a certain senior player for center and a certain junior player as a goal keeper. How many lineups are then possible?

When a particular senior player is always included in a team, the problem is to find the number of combinations of 3 seniors from the remaining 7 seniors, and with regard to juniors, to find the number of combinations of 1 junior from the remaining 6 juniors. Thus

3 seniors can be selected in $_7C_3$ ways

1 junior can be selected in $_6C_1$ ways

Hence a team of players can be selected in $_7C_3 \times _6C_1$ ways.

Since the positions of goal and center are already assigned, the remaining four positions in any one team can be filled in 4! ways. Thus the total number of possible lineups is $_7C_3 \times {}_6C_1 \times 4! = 5,040$.

It is important to observe that $_nC_r$ is the coefficient of the $(r + 1)$th term in the binomial expression $(a + b)^n$, whose expansion is:

$$(a + b)^n = a^n + na^{n-1}b + \frac{n(n - 1)}{2!} a^{n-2}b^2 + \cdots$$

$$+ \frac{n(n - 1) \cdots (n - r + 1)}{r!} a^{n-r}b^r + \cdots + b^n \qquad (5\text{-}6)$$

and can be conveniently written as:

$$(a + b)^n = a^n + {}_nC_1 a^{n-1}b + {}_nC_2 a^{n-2}b^2 + \cdots + {}_nC_r a^{n-r}b^r + \cdots + b^n$$

or

$$(a + b)^n = \sum_{r=0}^{n} {}_nC_r a^{n-r}b^r \qquad (5\text{-}7)$$

provided that we define $_nC_0 = 1$.

The use of binomial coefficients is considered again in Chapter 7.

PROBABILITY

Let us denote the occurrence of a certain event as success and its non-occurrence as failure. If we consider all the possible (imaginable) arrangements (or trials), and also the arrangements corresponding to success, then the ratio of the latter to the former defines the probability of success. All the arrangements considered must be mutually exclusive and equally likely, and, as stated before, exhaustive. If there are n possible arrangements, and success occurs in p cases, the probability of success is p/n, and the probability of failure is $1 - (p/n)$. Probability is thus expressed as a number not greater than 1. A value of unity denotes a certainty of success, and a value of zero means an impossibility of success.

Strictly speaking, we should distinguish two types of probability. In the first, probability of an event is established solely by the definition of the system, e.g., the probability of obtaining a given number on rolling a die is $\frac{1}{6}$. This is an *a priori* probability. In many other cases we are concerned with an *empirical* probability, which is based solely on experience, for example, on the past records of deaths, accidents, and so on. Engineering statistics are frequently concerned with a combination of both types of probabilities.

There are two rules of probability which are of fundamental importance:

(a) The probability of occurrence of several of a number of *independent* and *mutually exclusive* events is the sum of the probabilities of the separate events. An event is considered independent if its occurrence does not affect the probability of occurrence of other events. Events are said to be mutually exclusive if only one of them can occur at a time (e.g., a person in a sample can be either male or female but not both).

For example, in tossing a die, the probability of throwing a 3 *or* 6 is equal to the probability of throwing 3 plus the probability of throwing 6, that is, it is equal to

$$\frac{1}{6} + \frac{1}{6} = \frac{1}{3}$$

We may note that the sum of the probabilities of *all* the possible events is always 1.

(*b*) The probability of a *simultaneous* occurrence of a number of *independent* events is the product of the separate probabilities.

For example, in tossing two dice, the probability of throwing a double 6 is equal to the probability of throwing a 6 times the probability of throwing a 6, that is, it is equal to

$$\frac{1}{6} \times \frac{1}{6} = \frac{1}{36}$$

Example. Thirty high-strength bolts became mixed by mistake with 25 ordinary bolts, and it was not possible to tell them apart from appearance. If two bolts are drawn in succession, what is the probability that one of them is of the high-strength type and the other one is ordinary?

In this problem, the mutually exclusive events are:

(*a*) Drawing a high-strength bolt on the first trial and an ordinary one on the second.

(*b*) Drawing an ordinary bolt on the first trial and a high-strength one on the second.

Now the probability of (*a*) is

$$\frac{30}{55} \times \frac{25}{54} = \frac{25}{99}$$

and the probability of (*b*) is

$$\frac{25}{55} \times \frac{30}{54} = \frac{25}{99}$$

The probability of either (*a*) or (*b*) is the sum of the two probabilities:

$$\frac{25}{99} + \frac{25}{99} = \frac{50}{99}$$

SOLVED PROBLEMS

5-1. How many squads of 6 men can be selected from 60 men?

Solution:
This is a problem in combinations. Hence

$$_{60}C_6 = \frac{60!}{6!\,54!} = \frac{60 \times 59 \times 58 \times 57 \times 56 \times 55}{2 \times 3 \times 4 \times 5 \times 6} = 50{,}063{,}860 \text{ squads}$$

5-2. How many straight lines are determined by 10 points, no three of which are in the same straight line?

Solution:
The number of combinations of 2 points for a straight line from 10 points is:

$$_{10}C_2 = \frac{10!}{2!\,8!} = \frac{10 \times 9}{2} = 45 \text{ lines}$$

5-3. From 10 items, in how many ways can a selection of 6 be made:
(*a*)   when a specified item is always included;
(*b*)   when a specified item is always excluded?

Solution:
(*a*)   When a specified item is always included in the selection of 6 items, the problem is to find the number of combinations of 5 items from the remaining 9 items.
Hence

$$_9C_5 = \frac{9!}{5!\,4!} = \frac{9 \times 8 \times 7 \times 6}{2 \times 3 \times 4} = 126 \text{ selections of 6 items}$$

(*b*)   When a specified item is always excluded, the problem is to find the number of combinations of 6 items from the 9 remaining items. Hence,

$$_9C_6 = \frac{9!}{6!\,3!} = \frac{9 \times 8 \times 7}{2 \times 3} = 84 \text{ selections of 6 items}$$

5-4. A committee of 7 is to be chosen from 8 Canadians and 5 Americans. In how many ways can a committee be chosen if it is to contain:
(*a*)   just four Canadians;
(*b*)   at least four Canadians?

Solution:
(*a*)   To choose just 4 Canadians from 8 we have $_8C_4$ ways. Since there are only 3 positions remaining to be filled by the Americans, the number of ways in which 3 Americans can be selected from 5 is $_5C_3$.
Then the number of ways of selecting a committee of 7 is

$$_8C_4 \times {_5C_3} = \frac{8 \times 7 \times 6 \times 5}{2 \times 3 \times 4} \times \frac{5 \times 4}{2} = 700 \text{ ways}$$

(*b*)   When the committee is to include at least four Canadians, there are several possibilities:

Americans	Canadians	Number of ways
3	4	$_5C_3 \times {_8}C_4 = 700$
2	5	$_5C_2 \times {_8}C_5 = 560$
1	6	$_5C_1 \times {_8}C_6 = 140$
0	7	$_5C_0 \times {_8}C_7 = 8$
		Total $= 1{,}408$ ways

5-5. If $_nP_r = 110$ and $_nC_r = 55$, find n and r.

Solution:

$$_nP_r = \frac{n!}{(n-r)!}$$

and

$$_nC_r = \frac{n!}{r!\,(n-r)!}$$

Therefore,

$$\frac{_nP_r}{_nC_r} = r! = 2; \quad \text{hence } r = 2$$

Now

$$_nP_r = \frac{n!}{(n-r)!} = \frac{n!}{(n-2)!} = 110$$

But

$$\frac{n!}{(n-2)!} = n(n-1) = 110$$

Therefore,

$$n^2 - n - 110 = 0 \quad \text{or} \quad (n-11)(n+10) = 0$$

Hence

$$n = -10 \text{ (not possible)} \quad \text{or} \quad n = 11$$

Thus,

$$r = 2 \quad \text{and} \quad n = 11$$

5-6. (*a*) In how many ways can 6 soldiers stand in a line so that two soldiers in particular will not be next to one another?

(*b*) Show that

$$(1) \quad _nC_r + {_n}C_{r-1} = {_{n+1}}C_r$$

and

$$(2) \quad _{n+2}C_{r+1} = {_n}C_{r+1} + 2{_n}C_r + {_n}C_{r-1}$$

(*c*) A university senate is composed of 50 staff members of whom 6 are engineers. In how many ways can a committee of 10 be chosen so as to contain at least 4 engineers?

Solution:

(*a*) Let us consider five soldiers. These can be arranged in $n! = 5!$ ways. For each arrangement of these 5 soldiers, the sixth one can stand in four different locations without being adjacent to the particular soldier in question (see Fig. 5-1). Therefore,

$$\text{Total number of ways} = 4 \times 5! = 480$$

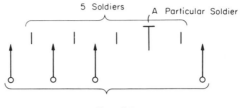

FIG. 5-1

(*b*) (1) Expanding the left-hand side we have:

$$_nC_r + {}_nC_{r-1} = \frac{n!}{r!\,(n-r)!} + \frac{n!}{(r-1)!\,(n-r+1)!}$$

$$= \frac{n!\,(n-r+1)}{r!\,(n-r+1)!} + \frac{n!\,r}{r!\,(n-r+1)!}$$

$$= \frac{n!\,(n+1)}{r!\,(n-r+1)!}$$

Therefore,

$$_nC_r + {}_nC_{r-1} = \frac{(n+1)!}{r!\,(n-r+1)!}$$

But

$$_{n+1}C_r = \frac{(n+1)!}{r!\,(n+1-r)!}$$

Thus

$$_nC_r + {}_nC_{r-1} = {}_{n+1}C_r$$

(2) Expanding the right-hand side of the given identity, we have:

$$_nC_{r+1} + 2{}_nC_r + {}_nC_{r-1} = \frac{n!}{(r+1)!\,(n-r-1)!}$$

$$+ \frac{2n!}{r!\,(n-r)!} + \frac{n!}{(r-1)!\,(n-r+1)!}$$

$$= \frac{n!\,[(n-r)(n-r+1) + 2(r+1)(n-r+1) + r(r+1)]}{(r+1)!\,(n-r+1)!}$$

$$= \frac{n!\,(n+1)(n+2)}{(r+1)!\,(n-r+1)!}$$

$$= \frac{(n+2)!}{(r+1)!\,(n-r+1)!}$$

But

$$_{n+2}C_{r+1} = \frac{(n+2)!}{(r+1)!\,(n+2-r-1)!} = \frac{(n+2)!}{(r+1)!\,(n-r+1)!}$$

Thus the two sides of the identity are equivalent.

(*c*)   A committee of 10 can be chosen so that there are either 4, 5, or 6 engineers on it. Hence, the number of possible selections is

$$(_6C_4 \times {}_{44}C_6) + (_6C_5 \times {}_{44}C_5) + (_6C_6 \times {}_{44}C_4)$$

$$= \frac{6!}{4!2!} \times \frac{44!}{6!38!} + \frac{6!}{5!1!} \times \frac{44!}{5!39!} + \frac{6!}{6!0!} \times \frac{44!}{4!40!}$$

$$= 112{,}537{,}579 \text{ ways (an adequate number even for academics)}$$

PROBLEMS

5-1.   From a box containing 20 balls, one-half of them white, one-half black, four balls are drawn at random. What is the probability of obtaining (*a*) all of them of the same color; (*b*) all of them black; (*c*) all of them black if each ball is replaced before the next one is drawn?

5-2.   In dealing a pack of 52 cards to four players, what is the probability of one of them obtaining 13 cards of a given suit?

5-3.   If one-quarter of the dancers are eliminated after each dance, the elimination being random, what is the mathematical probability of successfully completing five consecutive dances?

5-4.   A fair die is tossed twice. Find (*a*) the probability of a 3 turning up at least once, (*b*) the probability of getting a 3, 4, or 5 on the first toss and 1, 2, 3, or 6 on the second toss.

5-5.   In a classroom it was required to seat 7 men students and 6 women students in a row so that the women occupy the even places. How many such arrangements are possible?

5-6.   In the "football pools" operated in England one has to predict the result of 14 matches, there being three possible results of each match (home win, away win, draw). How many entries would you have to submit in order to make sure that the winning entry is included?

5-7.   A system has two components, *A* and *B*. If the probability of *A* failing is 0.7 and the probability of *B* failing is 0.8, what is the probability of (*a*) the system remaining sound; (*b*) both components failing; (*c*) either component failing?

chapter 6

Samples: Accuracy of the Mean

The previous chapter has interrupted our considerations of distributions, but the concepts introduced in it are necessary for the calculations to follow.

SAMPLING

We shall now consider more fully some of the properties of samples. Sampling is resorted to because testing the entire population is rarely practicable, especially in destructive tests or in tests involving a large· expense or effort. But the sample must be representative of the population from which it is drawn, and must, therefore, be drawn in a random manner—which means that every member of the population has an equal chance of being drawn in every trial.[1] How this is done in practice depends on the problem in hand, but the requirement of randomness should always be borne in mind.

We use the word *sample* in a very broad sense, meaning the observations (of any type) that have been made, while the term *population* refers to all the observations that could be made. Samples are tested for the purpose of making inferences about properties of the population, and the investigator must be clear what population he is interested in; for example, a particular batch of concrete, or all concrete placed in a given day, or all concrete in a given structure.

Tests on a sample can give results which are beyond doubt only so far as the sample itself is concerned. With respect to the underlying population a sampling investigation can give results only in terms of probability, and the confidence which we can have in our answers depends on the size of the sample.

MEAN OF SAMPLE MEANS

In Chapter 4 we showed how an estimate of the population variance can be made from the sample variance; we shall now consider the determination of the population mean from the sampling mean.

---

[1] The qualification "in every trial" precludes the use of methods such as choosing randomly a name in a list, and then taking every tenth name thereafter.

A problem that sometimes arises in the collection of data in practice is to decide how many observations to make.

Specifically, if we are taking measurements of what is presumed to be the same unique quantity, and if we are satisfied to take the mean of the observations as the appropriate single measure, how is the accuracy increased, if at all, as the number of observations is increased? For example, suppose that a certain length has been measured by four people who have found it to be: 100 ft 10 in., 100 ft 0 in., 99 ft 7 in., and 100 ft 3 in. The mean is 100 ft 2 in. Suppose that five more measurements are made by equally skilled people: 100 ft 1 in., 99 ft 9 in., 99 ft 7 in., 100 ft 5 in., 100 ft 3 in. The mean of all 9 measurements is 100 ft 1 in. instead of 100 ft 2 in. for the first four measurements. We can now ask: Is 100 ft 1 in., a more accurate result than 100 ft 2 in.? If so, how much more accurate can we expect it to be?

We should intuitively expect a larger sample to yield a more accurate result, but in order to have a quantitive appreciation, we have to determine how the representative nature of a sample improves with the sample size.

Suppose that we have a population of N observations from which we draw samples, each of n observations. We find the mean of each sample:

$$\bar{x} = \frac{x_1 + x_2 + \cdots + x_n}{n}$$

The number of different samples that can be drawn is the number of combinations of n elements from a population of N, that is

$$_N C_n = \frac{N!}{n!\,(N-n)!}$$

We shall now show that the mean of the means of all the samples is equal to the mean of the original population. Now, since there are $\dfrac{N!}{n!\,(N-n)!}$ samples, the mean of the means of all the samples is

$$\bar{\bar{x}} = \frac{\bar{x}_1 + \bar{x}_2 + \bar{x}_3 + \cdots}{\dfrac{N!}{n!\,(N-n)!}}$$

That is,

$$\bar{\bar{x}} = \frac{\dfrac{(x_1 + x_2 + \cdots)}{n} + \dfrac{(x_1 + x_3 + \cdots)}{n} + \dfrac{(x_2 + x_3 + \cdots)}{n} + \cdots}{\dfrac{N!}{n!\,(N-n)!}}$$

$$(6\text{-}1)$$

Consider all samples containing x_1. We obtain these by removing x_1 from the original N observations and selecting $n - 1$ observations out of the remaining $N - 1$. There are $\dfrac{(N - 1)!}{(n - 1)!(N - n)!}$ ways of doing this, and this will be the number of samples that contain x_1. Collecting all the terms of Eq. 6-1 containing x_1, we obtain the coefficient of x_1:

$$\frac{\dfrac{(N - 1)!}{(n - 1)!(N - n)!} \times \dfrac{1}{n}}{\dfrac{N!}{n!(N - n)!}} = \frac{1}{N}$$

Similarly, the coefficient of $x_2 = 1/N$, and the coefficient of $x_3 = 1/N$, and so on. Hence the mean of all the means is

$$\bar{\bar{x}} = \frac{x_1}{N} + \frac{x_2}{N} + \frac{x_3}{N} + \cdots + \frac{x_N}{N}$$

$$= \frac{x_1 + x_2 + x_3 + \cdots + x_N}{N}$$

$$= \text{mean of the original population}$$

Example. Consider observations: 1, 3, 4, 5, 12. Then $N = 5$. Take samples of 2 (that is, $n = 2$), and verify that the mean of all the sample means = mean of the population.

Sample	Mean of sample	Number of samples
1,3	2	
1,4	2.5	
1,5	3	$N - 1 = 4$
1,12	6.5	
3,4	3.5	
3,5	4	$N - 2 = 3$
3,12	7.5	
4,5	4.5	
4,12	8	$N - 3 = 2$
5,12	8.5	$N - 4 = 1$
Total		$= 10$

$$\text{Number of different samples} = \frac{N!}{n!(N - n)!} = \frac{5!}{2!\,3!} = 10$$

Mean of all sample means $= \bar{\bar{x}}$

$$= (2 + 2.5 + 3 + 6.5 + 3.5 + 4 + 7.5 + 4.5 + 8 + 8.5) \times \frac{1}{10} = 5$$

Mean of original population $= \mu = (1 + 3 + 4 + 5 + 12) \times \dfrac{1}{5} = 5$

Thus, $\bar{\bar{x}} = \mu$; that is, mean of all sample means = mean of original population.

DISTRIBUTION OF SAMPLE MEANS

So far we have established the value of the mean of all the sample means, but we still know nothing about how these sample means vary one from the other. We shall, therefore, now consider the distribution of the sample means, and also the relation between the standard deviation of the means and the standard deviation of the original population.

As before, we describe the population mean and standard deviation by μ and σ respectively. The number of different samples was shown to be:

$$\frac{N!}{n!\,(N-n)!}$$

Therefore, using Eq. 4-1, the variance of the means of samples of size n drawn from a population of N is:

$$\sigma_{\bar{x}}^2 = \frac{\Sigma\,(\bar{x}-\mu)^2}{\dfrac{N!}{n!\,(N-n)!}} \tag{6-2}$$

or, using the form of Eq. 4-4,

$$\sigma_{\bar{x}}^2 = \frac{\Sigma\,\bar{x}^2}{\dfrac{N!}{n!\,(N-n)!}} - \mu^2 \tag{6-3}$$

In each case the summation extends over all, that is, $\dfrac{N!}{n!\,(N-n)!}$, samples.

Now, the sum of squares of the sample means is

$$\Sigma\,\bar{x}^2 = \left(\frac{x_1+x_2+\cdots}{n}\right)^2 + \left(\frac{x_1+x_3+\cdots}{n}\right)^2$$
$$+ \left(\frac{x_2+x_3+\cdots}{n}\right)^2 + \cdots$$

Expanding the right-hand side,

$$\Sigma\,\bar{x}^2 = A\,(x_1^2 + x_2^2 + \cdots + x_N^2)$$
$$+ B\,(x_1 x_2 + x_1 x_3 + x_2 x_3 + \cdots) \tag{6-4}$$

To obtain A we have to determine the coefficient of x_1^2. The number of samples containing x_1 was shown to be $\dfrac{(N-1)!}{(n-1)!\,(N-n)!}$, and the number of samples containing x_1^2 is the same. Therefore, the coefficient of x_1^2 is

$$A = \frac{1}{n^2} \times \frac{(N-1)!}{(n-1)!\,(N-n)!} = \frac{(N-1)!}{n\,(n!)\,(N-n)!}$$

To obtain B in Eq. 6-4 we find the coefficient of $x_1 x_2$. The number of samples containing x_1 and x_2 is $\dfrac{(N-2)!}{(n-2)!\,(N-n)!}$. Hence the coefficient of $x_1 x_2$ is

$$B = \frac{2}{n^2} \times \frac{(N-2)!}{(n-2)!(N-n)!} = \frac{2(n-1)(N-2)!}{n(n!)(N-n)!}$$

Therefore the sum of the squares of sample means is

$$\Sigma \bar{x}^2 = \frac{(N-1)!}{n(n!)(N-n)!}(x_1^2 + x_2^2 + \cdots + x_N^2)$$

$$+ \frac{2(n-1)(N-2)!}{n(n!)(N-n)!}(x_1 x_2 + x_1 x_3 + x_2 x_3 + \cdots)$$

Also

$$\mu^2 = \left(\frac{x_1 + x_2 + \cdots + x_N}{N}\right)^2$$

$$= \frac{x_1^2 + x_2^2 + \cdots + x_N^2}{N^2} + \frac{2}{N^2}(x_1 x_2 + x_1 x_3 + x_2 x_3 + \cdots)$$

Substituting in

$$\sigma_{\bar{x}}^2 = \frac{\Sigma \bar{x}^2}{\dfrac{N!}{n!(N-n)!}} - \mu^2 \qquad \text{[6-3]}$$

we have

$$\sigma_{\bar{x}}^2 = (x_1^2 + x_2^2 + \cdots + x_N^2)\left(\frac{1}{Nn} - \frac{1}{N^2}\right)$$

$$+ (x_1 x_2 + x_1 x_3 + \cdots)\left(\frac{2(n-1)}{nN(N-1)} - \frac{2}{N^2}\right)$$

or

$$\sigma_{\bar{x}}^2 = (x_1^2 + x_2^2 + \cdots + x_N^2)\left(\frac{N-n}{N^2 n}\right)$$

$$- 2(x_1 x_2 + x_1 x_3 + \cdots)\left(\frac{N-n}{nN^2(N-1)}\right) \qquad (6\text{-}5)$$

We may remember that our intention is to compare the variance of the sample means with the variance of the original population. Using Eq. 4-4, the latter variance can be written

$$\sigma^2 = \frac{x_1^2 + x_2^2 + \cdots + x_N^2}{N} - \frac{(x_1 + x_2 + \cdots + x_N)^2}{N^2}$$

or

$$\sigma^2 = \frac{N-1}{N^2}(x_1^2 + x_2^2 + \cdots + x_N^2) - \frac{2}{N^2}(x_1 x_2 + x_1 x_3 + \cdots) \qquad (6\text{-}6)$$

STANDARD DEVIATION OF THE MEAN

Comparing Eqs. 6-5 and 6-6,

$$\sigma_{\bar{x}}^2 = \frac{N-n}{n(N-1)}\sigma^2 \qquad (6\text{-}7)$$

If, as is usually the case, N is very large (that is, $N \gg n$) then

$$\frac{N - n}{N - 1} \rightarrow 1$$

Thus Eq. 6-7 becomes

$$\sigma_{\bar{x}}^2 = \frac{\sigma^2}{n}$$

or, in terms of standard deviations

$$\sigma_{\bar{x}} = \frac{\sigma}{\sqrt{n}} \tag{6-8}$$

This equation is of considerable importance.[2]

In many cases, σ is not known but is estimated from the sample. Such an estimate is denoted by s and is more precise the larger the sample. Using this estimate, we can estimate the standard deviation of the mean to be

$$s_{\bar{x}} = \frac{s}{\sqrt{n}} \tag{6-9}$$

This shows that the standard deviation of the sample means varies inversely as the square root of the sample size. Since the standard deviation of the mean is a measure of the scatter of the sample means, it affords a measure of the precision that we can expect of a mean of one sample. For this reason $\sigma_{\bar{x}}$ is often called the *standard error of the mean*. We may observe that a sample of 16 observations is only twice as precise as a sample of 4, so that the gain in precision is small relative to the effort in taking the additional 12 observations. The argument cannot, however, be used too far as a sample of 2 is only $\sqrt{2}/2$ as precise as a sample of 4; here a doubling of the sample size may be well worthwhile.

It is further obvious that a sample of one tells us nothing about the precision of the estimated mean as s in Eq. 6-9 cannot be estimated.[3] With a number of samples of unit size the standard deviation could be estimated but $s_{\bar{x}}$ would be no smaller than the standard deviation of the underlying distribution.

Figure 6-1 shows a comparison between the (probability) distribution of individual observations and the (probability) distribution of means of samples drawn from this underlying distribution. The considerably narrower distribution of the sample means is apparent; this indicates that the

---

[2] It may be relevant to note that the standard deviation of the median is $\dfrac{1.25\,\sigma}{\sqrt{n}}$. We can see thus that for the same precision of the estimate the sample size in the case of an estimate of the median has to be $(1.25)^2$ times greater than in the case of the mean. We can say, therefore, that the median is less efficient than the mean as a measure of central tendency.

[3] The calculation of s (Eq. 4-3) involves $n - 1$ in the denominator.

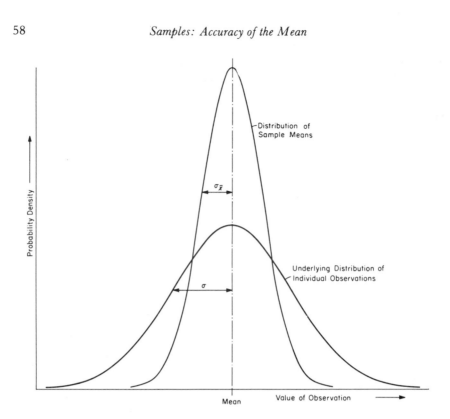

FIG. 6-1. Probability distribution of sample means compared with the underlying distribution; sample size = 4.

mean is an efficient measure of central tendency.[4] The higher peak of the curve for the means is due to the fact that the areas under the two curves are equal to one another and to unity as each represents the sum of all probabilities.

It may be interesting to note that means of samples are approximately normally distributed even when the underlying distribution is not normal; normal distribution is defined in Chapter 9, and the problem of distribution of means is considered more fully in Chapter 10.

We can now answer, at least in part, the question posed at the beginning of this chapter on the precision of length measurements.

Let us refer to the sample consisting of the first four measurements as sample 1, and to the sample consisting of all nine measurements as sample 2.

We have thus: $\bar{x}_1 = 100$ ft 2 in. $\bar{x}_2 = 100$ ft 1 in.

We calculate: $s_1 = 4.48$ in. $s_2 = 5.60$ in.

[4] The median is less efficient (see footnote 2).

From Eq. 6-9: $s_{\bar{x}_1} = 2.24$ in. $s_{\bar{x}_2} = 1.87$ in.

The standard error of sample 2 is thus smaller than that of sample 1, and we can write our estimates of the population mean (i.e., "true" length) as:

100 ft 2 in. $\pm 2\frac{1}{4}$ in. and 100 ft 1 in. $\pm 1\frac{3}{4}$ in. respectively

The exact interpretation of statements of this type is discussed in Chapter 10.

Example. To verify Eq. 6-7 for a population of observations: 2, 4, 6. Here

$$N = 3,$$
$$\mu = 4$$

Thus

$$\sigma^2 = \frac{2^2 + 0^2 + 2^2}{3} = \frac{8}{3}$$

Consider $n = 2$. The samples are then

2,4　　2,6　　4,6

and sample means are

3　　4　　5

Mean of sample means $= \dfrac{3 + 4 + 5}{3}$

$= 4$ (which checks with the population mean)

and

Variance of sample means $= \dfrac{1^2 + 0^2 + 1^2}{3} = \dfrac{2}{3}$

Substituting in Eq. 6-7,

$$\sigma_{\bar{x}}^2 = \frac{N - n}{n(N - 1)} \sigma^2$$

$$= \frac{1}{2 \times 2} \times \frac{8}{3} = \frac{2}{3}$$

which checks with the value calculated directly from the sample means.

Example. If we consider the results of strength tests on 270 bricks, given in Table 2-2, as a sample of the population consisting of all the bricks made by the given works during the sampling period, then we can say that the standard deviation of the sample mean (calculated in Chapter 3 to be 999.81 psi) is, from Eq. 6-9:

$$s_{\bar{x}} = \frac{s}{\sqrt{n}} = \frac{201.44}{\sqrt{270}} = 12.26 \text{ psi}$$

[201.44 is the value of the *sample* standard deviation (found in Chapter 4), but because n is large, the error involved in ignoring Bessel's correction is negligible].

The interpretation of the standard deviation of the mean in relation to the precision of the calculated mean is considered on page 111.

PROBLEMS

6-1. Calculate the standard deviation of the mean of Prob. 3-2.

6-2. Calculate the standard error of the mean tensile strength of rubber of Prob. 4-1. By what factor would this standard error be changed if we took 18 measurements? Assume that the estimated standard deviation is the same in both cases.

6-3. The coded length of specimens of a certain type was found to be: 17, 17, 12, 15, 20. By considering all possible samples of size two, drawn with replacement from the above population, find: (a) the population mean; (b) the population standard deviation; (c) the mean of the sample means; and (d) the standard deviation of the sample means.

Check (c) and (d) from (a) and (b), respectively, by using the appropriate formulae.

6-4. Determine the standard error of the mean precipitation found in Prob. 3-3.

6-5. Samples of four building blocks were taken, and the mean range of their weight was found to be 0.09 lb. Estimate the standard deviation of weight of the blocks. Estimate also the standard deviation of the mean weight of the sample.

6-6. The vibration time of a member was measured 13 times, the following values being obtained:

59.6, 60.4, 60.2, 60.7, 60.1, 59.8, 59.8, 60.3, 60.0, 59.9, 59.5, 60.2, 60.3 sec.

Find the mean and standard deviation for these values. Find also the standard deviation of the mean, mean deviation, and coefficient of variation.

chapter 7

Binomial Distribution

In some cases a population consists of only two classes of individuals, for example, alive or dead, even or odd, heads or tails, or simply possessing or not possessing a certain attribute (e.g., a defect). When one trial is made, for example, one ball is drawn at random from a collection containing a proportion p of black balls, the probability of the ball being black is p. The probability per trial is thus fixed. When a random sample of size n is drawn from the population (i.e., by making n trials), the distribution of the two classes of individuals (black balls and others) is, of course, discrete and is of the binomial type.

The name of the distribution arises from a similarity between the distribution of the probabilities of obtaining 0, 1, 2, ... items considered as a success in a sample of size n and the successive terms of the binomial expansion $(q + p)^n$, where p denotes the probability of success in a simple trial, and q (such that $p + q = 1$) the probability of failure. Success means simply encountering a certain class of individual (which in practice may be far from a success, e.g., a defective part), and failure means not encountering this class.

DERIVATION

Consider n trials in each of which the probability of success is p. Then the probability of failure is $1 - p = q$. To find the probability of r successes we observe that:

the probability of 1 success is p,
the probability of 2 successes is $p \times p$ or p^2,
the probability of 3 successes is $p \times p \times p$ or p^3,

the probability of r successes is p^r,
and the probability of $n - r$ failures is $(1 - p)^{n-r} = q^{n-r}$. From the rule given in Chapter 5, it follows that the probability of r successes and $(n - r)$ failures is $p^r(1 - p)^{n-r}$.

The number of selections for r successes and $(n - r)$ failures in n trials is $\dfrac{n!}{r!\,(n - r)!}$ (see Eq. 5-4).

Therefore the probability P_r of an event succeeding r times is

$$P_r = \frac{n!}{r!\,(n-r)!}\, p^r(1-p)^{n-r} \qquad (7\text{-}1a)$$

or

$$P_r = {}_nC_r\, p^r q^{n-r} \qquad (7\text{-}1b)$$

It may be observed that this term is similar to the rth term of the binomial expansion $(q+p)^n$ (see Eq. 5-6 or 5-7) which can be written

$$(q+p)^n = \sum_{r=0}^{n} {}_nC_r\, p^r q^{n-r} \qquad (7\text{-}2)$$

The successive terms of the expansion give the probability P_r of an event succeeding r times in n trials for values of r varying in steps of one from 0 to n.

In many cases, we are interested not in the probability of an event succeeding exactly r times but in the probability of its succeeding *at least* r times in n trials. This is given by the *theorem of repeated trials* as

$$P_r + P_{r+1} + \cdots + P_n$$

It should be emphasized that for the binomial distribution to be applicable, the probability of success must be constant from trial to trial, and all the trials must be independent events. Thus, the conditions (e.g., the method of manufacture) must not change while the samples are being taken, and the sampling must be done in a random manner, each selection being independent.

Let us consider now several simple examples of binomial distribution.

Example. Two coins are tossed (i.e., we take samples of two from an infinite population of coins). There are three possibilities for each toss or observation:

no heads   one head   two heads

Two coins can fall in $2^2 = 4$ ways. They give us no heads in only one case (when they both fall tails), so that the probability of no heads is $\frac{1}{4}$. For there to be one head there are two possible arrangements: a head on the first coin or a head on the second coin; hence the probability of one head is $\frac{2}{4}$. Finally, for there to be two heads both coins have to fall heads, and thus the probability of two heads is $\frac{1}{4}$. We can, therefore, write the probabilities:

no heads   one head   two heads
$\frac{1}{4}$ $\frac{1}{2}$ $\frac{1}{4}$

Denoting the probability of success (heads) in one trial as p and the probability of failure (no heads) as q, we can write the binomial expansion for two tosses:

$$(q+p)^2 = q^2 + 2qp + p^2$$

Since $p = q = \frac{1}{2}$, the expansion gives the probabilities for the three possible cases respectively:

$$(q + p)^2 = \quad (\tfrac{1}{2})^2 \quad + \quad 2(\tfrac{1}{2})(\tfrac{1}{2}) \quad + \quad (\tfrac{1}{2})^2$$

Probability of: no heads   one head   two heads

Example. If four coins are tossed, what are the probabilities of obtaining various numbers of heads?

The number of possible ways in which 4 coins can be tossed is $2^4 = 16$.

For no heads, the number of favorable events is 1 (probability $= \frac{1}{16}$), since to get no heads all four coins have to be tails.

For one head, the number of favorable events is 4 (probability $= \frac{4}{16}$), since

the 1st coin could be tossed as a head,
the 2nd coin could be tossed as a head,
the 3rd coin could be tossed as a head,
the 4th coin could be tossed as a head.

For two heads, the number of favorable events is the number of ways in which one can select 2 items out of 4, that is

$$_4C_2 = \frac{4 \times 3}{2} = 6 \text{ (probability } = \tfrac{6}{16})$$

For three heads, the number of favorable events is $_4C_3 = 4$ (probability $= \frac{4}{16}$).

For four heads, the number of favorable events is $_4C_4 = 1$ (probability $= \frac{1}{16}$).

Compare these values with the binomial expansion of

$$\left(\frac{1}{2} + \frac{1}{2}\right)^4 = \left(\frac{1}{2}\right)^4 + 4\left(\frac{1}{2}\right)^3 \frac{1}{2} + \frac{4 \times 3}{2}\left(\frac{1}{2}\right)^2\left(\frac{1}{2}\right)^2 + \frac{4 \times 3 \times 2}{2 \times 3}\frac{1}{2}\left(\frac{1}{2}\right)^3 + \left(\frac{1}{2}\right)^4$$

$$= \frac{1}{16} + \frac{4}{16} + \frac{6}{16} + \frac{4}{16} + \frac{1}{16}$$

Probability of: no heads   1 head   2 heads   3 heads   4 heads

This distribution is shown in the frequency diagram of Fig. 7-1, and it can be seen that when $p = q$ the distribution of the probabilities is (as expected) symmetrical.

Nonsymmetrical distribution is illustrated by the following case.

Example. Consider a population consisting of equal numbers of balls of three different colors (a type of population favored by statisticians!) from which we draw four balls at a time, replacing the balls every time. What is the probability of obtaining in our sample 0, 1, ..., 4 balls of a given color, say black?

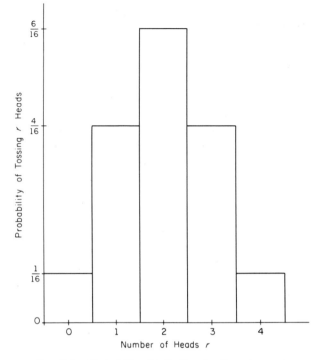

FIG. 7-1. Probability distribution for throwing various numbers of heads in tossing four coins.

For each ball drawn, the probability of success (black ball) is $p = \frac{1}{3}$; the probability of failure is $q = \frac{2}{3}$. Using binomial distribution, we have:

$$\left(\frac{2}{3} + \frac{1}{3}\right)^4 = \frac{16}{3^4} + \frac{32}{3^4} + \frac{24}{3^4} + \frac{8}{3^4} + \frac{1}{3^4}$$

$$= \quad 0.1975 \quad 0.3951 \quad 0.2963 \quad 0.0988 \quad 0.0123$$

Probability of drawing:	no black balls	1 black ball	2 black balls	3 black balls	4 black balls

The probability distribution (plotted in Fig. 7-2) is nonsymmetrical.

Example. Seven races are to be held, the same six dogs taking part in each race. What are the probabilities of one particular dog winning 1, 2, ..., 7 races, assuming that all dogs are "equally good."[1]

In any one race our dog has a $\frac{1}{6}$ chance of winning (probability of suc-

---

[1] An assumption of doubtful validity.

cess $= p = \frac{1}{6}$) and a $\frac{5}{6}$ chance of not winning (probability of failure $=$ $q = \frac{5}{6}$). Binomial expansion gives:

$$\left(\frac{5}{6} + \frac{1}{6}\right)^7 = \left(\frac{5}{6}\right)^7 + 7\left(\frac{5}{6}\right)^6\left(\frac{1}{6}\right) + \frac{7 \times 6}{2}\left(\frac{5}{6}\right)^5\left(\frac{1}{6}\right)^2 + \frac{7 \times 6 \times 5}{2 \times 3}\left(\frac{5}{6}\right)^4\left(\frac{1}{6}\right)^3 + \cdots + \left(\frac{1}{6}\right)^7$$

| Probability of: | no wins | 1 win | 2 wins | 3 wins | 7 wins |

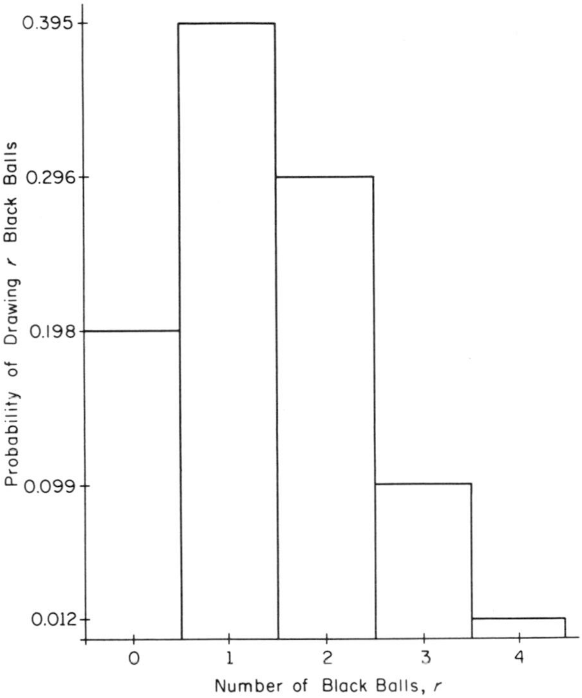

FIG. 7-2. Probability distribution for drawing different numbers of black balls in a sample of 4 balls drawn from a population of balls of 3 colors in equal proportions.

PASCAL'S TRIANGLE

The binomial coefficients can be obtained from Pascal's triangle; this is constructed so that each term is the sum of the two terms immediately above and to either side, as shown in Fig. 7-3. The second term of each line corresponds to the value of n in $(q + p)^n$, and the sum of coefficients in any line is equal to 2^n.

The coefficients of the binomial expansion can, of course, be computed quite rapidly using tables of factorial values. If, however, appropriate fac-

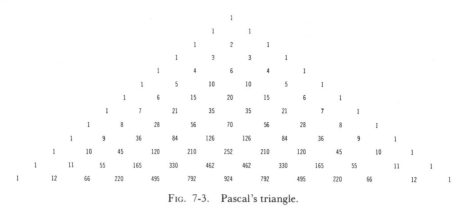

Fig. 7-3. Pascal's triangle.

torial values are not available and n is large, Stirling's formula can be used. This gives the factorial:

$$n! = e^{-n} n^n \sqrt{2\pi n} \qquad (7\text{-}3)$$

The error involved is less than 0.1 percent for n greater than 100 and less than 1 percent for n greater than 10.

Binomial distribution is used extensively in quality testing; a very simple illustration follows.

Example. In the production of wire connections consisting of four wires in parallel it was found that on the average one wire in ten was not tightened. If the strength of each wire is 250 lb, find the proportion of connections which can withstand 750 lb.

We assume that a wire which has not been tightened carries no load.

$$\text{Probability of a good wire} \quad = p = 0.9$$
$$\text{Probability of a defective wire} = q = 0.1$$

Using the binomial distribution,

$$(0.1 + 0.9)^4 = (0.1)^4 + 4(0.1)^3(0.9) + \frac{4 \times 3(0.1)^2(0.9)^2}{2}$$

$$= 0.0001 \qquad 0.0036 \qquad 0.0486$$

Probability of: all   3 defective,   2 defective,
                 defective   1 good   2 good

$$+ \frac{4 \times 3 \times 2(0.1)(0.9)^3}{2 \times 3} + (0.9)^4$$

$$0.2916 \qquad 0.6561$$

                 1 defective,   all good
                 3 good

We can say, therefore, that of all connections made,

$$65.61\% \text{ will have a strength of } 4 \times 250 = 1{,}000 \text{ lb}$$
$$65.61 + 29.16 = 94.77\% \text{ will have a strength of } 3 \times 250 = 750 \text{ lb or more}$$
$$94.77 + 4.86 = 99.63\% \text{ will have a strength of } 2 \times 250 = 500 \text{ lb or more}$$
$$99.63 + 0.36 = 99.99\% \text{ will have a strength of } 1 \times 250 = 250 \text{ lb or more}$$
$$\text{and} \qquad 0.01\% \text{ will have no strength}$$

Example. Wireless sets are manufactured with 25 soldered joints each. On the average 1 joint in 500 is defective. How many sets can be expected to be free from defective joints in a consignment of 10,000 sets?

Let the probability of a defective joint ("success") be $p = 0.002$. Then $q = 0.998$. Using the binomial expansion,

$$(0.998 + 0.002)^{25} = \underset{\substack{\text{no defective} \\ \text{joints}}}{(0.998)^{25}} + \underset{\substack{1 \text{ joint} \\ \text{defective}}}{25 \times (0.998)^{24} \times 0.002} + \cdots$$

Thus the proportion of sets with no defective joints is $(0.998)^{25} = 0.95118$ so that in 10,000 sets, 9,512 would be expected to be free from defective joints. It is clear that some sets would have more than one defective joint.

MEAN AND STANDARD DEVIATION

Let us now further consider the properties of the binomial distribution. If p is the proportion of successes in the population, then the mean number of successes in n trials is

$$\mu = np \tag{7-4}$$

This is obvious, as the mean number of successes in n trials is equal to the probability of success in one trial times the number of trials.

The standard deviation for a binomial frequency distribution is

$$\sigma = \sqrt{npq} \tag{7-5}$$

Since q is not independent but is equal to $(1 - p)$, we can see that the binomial distribution can be expressed in terms of two parameters, n and p.

Equations 7-4 and 7-5 are proved in Appendix B; a simple verification is afforded by the following example.

Example. Consider 32 trials, each consisting of tossing four coins. The theoretical frequencies are given by $32(\frac{1}{2} + \frac{1}{2})^4$, namely:

Number of heads x_i	Theoretical frequency f_i	$f_i x_i$	$f_i x_i^2$
0	2	0	0
1	8	8	8
2	12	24	48
3	8	24	72
4	2	8	32
Totals	$\Sigma f_i = 32$	$\Sigma f_i x_i = 64$	$\Sigma f_i x_i^2 = 160$

Using the general expressions for mean and standard deviation (Eqs. 3-2 and 4-4), we have

$$\text{Mean} = \mu = \frac{\Sigma f_i x_i}{\Sigma f_i} = \frac{64}{32} = 2 \text{ (as, indeed, expected)}$$

$$\text{Standard deviation} = \sigma = \sqrt{\frac{\Sigma f_i x_i^2 - \frac{(\Sigma f_i x_i)^2}{\Sigma f_i}}{\Sigma f_i}} = \sqrt{\frac{160 - \frac{(64)^2}{32}}{32}} = 1$$

We can now check these results against Eqs. 7-4 and 7-5.

$$n = 4$$
$$p = \tfrac{1}{2}$$
$$q = \tfrac{1}{2}$$

Then

$$\mu = np = 4 \times \tfrac{1}{2} = 2$$

and

$$\sigma = \sqrt{npq} = \sqrt{4 \times \tfrac{1}{2} \times \tfrac{1}{2}} = 1$$

COMPARISON OF EXPERIMENTAL AND BINOMIAL DISTRIBUTIONS

Let us now consider an actual experiment in which the following results were obtained:

Number of heads x_i	Observed frequency f_i	$f_i x_i$	$f_i x_i^2$
0	0	0	0
1	8	8	8
2	15	30	60
3	6	18	54
4	3	12	48
Totals	$\Sigma f_i = 32$	$\Sigma f_i x_i = 68$	$\Sigma f_i x_i^2 = 170$

Then

$$\mu = \frac{68}{32} = 2.12$$

and

$$\sigma = \sqrt{\frac{170 - \frac{(68)^2}{32}}{32}} = 0.89$$

A comparison of the observed distribution with the preceding theoretical distribution is shown in Fig. 7-4.

We should note that if the comparison is made in terms of frequencies rather than of probabilities, the expected frequency has a mathematical

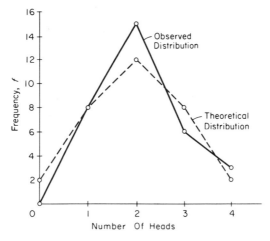

Fig. 7-4. Theoretical and experimental distribution for 32 throws of 4 coins.

and not a strictly physical meaning, as fractions of, (say) heads are not possible.

A practical problem of this type arises in acceptance tests. For example, let us imagine that a manufacturer delivers a product on the understanding that 90 percent of the items are free from defect. We take a sample of 4 items and find 2 of them defective. Are we justified in rejecting the entire consignment?

To answer this question we have to know the probability P of obtaining at least 2 defectives in a sample of 4. We have:

$$n = 4, \quad p = 0.1, \quad q = 0.9$$

Now

$$P = P_2 + P_3 + P_4$$
$$= {}_4C_2 (0.1)^2 (0.9)^2 + {}_4C_3 (0.1)^3 (0.9) + {}_4C_4 (0.1)^4$$
$$= 0.0523$$

Thus there is a probability of only 0.0523 (or approximately 1 in 20) of drawing at least 2 defectives in a sample of 4, and we would be far from unreasonable if we rejected the consignment.

It should be stressed that intuitive approach to problems of this type can often be misleading. For example, what answer would the reader expect to the following problem?

Lottery tickets are sold, it being advertised that every fourth ticket carries a prize. If we buy 4 tickets, this being a random sample, what is the probability that we get at least one winning ticket?

The probability of having at least one winning ticket is

$$P = 1 - P_0$$

where P_0 is the probability of having no winning ticket in a sample of 4, and the term 1 represents all the possible cases. We have $p = 0.25$ and $n = 4$. Thus,

$$P = 1 - {}_4C_0 (0.25)^0 (0.75)^4$$
$$= 0.684$$

i.e., there is a 68.4 percent probability of having at least one winning ticket. This may interest those who did not get a winning ticket under similar circumstances and ended up by suspecting the promoters.

The answer to our problem could also be obtained by adding the probabilities of drawing 1, 2, 3, and 4 winning tickets, but the method used here involves less effort.

Another comparison between an experimental distribution and the theoretical binomial distribution may be of interest.

Example. Ten tosses of a suspected die gave the results 1, 1, 1, 6, 1, 1, 3, 1, 1, 4. What is the probability of at least this many aces if the die is true?

The event "at least 7 aces" can materialize in four mutually exclusive ways: 7 aces, 8 aces, 9 aces, 10 aces.

The probability of throwing at least 7 aces, P, is the sum of the probabilities for 7, 8, 9, and 10 aces, that is

$$P = P_7 + P_8 + P_9 + P_{10}$$

We have $n = 10$, and the probability of throwing an ace in any one throw is $p = \frac{1}{6}$.
Therefore

$$P = {}_{10}C_7 \left(\frac{1}{6}\right)^7 \left(\frac{5}{6}\right)^3 + {}_{10}C_8 \left(\frac{1}{6}\right)^8 \left(\frac{5}{6}\right)^2 + {}_{10}C_9 \left(\frac{1}{6}\right)^9 \left(\frac{5}{6}\right) + {}_{10}C_{10} \left(\frac{1}{6}\right)^{10}$$
$$= 0.000027$$

This probability is so small that it is most unlikely that the observed 7 aces in 10 throws could be obtained with $p = \frac{1}{6}$. We conclude, therefore, that the hypothesis $p = \frac{1}{6}$ should be rejected, i.e., the die is biased or "loaded."

We can, of course, test the agreement between the two distributions quantitatively in terms of probability; the appropriate methods are dealt with in Chapter 12.

SOLVED PROBLEMS

7-1. If the probability of a weld being defective is 0.1, what is the probability of obtaining exactly 0, 1, 2, and 3 defective welds in a sample of 5 welds? What is the probability of obtaining less than 2 defective welds? If a structure has 100 welds, how many of them would you expect to be defective? What is the probability of there being at least 90 welds free from defect in a structure containing 100 welds?

Solution:

The probability of a defective weld is $p = 0.1$; then $q = 0.9$.

Using the binomial expansion:

$$(0.9 + 0.1)^5 = (0.9)^5 + 5(0.9)^4(0.1) + \frac{5 \times 4}{2!}(0.9)^3(0.1)^2 + \frac{5 \times 4 \times 3}{3!}(0.9)^2(0.1)^3 + \cdots$$

Probability of:	0.59049	0.32805	0.0729	0.0081
	all good	one defective	two defectives	three defectives

Probability of obtaining less than two defective welds $= 0.59049 + 0.32805$

$$= 0.91854$$

Of 100 welds we would expect $0.1 \times 100 = 10$ to be defective (on the average). The probability of there being at least 90 welds free from defect is

$$\sum_{r=90}^{100} P_r$$

where $P_r = {}_{100}C_r(0.1)^{100-r}(0.9)^r$

7-2. If the probability of a structure collapsing after 30 years of service is 0.01, find the probability that out of 10 such structures

(a)   none,
(b)   exactly one,
(c)   not more than one,
(d)   more than one,
(e)   at least one

will collapse after 30 years of service.

Solution:

The probability of a sound structure is $p = 0.99$, and the probability of a collapse is $q = 0.01$. Therefore

$$(0.99 + 0.01)^{10} = (0.99)^{10} + 10(0.99)^9(0.01) + \cdots$$

$$= 0.9036 \qquad\qquad 0.0913$$

Probability of:	no collapse	one collapse

Logarithms are used to obtain the above results. For example, put

$$(0.99)^{10} = y$$

Then

$$\log y = 10 \log 0.99 = \bar{1}.9956 \times 10$$

$$= \overline{10} + 9.956$$

$$= \bar{1}.9560$$

Hence $y = 0.9036$. Thus the probabilities are:

(a)   0.9036
(b)   0.0913

(c) $0.9036 + 0.0913 = 0.9949$
(d) $1 - 0.9949 = 0.0051$
(e) $1 - 0.9036 = 0.0964$

PROBLEMS

7-1. On checking assembly lines it was found that one of the ten lines produced defective items. The products of all the lines were mixed by then, and the defectives could not be easily separated out. If a random sample of ten items is taken, what is the probability of its containing (a) no defective items; (b) one defective item; (c) not more than two defective items; (d) more than one defective item?

7-2. If the probability of a child being male is 0.55, what is the probability of having three daughters in succession?

7-3. A product is supposed to contain 5 percent of defective items. We take a sample of 10 items and find it to contain 2 defectives. Are we justified in suspecting that the consignment is not up to specification?

7-4. A manufacturing process is intended to produce precast units with no more than 2 percent defective. It is checked every day by testing 10 units selected at random from the day's production. If one or more of the 10 fails, the process is halted and carefully examined. If in fact its probability of producing a defective unit is 0.01,

(a)   What is the probability of obtaining one or more defective units?

(b)   What is the probability of obtaining no defectives in a given test?

(c)   Find the mean and the standard deviation of the number of defective units in a sample of 10 units.

7-5. The foreman of a casting section in a certain factory finds that on the average 1 in every 5 castings made is defective. If the section makes 8 castings a day, what is the chance that 2 of these will be defective? What is the chance that five or more defective castings are made in one day?

7-6. Samples of 6 items are drawn at random from a supply source which contains 9 percent defectives. Draw a histogram showing the probabilities of having 0, 1, . . . , 6 defectives in the sample.

7-7. In a game of Russian roulette one chamber of a six-chamber gun is loaded. The cylinder is spun around, and the trigger is pulled. Three men are playing the "roulette," taking 3 turns each at pulling the trigger. What is the probability that (a) a particular man will survive the game; (b) one of the three men will survive the game; (c) all the men will survive?

7-8. From seven different concrete mixes a number of compression test specimens of two sizes were made, the following results being obtained.[2] Test the hypothesis that there is no difference between the strength of specimens of 10-cm and 20-cm size.

[2]A. M. Neville, "Some Aspects of the Strength of Concrete," Part II, *Civil Engineering and Public Works Review*, Vol. 54, No. 640 (Nov. 1959), pp. 1308–1310.

Mix	10-cm specimens		20-cm specimens	
	Sample size	Mean strength (kg/cm²)	Sample size	Mean strength (kg/cm²)
A	6	141	6	115
B	27	237	21	218
C	15	289	12	275
D	6	367	9	324
E	12	452	7	434
F	18	591	6	517
G	11	739	9	647

[HINT: Calculate the probability of obtaining the observed number of differences of the same sign, if positive and negative differences occur equally often in the parent population.]

chapter 8

Poisson Distribution

The Poisson distribution represents the probability of an isolated event occurring a specified number of times in a given interval of time (or space) when the rate of occurrence in a continuum of time (or space) is fixed. The occurrence of events must be affected by chance alone, and the Poisson distribution is therefore such that information about the position of one event is of no help in predicting the position of any other specific event; furthermore, data on one interval of time (or space) are of no help in predicting how many events will occur in any other interval. A characteristic feature of the Poisson distribution is the fact that only the occurrence of an event can be counted; its nonoccurrence cannot, as it has no physical meaning. Thus the total number of events n cannot be measured, and, in consequence, the binomial distribution is not precisely applicable.

Some of the phenomena which follow the Poisson distribution are: flaws in castings, number of vehicles on a highway, number of telephone calls, clicks of a Geiger counter, or the celebrated case of cavalrymen killed by a horse-kick (discussed later in this chapter).

TERMS OF THE POISSON DISTRIBUTION

The Poisson distribution is made up of a series of terms:

$$e^{-\mu}, \quad e^{-\mu}\mu, \quad e^{-\mu}\frac{\mu^2}{2!}, \quad e^{-\mu}\frac{\mu^3}{3!}, \quad e^{-\mu}\frac{\mu^4}{4!}, \ldots$$

representing, respectively, the probability of the occurrence of 0, 1, 2, 3, 4, etc., events, where e is the base of natural logarithms and μ is the mean frequency of occurrence. The sum of all terms of the series is unity, as must be the case with a sum of all probabilities.

If r is the number of occurrences whose probability we require, we can write the general term of the series

$$P_r = \frac{e^{-\mu}\mu^r}{r!} \tag{8-1}$$

The values of $e^{-\mu}$ for values of μ between 0.01 and 5 are given in Table A-2, but it is clear that such a computation is tiresome, and the use of tabulated or plotted values such as shown in Fig. 8-1 is preferable.

The Poisson distribution is asymmetrical (skewed) and the relation between the mode and the mean μ is such that the mode is at 0 occurrence when $\mu < 1$,

at 1 occurrence when $1 \leqslant \mu < 2$,

at 2 occurrences when $2 \leqslant \mu < 3$, etc.

DERIVATION FROM BINOMIAL DISTRIBUTION

It was shown earlier (Eq. 7-1a) that in n trials the probability of an event succeeding r times is

$$P_r = \frac{n!}{r!\,(n-r)!}\,p^r q^{n-r} \tag{8-2}$$

When n is large compared with r,

$$\frac{n!}{(n-r)!} = n(n-1)(n-2)\ldots(n-r+1)$$

$$\simeq n^r$$

Therefore the probability of r successes becomes

$$P_r = \frac{n^r}{r!}\,p^r q^{n-r} \tag{8-3}$$

Now if p is very small and r is not large,

$$q^r = (1-p)^r \simeq 1$$

and

$$q^{n-r} \simeq q^n = (1-p)^n$$

Hence

$$P_r = \frac{(np)^r}{r!}\,(1-p)^n$$

$$= \frac{(np)^r}{r!}\left[1 - np + \frac{n(n-1)(-p)^2}{2!} + \frac{n(n-1)(n-2)(-p)^3}{3!} + \cdots\right]$$

$$\simeq \frac{(np)^r}{r!}\left[1 - np + \frac{(np)^2}{2!} - \frac{(np)^3}{3!} + \cdots\right]$$

Thus

$$P_r = \frac{(np)^r}{r!}\,e^{-np} \tag{8-4}$$

This, then, is the probability of r successes in n trials.

MEAN AND STANDARD DEVIATION

The mean number of occurrences of an event per unit of time (or space) is

$$\mu = np \tag{8-5}$$

and the standard deviation of the numbers of events is

$$\sigma = \sqrt{np} \tag{8-6}$$

Thus the mean and variance are equal to one another:

$$\mu = \sigma^2 = np \tag{8-7}$$

It may be observed that Eq. 8-5 is identical with Eq. 7-4 derived for the binomial distribution. Likewise, Eqs. 8-6 and 7-5 are identical, provided that we remember that the Poisson distribution was derived for $q \backsim 1$.

It is important to note that the Poisson distribution contains only one parameter, np, the mean occurrence of an event, and we do not know the value of n. On the other hand, in the binomial distribution we know the number of times an event occurs and the number of times an event does not occur.

POISSON DISTRIBUTION AS AN APPROXIMATION TO BINOMIAL DISTRIBUTION

The Poisson distribution can thus be used as an approximation to the binomial distribution when the sample size n is large and the probability of success p is small (the same applies when q is small, p and q being of course interchangeable), i.e., when the binomial distribution is highly skewed. As a guide, we can say that a good approximation is obtained when $n \geq 20$ and $p \leq 0.05$, and the approximation improves with a decrease in p.

Example. In making glass, undissolved particles called "stones" sometimes occur. Let us assume that there is an average of 1 stone per pound of glass made. If there are 100,000 "particles" in 1 lb of glass, then the probability of a stone is

$$p = 10^{-5}$$

If we are making glass lenses of 1/10 lb weight each, then there will be on the average 1 stone in every ten lenses. Thus, $np = 0.1$.

What is the proportion of lenses free from stones? The probability P_r of finding r stones in a lens is given by Eq. 8-4:

$$P_r = \frac{(np)^r}{r!} e^{-np}$$

and is tabulated below:

Number of stones in a lens, r	0	1	2	3	4
Probability P_r	0.9048	0.09048	0.004524	...	...

Therefore

90.48% of all lenses made will be free from stones

9.05% of all lenses made will contain 1 stone

0.45% of all lenses made will contain 2 stones

and so on.

If each lens weighed 1 lb, then we would have $np = 1$, and hence the following values of probability of obtaining a lens containing r stones:

Number of stones in a lens, r	0	1	2	3	4	5
Probability P_r	0.367	0.367	0.183	0.061	0.015	...

Therefore

36.7 percent of all lenses made will be free from stones

36.7 percent of all lenses made will contain 1 stone

18.3 percent of all lenses made will contain 2 stones

6.1 percent of all lenses made will contain 3 stones

1.5 percent of all lenses made will contain 4 stones

and so on.

The Poisson distribution (instead of binomial expansion) is particularly useful when n is extremely large and p very small as it then becomes virtually impossible to compute the binomial terms. For example, assume that we have n radioactive nuclei such that the probability of one of these decaying in a time interval t is p. We want to calculate the probability of r of these undergoing decay in time t.

In terms of binomial distribution the required probability is (from Eq. 7-1b):

$$P_r = {}_nC_r \, p^r (1 - p)^{n-r}$$

If $n = 10^{23}$ and $p = 10^{-22}$, the probability becomes

$$P_r = \frac{(10^{23})!}{(10^{23} - r)! \, r!} \, p^r (1 - p)^{10^{23} - r}$$

which is difficult to evaluate. We prefer, therefore, to work in terms of $np = 10$ and use the Poisson approximation (Eq. 8-4)

$$P_r = \frac{10^r}{r!} \, e^{-10}$$

SIGNIFICANCE OF POISSON DISTRIBUTION

In many cases we may suspect that a set of occurrences is completely random in nature, and we may want to determine whether this is so. We proceed to compare the experimental distribution with an assumed Poisson distribution, and if the agreement is good, we conclude that the distribution of occurrences is influenced by chance alone. If the agreement is not good, we suspect that some definite influences may exist. We then have to study the data further, e.g., by examining the periods of tests and seeking a correlation between these and some other, possibly intermittent, influence.

The goodness of fit of the observed distribution to the assumed Poisson distribution may be tested by the χ^2 test, discussed in Chapter 12. At this stage we shall only make a simple comparison.

Example. Records of deaths due to horse-kicks were kept in 10 army corps over a period of 20 years:[1]

Number of deaths per corps per annum r	0	1	2	3	4	5 or more
Number of corps per annum with r deaths f	109	65	22	3	1	0

Compare these values with a Poisson distribution derived from the observed mean frequency of death.

We take an army corps per annum as a unit. We have thus $20 \times 10 = 200$ observations.

The mean number of deaths per corps per annum is

$$np = \frac{\Sigma fr}{\Sigma f} = \frac{0 \times 109 + 1 \times 65 + 2 \times 22 + 3 \times 3 + 4 \times 1 + 5 \times 0}{200}$$

$$= \frac{122}{200} = 0.61$$

Substituting in Eq. 8-4, we obtain the following:

Number of deaths per corps per annum r	0	1	2	3	4	5
Probability of an army corps with r deaths P_r	$e^{-0.61}$ $= 0.545$	$0.61e^{-0.61}$ $= 0.331$	$\dfrac{(0.61)^2 e^{-0.61}}{2}$ $= 0.101$	$\dfrac{(0.61)^3 e^{-0.61}}{2 \times 3}$ $= 0.020$	$\dfrac{(0.61)^4 e^{-0.61}}{2 \times 3 \times 4}$ $= 0.003$	...
Calculated number of army corps per annum with r deaths $= 200P_r$ ...	109	66	20	4	$0.6 \simeq 1$	...
Observed number of army corps per annum with r deaths	109	65	22	3	1	0

As shown by the two last lines of the preceding table the agreement is extremely close, and we conclude that the distribution of deaths is due to chance alone, and not to such factors as the locality where different corps are stationed or the personality of the general commanding.

[1] Obtained by Bortkewitch and quoted in R. A. Fisher, *Statistical Methods for Research Workers* (New York: Hafner Publishing Co., 1958), p 55.

POISSON PROBABILITY PAPER

A graph paper ruled so that the abscissae represent, to a logarithmic scale, the expected average number of events and the ordinates give the probability of occurrence to a Poisson probability scale is called a Poisson probability paper. Lines can be drawn showing the probability of an event occurring not more than r times for values of $r = 0, 1, 2, 3, \ldots 15$. This is represented in Fig. 8-1.

If we require the probability of an event occurring exactly a certain number of times, we have to use differences. For example, if the average number of events is 1, and we require the probability of an event occurring 3 times, we find from Fig. 8-1 that the probability of its occurring not more than 3 times is 0.981. The probability of occurring not more than 2 times is 0.920. Hence, the probability of occurring 3 times is 0.981 − 0.920 = 0.061.

Poisson probability paper can also be used to check whether an actual distribution agrees closely with the Poisson distribution, and, if so, what is the expected number of occurrences. From the experimental data we calculate the frequency and (by dividing by the total frequency) the proba-

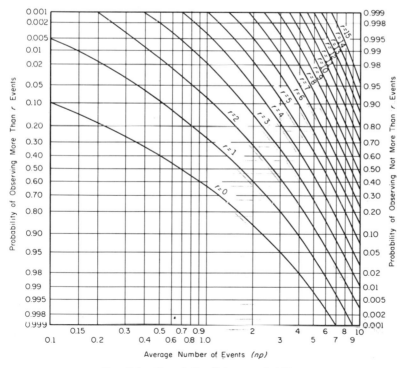

Fig. 8-1. Cumulative Poisson probability

bility of an event occurring not more than 1, 2, 3, etc. times. For a Poisson distribution the points corresponding to a calculated probability and the average number of events would lie on a vertical line; the proximity of the actual points to such a line indicates the agreement with a Poisson distribution, and the abscissa of the line gives the expected (average) number of events.

The paper is generally valuable when we can use the Poisson distribution as an approximation to the binomial distribution, i.e., when the latter is highly skewed.

SOLVED PROBLEMS

8-1. The number of cars passing over a toll bridge during the time interval 10 to 11 A.M. is 1,200. The cars pass individually and collectively at random. Write an expression for the probability that not more than 4 cars will pass during the 1-min interval 10:45 to 10:46. Derive an expression for the probability that 5 or more cars will pass during the same interval.

Solution:

Number of cars in 60 min $= 1,200$.

Mean number of cars in 1-min interval $= \dfrac{1200}{60} = 20 = np$.

The probability of not more than 4 cars passing in that given interval

$= $ sum of probabilities of zero cars to and including 4 cars

$$= \sum_{r=0}^{4} \frac{(np)^r e^{-np}}{r!} = \left[\frac{(20)^0}{0!} + \frac{(20)^1}{1!} + \frac{(20)^2}{2!} + \frac{(20)^3}{3!} + \frac{(20)^4}{4!} \right] e^{-20}$$

Hence probability of 5 or more cars

$$= 1 - \sum_{r=0}^{4} \frac{(20)^r e^{-20}}{r!}$$

8-2. If the probability of a concrete beam failing in compression is 0.05, use the Poisson approximation to obtain the probability that from a sample of 50 beams
(*a*) at least three will fail in compression;
(*b*) no beam will fail in compression.

Solution:

Here, $p = 0.05$. Mean number of failures in compression $= np = 0.05 \times 50 = 2.5$.

(*a*) Probability of at least 3 beams failing

$$= 1 - \sum_{r=0}^{2} \frac{(np)^r e^{-np}}{r!}$$

$$= 1 - \left[\frac{(2.5)^0 e^{-2.5}}{0!} + \frac{(2.5)^1 e^{-2.5}}{1!} + \frac{(2.5)^2 e^{-2.5}}{2!} \right]$$

$$= 1 - e^{-2.5}[1 + 2.5 + 3.125]$$

$$= 1 - 0.082 \times 6.625 = 0.4575$$

(b) Probability of no beam failing in compression

$$= \frac{(2.5)^0 e^{-2.5}}{0!} = 0.082$$

Alternatively, we can use Poisson probability paper (see Fig. 8-1). For $np = 2.5$, the probability of at least 3 beams failing $= 1$ − probability of not more than 2 beams failing. For $r = 2$, probability $= 0.54$. Therefore the required probability of at least 3 beams failing is $1 - 0.54 = 0.46$. This can be found directly from the vertical scale on the left in Fig. 8-1.

For $r = 2$, probability $= 0.46$. Also, from Fig. 8-1 the probability of no failure, for $np = 2.5$ and $r = 0$, is 0.08.

8-3. If the probability of a Bailey bridge collapsing after 10 years of service without maintenance is 0.02, find the probability that out of 30 such bridges (having 10 years of service) (a) none, (b) exactly two, (c) not more than one, (d) more than two, (e) at least one, will collapse.

Solution:

Since the probability of success (bridge collapsing) $p < 0.05$ and the sample size $n > 20$, we can conveniently use the Poisson distribution as a good approximation to the binomial distribution. We have:

$$p = 0.02, \qquad n = 30$$

Therefore

$$np = 0.6$$

Using the cumulative Poisson probability graph of Fig. 8-1 with $np = 0.6$ and the appropriate r, we obtain:

(a) for $r = 0$, probability $= 0.54$ or 54 percent
(b) for $r = 2$, probability $= 0.975 - 0.875 = 0.10$ or 10 percent
(c) for $r \not> 1$, probability $= 0.875$ or 87.5 percent
(d) for $r > 2$, probability $= 0.025$ or 2.5 percent
(e) for $r \geq 1$, read off for $r > 0$ (i.e., left-hand ordinate),
      probability $\doteq 0.44$ or 44 percent

PROBLEMS

8-1. The numbers of road accidents per day reported in a given city on 100 consecutive days are as follows.

No. of accidents	0	1	2	3	4	5	6
No. of days	19	26	26	15	9	4	1

(a) Check whether the distribution of accidents can be considered to be a Poisson distribution.
(b) Compare the standard deviation of the given data with that of the Poisson distribution.

8-2. The probability for people of a certain age of dying within a year of their birthday is 0.0038. If there are 1,000 people of this age in a certain town, what is the probability of 10 of them dying during the year?

8-3. Cosmic ray counts are believed to be completely random, i.e., follow a Poisson distribution. Is this true of the following data?

Number of counts in 1 minute, r	0	1	2	3	4	5	6	7
Number of minutes having r counts	40	70	41	20	13	0	1	0

8-4. If a product is supposed to contain 2 percent of defective items, would we be justified in rejecting a consignment if, after testing 50 items, we find it to contain 5 defectives?

8-5. If the proportion of defective bearings being manufactured is 1/25, approximate by means of a Poisson distribution the probability that a random sample of 75 bearings will contain 3 or fewer defectives.

8-6. The number of failures of telephones connected to a private exchange is as follows:

No. of failures reported in a day, r	No. of days with r failures
0	101
1	60
2	31
3	8
4	0
5	1
6	0

Test the assumption that the failures occur randomly.

chapter 9

Normal Distribution

Chapters 7 and 8 dealt with distributions of occurrences of distinct events, i.e., with discrete variables. We shall now return to a consideration of quantities which vary continuously, and, specifically, to the properties of populations (and of samples drawn from such populations) whose individual members vary due to what is commonly referred to as errors.

ERRORS

There are two broad types of errors: *systematic* errors and *random* errors. The former arise from causes which act consistently under the given circumstances, e.g., a rule calibrated at one temperature will read systematically incorrectly at another, and the same applies in the simpler case of a false zero through the end of the rule having been cut off. Such an error can and should be avoided by suitable experimental techniques.

But even when all systematic errors have been eliminated there still remain accidental or random errors, which consist of a large number of very small effects, such as imprecision in an estimate of a fraction of a division on a scale, or a small, natural (random) variation in temperature from the standard at which the equipment has been calibrated (but not a seasonal variation which would introduce a systematic error and should be allowed for). Some of these effects are positive, others negative—i.e., they affect the value of the observation being made in a plus or minus direction with an equal probability. Thus the probability p of the occurrence of a positive error is $\frac{1}{2}$, and the probability q of its nonoccurrence (i.e., occurrence of a negative error) is also $\frac{1}{2}$. This fact is of fundamental importance and will be used in deriving the equation to the normal curve from the binomial distribution.

It is convenient to assume that all the small contributory errors are of equal absolute magnitude $|E|$, and in any particular case there are $2n$ of them. Thus, the total error will range from $-2nE$ (when all the contributory errors are negative) to $+2nE$ (when they are all positive). In any intermediate case, there will be a surplus (or a deficiency) of positive errors equal in number to $2r$, so that the resultant positive error is $2rE = X$. It is this error that causes variation between observations even under most carefully controlled conditions.

GAUSS FUNCTION

The distribution of these errors can be derived from mathematical considerations, and is given by the so-called Gauss function:

$$y = Ce^{-h^2 X^2} \qquad (9\text{-}1)$$

where

X = error (i.e., deviation from the mean or "true" value)

y = probability of occurrence of this error (or, strictly speaking, of an error in the range X to $X + \Delta X$)

e = base of natural logarithms

C = constant which determines, as will be shown later, the maximum height of the curve

h = constant which determines the spread of the curve, i.e., expresses the precision of the measurement, and is known as the *precision constant*.

The Gauss function, given by Eq. 9-1, can be viewed also from another standpoint, namely, as an empirical (approximate) formula for the distribution of many physical quantities which have a continuously variable magnitude. These twin *raisons d'être* of the Gauss function make it particularly important in statistical work. We may note in passing that the function was derived not only by Gauss but also by Laplace and de Moivre.

The distribution described by the Gauss function (Eq. 9-1) is commonly known as the *normal* distribution, but the name should not be construed to mean that the distribution is any more normal than other distributions.

DERIVATION OF THE FUNCTION

A general mathematical derivation of the Gauss function is not considered appropriate in this book, but a derivation from the binomial distribution should be of engineering interest.

Let us consider the binomial distribution $(q + p)^n$ with $p = q = \frac{1}{2}$. The mean is then $\mu = np = \frac{1}{2}n$. The frequency polygon for this distribution with $n = 8$ is shown in Fig. 9-1. As n increases indefinitely the frequency polygon will approach a smooth curve, symmetrical about a vertical line through the mean, and we can consider the normal curve to be the limit of the binomial expansion $(\frac{1}{2} + \frac{1}{2})^n$ as $n \to \infty$. The normal curve is plotted in Fig. 9-1 to the same scale as the frequency polygon, i.e., the area under each is the same.

Let us consider the expansion

$$\left(\frac{1}{2} + \frac{1}{2}\right)^{2n} = 2^{-2n}(1 + {}_{2n}C_1 + {}_{2n}C_2 + \cdots + {}_{2n}C_{n+r} + \cdots + 1) \qquad (9\text{-}2)$$

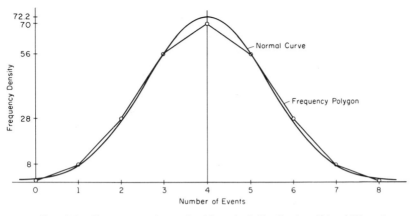

Fig. 9-1. Frequency polygon for binominal distribution $(\frac{1}{2} + \frac{1}{2})^8$ and the normal distribution curve, drawn to the same scale.

The successive terms in brackets are plotted in Fig. 9-2 as ordinates at intervals Δx, beginning with the first term at the origin $x = 0$. The maximum term in Eq. 9-2 is $2^{-2n} \times {}_{2n}C_n$, and this is the ordinate at the mean μ. It is convenient to transfer the origin to the mean, so that

$$\left.\begin{array}{l} X = x - \mu \\ \Delta X = \Delta x \end{array}\right\} \tag{9-3}$$

The y coordinate remains unaltered.

Consider points U and V in Fig. 9-2.

Their ordinates are:

$$y_U = {}_{2n}C_{n+r}$$

and

$$y_V = y_U + \Delta y = {}_{2n}C_{n+r+1}$$

But

$${}_{2n}C_{n+r+1} = \frac{{}_{2n}C_{n+r}(n-r)}{n+r+1}$$

(see footnote[1]).

Therefore

$$\Delta y = y_V - y_U$$

$$= {}_{2n}C_{n+r+1} - {}_{2n}C_{n+r}$$

$$= {}_{2n}C_{n+r}\left(\frac{n-r}{n+r+1} - 1\right)$$

[1] Since $\displaystyle {}_mC_{k+1} = \frac{m!}{(m-k-1)!\,(k+1)!} = \frac{m!}{(m-k)!\,k!} \times \frac{(m-k)}{(k+1)} = {}_mC_k \times \frac{(m-k)}{(k+1)}$.

or

$$\Delta y = {}_{2n}C_{n+r} \times \frac{n - r - n - r - 1}{n + r + 1}$$

$$= {}_{2n}C_{n+r} \times \left(\frac{-2r - 1}{n + r + 1}\right)$$

$$= y \times \left(\frac{-2r - 1}{n + r + 1}\right)$$

Hence

$$\frac{\Delta y}{\Delta X} = \frac{y}{\Delta X}\left(\frac{-2r - 1}{n + r + 1}\right) \tag{9-4}$$

The abscissa of point U is

$$X = r\,\Delta X$$

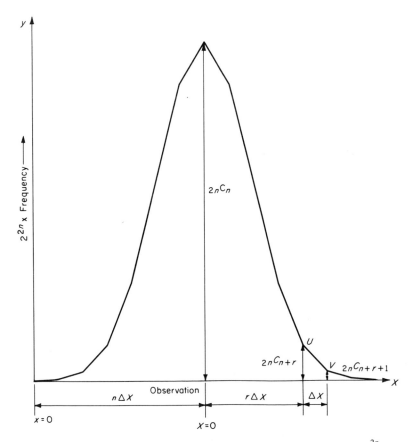

Fig. 9-2. Frequency polygon for binominal distribution $(\frac{1}{2} + \frac{1}{2})^{2n}$.

Hence

$$r = \frac{X}{\Delta X}$$

Substituting in Eq. 9-4,

$$\frac{\Delta y}{\Delta X} = \frac{y}{\Delta X} \left(\frac{-\dfrac{2X}{\Delta X} - 1}{n + \dfrac{X}{\Delta X} + 1} \right)$$

or

$$\frac{\Delta y}{\Delta X} = \frac{y}{\Delta X} \left[\frac{-(2X + \Delta X)}{n \, \Delta X + X + \Delta X} \right] \tag{9-5}$$

It is shown in Appendix C that in the expansion $(\frac{1}{2} + \frac{1}{2})^{2n}$ the mean of all the terms is

$$\mu = n \, \Delta x = n \, \Delta X \tag{9-6}$$

and the variance is

$$\sigma^2 = \frac{n}{2} (\Delta x)^2 = \frac{n}{2} (\Delta X)^2 \tag{9-7}$$

Substituting in Eq. 9-5, we obtain

$$\frac{\Delta y}{\Delta X} = \frac{-y(2X + \Delta X)}{2\sigma^2 + X \Delta X + (\Delta X)^2}$$

As $n \to \infty$,

$$\Delta X \to 0 \quad \text{and} \quad \frac{\Delta y}{\Delta X} \to \frac{dy}{dX}$$

Therefore

$$\frac{dy}{dX} = -y \frac{X}{\sigma^2}$$

or

$$\frac{dy}{y} = -\frac{X \, dX}{\sigma^2}$$

Integrating,

$$y = Ce^{-\frac{X^2}{2\sigma^2}} \tag{9-8}$$

Putting

$$h = \frac{1}{\sqrt{2}\,\sigma} \tag{9-9}$$

(h being the precision constant of the Gauss function), we can write Eq. 9-8 as

$$y = Ce^{-h^2 X^2}$$

which is Eq. 9-1.

THE NORMAL CURVE

The equation to the normal distribution curve can be written in several different forms. If we require the normal *frequency distribution* curve, the equation must satisfy the condition that the area under the curve is equal to the total number of observations *n*. Thus

$$\int_{-\infty}^{+\infty} y \, dX = n \tag{9-10}$$

The integration extends between $-\infty$ and $+\infty$ because when we postulated in our derivation that $n \longrightarrow \infty$, we extended the curve to infinity in either direction from the mean μ.

Such a curve can be directly compared with a histogram because the area under the histogram is also equal to the total number of observations.

Substituting in Eq. 9-10 from Eq. 9-8, we have

$$C \int_{-\infty}^{+\infty} e^{-\frac{X^2}{2\sigma^2}} \, dX = n \tag{9-11}$$

It is shown in Appendix D that

$$\int_{-\infty}^{+\infty} e^{-\frac{X^2}{2\sigma^2}} \, dX = \sigma\sqrt{2\pi} \tag{9-12}$$

Hence the maximum height of the curve is

$$C = \frac{n}{\sigma\sqrt{2\pi}} \tag{9-13}$$

and the equation to the normal frequency distribution curve can be written:

$$y = \frac{n}{\sigma\sqrt{2\pi}} \, e^{-\frac{X^2}{2\sigma^2}} \tag{9-14}$$

As previously defined, σ is the standard deviation of the population.

If we operate in terms of actual observations *x* (rather than deviations from the mean *X*) we can substitute from Eq. 9-14:

$$y = \frac{n}{\sigma\sqrt{2\pi}} \, e^{-\frac{(x-\mu)^2}{2\sigma^2}} \tag{9-15}$$

For many purposes it is preferable to deal with probability rather than frequency distribution. Since the sum of all probabilities is unity, the area under the normal *probability distribution* curve must be equal to unity. Such a curve is said to be *normalized,* and is given by

$$y = \frac{1}{\sigma\sqrt{2\pi}} \, e^{-\frac{(x-\mu)^2}{2\sigma^2}} \tag{9-16}$$

where y is the *probability density* for the deviation $(x - \mu)$, and represents the rate of change of probability with x.

Since the mean μ is constant for any one distribution, the effect of μ is to move the position of the normal curve along the x-axis but not to change the shape of the curve, which depends on the value of standard deviation σ only. Thus σ determines the horizontal spread, and it is for many purposes convenient to use σ as a unit of deviation from the mean. We put

$$z = \frac{x - \mu}{\sigma} = \frac{X}{\sigma} \tag{9-17}$$

Hence

$$dz = \frac{1}{\sigma} dX$$

and the equation to the normal probability distribution curve becomes:

$$y = \frac{1}{\sqrt{2\pi}} e^{-\frac{z^2}{2}} \tag{9-18}$$

This equation for a normal probability distribution is said to be in a standard form,[2] and it is for this form that most statistical tables have been prepared. Table A-3 gives the values of y. (To standardize a variate we transform it using Eq. 9-17, that is, we subtract the mean from all values and divide the results by the standard deviation.)

From the above argument it is clear that μ and σ are the parameters of the normal distribution.

PHYSICAL SIGNIFICANCE OF STANDARD DEVIATION

Consider Eq. 9-16 using $X = x - \mu$. In order to find the point at which the curvature of this curve changes sign, we equate the second differential coefficient of the equation to zero. Thus

$$\frac{d^2 y}{dX^2} = \frac{-1}{\sigma^3 \sqrt{2\pi}} \left(e^{-\frac{X^2}{2\sigma^2}} - \frac{X^2}{\sigma^2} e^{-\frac{X^2}{2\sigma^2}} \right) = 0$$

whence

$$1 - \frac{X^2}{\sigma^2} = 0$$

or

$$X = \pm\sigma$$

In other words, the point of inflection occurs on either side of the mean at a distance equal to the standard deviation, that is, $z = 1$. This establishes a physical significance of the standard deviation, and should be remembered when sketching the normal curve.

[2] It applies to x when $\mu = 0$ and $\sigma = 1$.

AREA UNDER THE NORMAL CURVE

Since $dz = \dfrac{1}{\sigma} dx$, the area under the curve between the mean and $z = z$ is

$$F(z) = \int_{\mu}^{x} y \, dx$$

$$= \sigma \int_{0}^{z} y \, dz$$

that is (from Eqs. 9-16 and 9-17),

$$F(z) = \frac{1}{\sqrt{2\pi}} \int_{0}^{z} e^{-\frac{z^2}{2}} \, dz \qquad (9\text{-}19)$$

Figure 9-3 shows the normal probability curve, the abscissae being marked in terms of both X and z. The areas under the curve $F(z)$ cor-

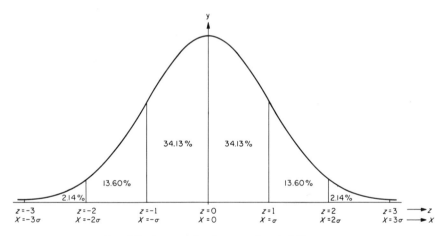

Fig. 9-3. Areas under the normal probability curve.

responding to deviations in steps of one standard deviation are written on the figure. It may be noted that Eq. 9-19 cannot be integrated directly, and $F(z)$ must be obtained by numerical methods (see Appendix D). The full range of values of $F(z)$ is given in Table A-4. A selection of values of $F(z)$ is given in Table 9-1, together with areas for the range ($\mu - z\sigma$, $\mu + z\sigma$), that is, corresponding to a deviation from the mean not exceeding $\pm z\sigma$. The latter areas are equal to $2 \times F(z)$, and give the probability of a given deviation in *either* direction not being exceeded, while $F(z)$ gives values for a positive *or* a negative deviation not being exceeded. The distinction is obvious, but it is important to remember it at all times.

TABLE 9-1

AREAS UNDER THE NORMAL CURVE

(See Eq. 9-19)

z	$F(z)$	$2 \times F(z)$
0	0.0000	0.0000
0.25	0.0987	0.1974
0.50	0.1915	0.3830
0.67	0.2486	0.4972
0.6745	0.2500	0.5000
0.68	0.2518	0.5035
1.00	0.3413	0.6826
1.96	0.4750	0.9500
2.00	0.4772	0.9544
2.50	0.4938	0.9876
2.576	0.4950	0.9900
3.00	0.4987	0.9974

The probability of a deviation lying between two values of z is given by the area under the normal curve between these limits. Since Table A-4 (and, indeed, all statistical tables) gives the values of $F(z)$ with one limit of $z = 0$ only,[3] we have to use differences. For example, the probability of a deviation z such that $1 \leq z \leq 2$ is obtained by subtraction of $F(z)$ for $z = 1$ from $F(z)$ for $z = 2$, namely, $0.4772 - 0.3413 = 0.1359$. Thus the probability of an observation having a deviation from the mean not smaller than σ and not greater than 2σ is 0.1359.

Example. Find the probabilities of a set of observations, believed to be normally distributed, having values that fall outside the range specified in column 1 of the following table. Hence, find the number per 1,000 outside the specified range.

(1) Range	(2) Probability of falling inside the range	(3) Number of observations per 1,000 outside the specified range
$-\tfrac{1}{4}\sigma,\ +\tfrac{1}{4}\sigma$	0.1974	803
$-1\tfrac{1}{2}\sigma,\ +\tfrac{1}{2}\sigma$	0.6247	375
$-\tfrac{1}{2}\sigma,\ +1\tfrac{1}{2}\sigma$	0.6247	375
$-\tfrac{1}{2}\sigma,\ +3\sigma$	0.6902	310
$+2\sigma,\ +4\sigma$	0.0228	977

To obtain column 2 we find $F(z)$ from Table A-4.

For example, in order to find the probability for the range $-\tfrac{1}{4}\sigma$ to $+\tfrac{1}{4}\sigma$, we observe that the area under the normal curve between $z = 0$ and $z - \tfrac{1}{4}$ is 0.0987. Since the curve is symmetrical, the probability for the range $-\tfrac{1}{4}\sigma$ to $+\tfrac{1}{4}\sigma$ is $2 \times 0.0987 = 0.1974$. To obtain column 3 we

[3] Or $z = -\infty$, but not finite values.

multiply the probability of falling inside the range by 1,000 and subtract the result from 1,000.

To find the probability for the range $-1\frac{1}{2}\sigma$ to $+\frac{1}{2}\sigma$ we have to find $F(z)$ for 0 to $\frac{1}{2}\sigma$ (0.1915), and $F(z)$ for 0 to $1\frac{1}{2}\sigma$ (0.4332) and add the two results (obtaining 0.6247). We utilize the fact that $F(z)$ for 0 to $-1\frac{1}{2}\sigma$ is the same as $F(z)$ for 0 to $+1\frac{1}{2}\sigma$. For the same reason we can write the probability for the range $-\frac{1}{2}\sigma$ to $1\frac{1}{2}\sigma$, without further calculations.

For the probability for the range $+2\sigma$ to $+4\sigma$ we have to subtract $F(z)$ for 0 to 2σ (0.4772) from $F(z)$ for 0 to 4σ (0.49997); the answer is 0.02277.

SOLVED PROBLEMS

9-1. The finished inside diameter of a piston ring is normally distributed with a mean of 4.50 in. and a standard deviation of 0.005 in. What is the probability of obtaining a diameter exceeding 4.51 in.?

Solution:

Given $\mu = 4.50$ in. and $\sigma = 0.005$ in.

Deviation from the mean:

$$x - \mu = 4.51 - 4.50 = 0.01$$

Hence

$$z = \frac{x - \mu}{\sigma} = \frac{0.01}{0.005} = 2.0$$

From Table A-4 for $z = 2.0$, $F(z) = 0.4772$. Therefore required probability

$$= 0.5000 - 0.4772$$

$$= 0.0228$$

$$= 2.28 \text{ percent (a chance of 1 in 44)}$$

9-2. The resistance of a foil strain gage is normally distributed with a mean of 120.0 ohms and a standard deviation of 0.4 ohm. The specification limits are 120.0 ± 0.5 ohms. What percentage of gages will be defective?

Solution:

Given $\mu = 120.0$ ohms and $\sigma = 0.4$ ohm.

Allowable deviation from the mean:

$$x - \mu = \pm 0.5 \text{ ohm}$$

Hence

$$z = \frac{x - \mu}{\sigma} = \frac{0.5}{0.4} = 1.25$$

From Table A-4, for $z = 1.25$, $F(z) = 0.3944$. Therefore, the probability of a defective gage

$$= 1 - 2 \times 0.3944$$

$$= 1 - 0.7888$$

$$= 0.2112$$

$$- 21.12 \text{ percent}$$

9-3. The measurement of the inside diameter of a cast-iron pipe is normally distributed with a mean of 5.01 in. and standard deviation of 0.03 in. The specification limits are 5.00 ± 0.05 in. What percentage of pipes is not acceptable?

Solution:

Refer to Fig. 9-4. For the upper range,

$$z = \frac{5.05 - 5.01}{0.03} = 1.33$$

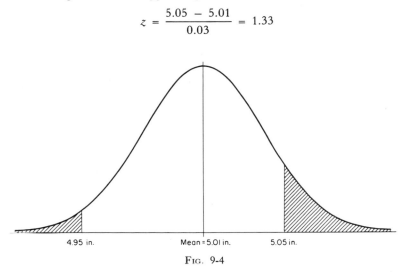

4.95 in.   Mean = 5.01 in.   5.05 in.

FIG. 9-4

From Table A-4, for $z = 1.33$, $F(z_1) = 0.4082$. For the lower range,

$$z = \frac{5.01 - 4.95}{0.03} = \frac{0.06}{0.03} = 2.0$$

The corresponding $F(z_2) = 0.4772$. The probability of falling within the specified limits

$$= F(z_1) + F(z_2)$$
$$= 0.4082 + 0.4772$$
$$= 0.8852$$

Probability of falling outside the limits

$$= \text{percentage of unacceptable pipes}$$
$$= 1 - 0.8852 = 0.1148$$
$$= 11.48 \text{ percent}$$

PROBLEMS

9-1. If μ is the mean and σ is the standard deviation of the diameters of ball bearings, which follow a normal distribution, what percentage of ball bearings would have diameters: (*a*) within the range ($\mu \pm 2\sigma$); (*b*) outside the range ($\mu \pm 0.9\sigma$); (*c*) greater than ($\mu - 1.5\sigma$)?

9-2. The strength of a plastic produced by a certain method is known to be normally distributed. If 10 percent of the results exceed 8,000 lb and 70 percent exceed 6,000 lb, what are the mean and the standard deviation?

9-3. If x is normally distributed with a mean of 100 and a standard deviation of 18, find the probability of a random observation falling between (*a*) 115 and 140; (*b*) 90 and 120.

9-4. If the I.Q. scores of recruits are normally distributed with a mean of 100 and a standard deviation of 13, find (*a*) the fraction who have an I.Q. greater than 133; (*b*) the fraction who have an I.Q. greater than 90; (*c*) the I.Q. exceeded by the upper quartile of recruits.

9-5. The navy uses stockings which have a mean life of 50 days with a variance of 64 days. Assuming that the life of such stockings is normally distributed, of 150,000 pairs issued how many would be expected to need replacement after 42 days? after 63 days?

9-6. Electric bulbs bought for lighting an outdoor rink have a mean life of 3,000 hours with a coefficient of variation of 11.3 percent. If it is more economical to replace all the bulbs when 20 percent of them have burned out than to change them as needed, after how many hours should the bulbs be changed?

Assuming that the lamps have not been changed, find the period after which an additional 20 percent of the lamps will have burned out.

chapter 10

Use of Normal Distribution

Two comments on normal distribution may now be in order. In a mathematical derivation of the normal distribution curve, x (or X) is assumed to be a continuous variable. For this reason the probability of x having *exactly* a particular value is zero, and we consider only the probability of x, when chosen at random, falling between x and $x + \Delta x$; this is given by the area $y \Delta x$. In the limit this area becomes $y\,dx$. As mentioned before, y represents the probability density.

LIMITS OF PRACTICAL DISTRIBUTIONS

The second comment concerns limits of the normal distribution curve. Equation 9-11 shows these as $-\infty$ and $+\infty$, and yet in many cases the observed values cannot extend so far from the mean; furthermore, negative values of x may sometimes have no physical meaning. To explain this anomaly we should remember that we use the normal distribution as an approximation to physical observations, the mathematical equation being valid only between finite limits. The approximation is, however, very good as 99.9936 percent of the area under the normal curve lies within a range of four standard deviations from the mean; for three standard deviations the area contained is 99.740 percent (see Table A-4). We are, therefore, justified in the majority of cases in ignoring the *tails* of the distribution beyond $z = 4$, or some other appropriate value.

SOME IMPORTANT PROBABILITIES

Several values of area under the normal probability curve are of especial interest and are shown diagrammatically in Fig. 10-1. Figure 10-1*a* illustrates the fact that one-half of the area under the curve lies within $\pm 0.6745\,\sigma$ from the mean. Thus a single observation has an equal chance of falling within or without this range. For this reason such a deviation has in the past been called the *probable error*, but the term is not often used nowadays.[1]

---

[1] The probable error of the mean $\bar{x}$ is a value E such that there is a 50 percent probability that $\bar{x}$ does not differ from μ by more than E.

Figure 10-1*b* shows that within a range of $\pm\sigma$ from the mean are contained 68.26 percent of all observations. A deviation of $\pm\sigma$ is referred to as a *standard error*, and is often quoted as a measure of precision. Thus if a mean value of a quantity is given, for example, as 27.05 ± 0.042, we interpret this to mean that the "true" value of the mean lies between $(27.05 - 0.042)$ and $(27.05 + 0.042)$, and there is a 68.26 percent probability of our being correct. In other words, if we present results in this form on a number of occasions, we shall be correct in our statements in 68.26 percent of all cases.

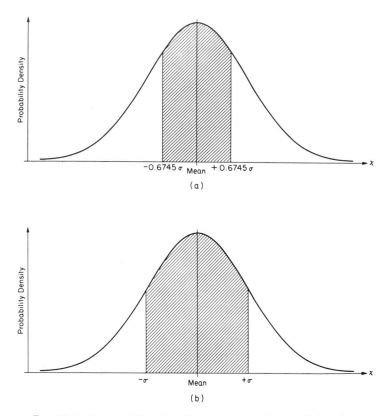

Fig. 10-1.   Range of deviations from the mean for specified probabilities of an observation falling within the range: (*a*) 50 percent; (*b*) 68.26 percent; (*c*) 95 percent; (*d*) 99 percent.

Figures 10-1*c* and 10-1*d* are of particular interest as they show the values of a deviation, positive or negative, exceeded by chance in 5 percent and 1 percent of all cases respectively, these percentages being extensively used in statistical treatments of data. If we are interested in a deviation of a specified sign only, say positive, the probability would be given by the area under the normal curve from the specified deviation to $+\infty$. Thus, the magnitude of a positive deviation which would be exceeded in 1 percent of all cases is given by

$$0.5 + F(z) = 0.99$$

Hence

$$F(z) = 0.49$$

From Table A-4

$$z = 2.33$$

i.e., a deviation of $+2.33\,\sigma$ is exceeded by chance in 1 percent of all cases.

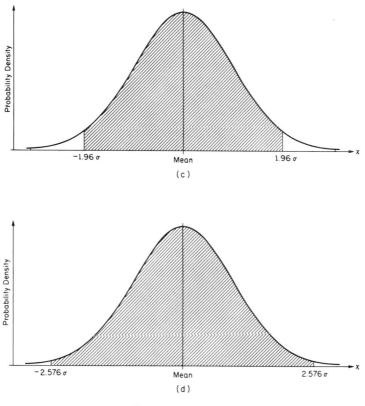

Fig. 10-1 (*Continued*)

FITTING A NORMAL CURVE

In experimental work we frequently obtain a set of observations which we consider as members of a population, but we may have no assurance that the data follow a normal distribution, or any other standard distribution. We may, however, suspect on the basis of past experience that certain observations conform to a given distribution, and it is one of the more important applications of statistics to the problems of measurement to investigate whether the data in hand fit an assumed distribution.

We shall now consider fitting a normal curve by following a numerical example. Before proceeding, however, we should recall two assumptions made in our derivation of the normal frequency curve:

(a)   The mean and the standard deviation of the normal frequency distribution are equal, respectively, to the mean and standard deviation of the actual observations.

(b)   The area under the normal frequency distribution curve is equal to the total number of observations, i.e., to the area under the histogram.

Example. Let us fit the normal curve to the theoretical frequency distribution of heads when eight coins are tossed.

In Fig. 9-1 the binomial expansion of $(\frac{1}{2} + \frac{1}{2})^8$ was shown to have the following values:

Number of successes..........	0	1	2	3	4	5	6	7	8
Frequency	1	8	28	56	70	56	28	8	1

Thus, the total number of observations is $n = 256$.

$$\text{Mean} = \mu = n'p = \frac{1}{2} \times 8 = 4$$

and

$$\sigma = \sqrt{n'pq} = \sqrt{8 \times \frac{1}{2} \times \frac{1}{2}} = \sqrt{2}$$

Substituting in Eq. 9-15 for the normal frequency distribution,

$$y = \frac{n}{\sigma\sqrt{2\pi}} e^{-\frac{(x-\mu)^2}{2\sigma^2}} \tag{10-1}$$

that is

$$y = \frac{128}{\sqrt{\pi}} e^{-\frac{(x-4)^2}{4}} \tag{10-2}$$

We can now plot y for various values of x and draw a smooth curve through the points. This has been done in Fig. 10-2, which shows also the frequency polygon and histogram for the binomial distribution. Since we are dealing with an ideal distribution, the agreement between the curves is of course good, the discrepancy being due solely to the discontinuous character of the binomial distribution.

In practice, instead of calculating the values from Eq. 10-2, we use tabulated values of the ordinate of the normal curve. Table A-3 gives the or-

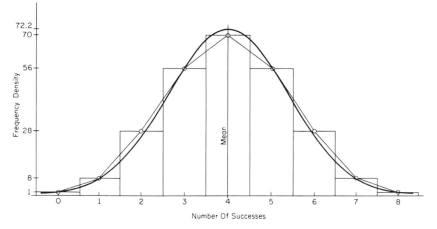

Fig. 10-2. Frequency density: histogram, polygon, and fitted normal curve for example.

dinates for the normal curve in the standard form (Eq. 9-18), that is,

$$y = \frac{1}{\sqrt{2\pi}} e^{-z^2/2}$$

In our case, the tabulated ordinates would have to be multiplied by

$$\frac{n}{\sigma} = \frac{256}{\sqrt{2}}$$

Let us now consider an example based on experimental results, as distinct from a theoretical distribution.

Example. Two hundred and fifty-five lengths of wire were roughly cut to a length of 300 ft 6 in. each. When measured, they were found to range between 300 ft $0\frac{1}{2}$ in. and 301 ft $0\frac{1}{2}$ in. The measured lengths in excess of 300 ft 0 in. were recorded for intervals of $\frac{1}{2}$ to $1\frac{1}{2}$ in., $1\frac{1}{2}$–$2\frac{1}{2}$ in., ..., $11\frac{1}{2}$–$12\frac{1}{2}$ in , with the following observed frequency distribution:

Class midpoint (in.), x_i	1	2	3	4	5	6	7	8	9	10	11	12
Frequency, f_i	2	10	19	25	40	44	41	28	25	15	5	1

In order to fit the normal curve to this distribution, we have to find the mean and the standard deviation of the observed data. It is convenient to assume a fictitious mean $\overline{X}_0 = 6$ in. We can then use a new variable $X_i' = x_i - \overline{X}_0$ and tabulate the results as follows:

x_i	f_i	Deviation from fictitious mean X_i'	$f_i X_i'$	$f_i X_i'^2$
1	2	-5	-10	50
2	10	-4	-40	160
3	19	-3	-57	171
4	25	-2	-50	100
5	40	-1	-40	40
6	44	0	0	0
7	41	1	41	41
8	28	2	56	112
9	25	3	75	225
10	15	4	60	240
11	5	5	25	125
12	1	6	6	36
Totals	$\Sigma f_i = 255$		$\Sigma f_i X_i' = -197 + 263$ $= 66$	$\Sigma f_i X_i'^2 = 1,300$

Hence

$$\text{Mean} = \bar{X} = \bar{X}_0 + \frac{\Sigma f_i X_i'}{\Sigma f_i} = 6 + \frac{66}{255} = 6.26 \text{ in.}$$

and

$$\sigma = \sqrt{\frac{\Sigma f_i X_i'^2 - \dfrac{(\Sigma f_i X_i')^2}{n}}{n-1}} = \sqrt{\frac{1,300 - \dfrac{66^2}{255}}{254}} = 2.25 \text{ in.}$$

Substituting in Eq. 9-14, we obtain

$$y = \frac{255}{2.25\sqrt{2\pi}} e^{-\frac{X^2}{2(2.25)^2}}$$

$$= 45.21 \, e^{-0.0986 X^2}$$

where

$$X = x - \bar{X}$$

For the purpose of plotting the curve, we multiply the values of the ordinate of the normal curve in the standard form y (Table A-3) by $n/\sigma = 255/2.25$ and obtain:

$z = \dfrac{X}{\sigma}$ =	0	± 0.5	± 1.0	± 1.5	± 2.0	± 2.5	± 3.0
y =	0.3989	0.3521	0.2420	0.1295	0.0540	0.0175	0.0044
$y\,(n/\sigma)$ =	45.21	39.90	27.43	14.68	6.12	1.98	0.05
X =	0	1.12	2.25	3.37	4.50	5.62	6.75
x = 6.26		$\begin{cases} 5.14 \\ 7.38 \end{cases}$	$\begin{matrix} 4.01 \\ 8.51 \end{matrix}$	$\begin{matrix} 2.88 \\ 9.63 \end{matrix}$	$\begin{matrix} 1.76 \\ 10.76 \end{matrix}$	$\begin{matrix} 0.63 \\ 11.88 \end{matrix}$	$\begin{matrix} -0.49 \\ 13.01 \end{matrix}$

Figure 10-3 shows the plot of $y\,(n/\sigma)$ against x.

It is important to note that the ordinates of the normal curve have been calculated for deviations of X from the mean, while the histogram is plotted

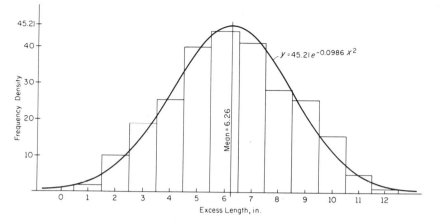

FIG. 10-3.   Histogram and fitted normal curve for example; the lengths plotted
are those in excess of 300 ft 0 in.

for the arbitrary intervals of 1 in., 2 in., 3 in., and so on. The height of the histogram blocks is obtained by dividing each class frequency by the class width; the histogram will then be plotted to the same scale as the normal curve. Since in our case the class width is unity, the heights are numerically equal to frequencies.

Finally, we must not forget that the lengths plotted are those in excess of 300 ft 0 in.

Example. Find the probability of obtaining between 4 and 7 heads in 10 throws of a coin, using the binomial expansion, and approximating by the normal distribution.

Using the binomial distribution, we write by virtue of the theorem of repeated trials, and from Eq. 7-1 b,

$$P = \sum_{i=4}^{7} {}_{10}C_i \left(\frac{1}{2}\right)^{10}$$

$$= \frac{210 + 252 + 210 + 120}{1024}$$

$$= 0.7734$$

that is, the probability of obtaining the required number of heads is 77.34 percent.

In the approximation based on the normal distribution we obtain a more accurate result if we recognize that the extreme values (4 and 7 heads) represent class midpoints; the actual class intervals extend to the (rather theoretical) values of $3\frac{1}{2}$ and $7\frac{1}{2}$ respectively (Fig. 10-4). Thus the area under the histogram, which is to be equaled by the fitted normal curve,

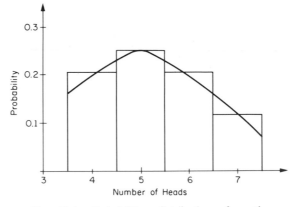

FIG. 10-4. Probability distribution for the example.

should be taken to these extremes. We have

$$p = q = \frac{1}{2}$$

$$\mu = np = 5$$

$$\sigma = \sqrt{npq} = 1.58$$

$$X_1 = 3.5 - 5 = -1.5$$

$$X_2 = 7.5 - 5 = +2.5$$

Therefore

$$z_1 = \frac{-1.5}{1.58} = -0.95$$

and

$$z_2 = \frac{2.5}{1.58} = 1.58$$

The areas under the normal curve between these values of z and the mean are found from Table A-4 to be $0.3289 + 0.4429 = 0.7718$. The approximation is thus very close.

PROBABILITY PAPER

We may recall the cumulative frequency curve, mentioned in Chapter 2. When a variate follows a normal distribution, the cumulative frequency plots as an S-shaped curve. A curve of such shape is not convenient to use, and it is preferable to rectify it. This is achieved by the use of probability paper.

The construction of this paper is based on the fact that the cumulative frequency represents the area under the normal probability curve between $-\infty$ and the value of the variate up to which the cumulative frequency is required. Thus we make the increments in the ordinates (labeled as the cumulative area under the normal curve) equal for equal increments in the abscissae (representing the variate). On commercial probability paper the ordinates are marked off for probabilities of 0.01, 0.02, ..., 0.1, 0.2, ..., 1.0, 1.2, ..., 2, 3, ..., 20, 22, ..., 50 and on to 100 percent. Since the normal distribution is symmetrical, the spacing is symmetrical about the ordinate of 50 percent. The abscissae represent the variate to a linear scale. The normal probability paper is shown in Fig. 10-6.

We may note that the areas used in constructing the probability paper are the tail areas while the area $F(z)$ given in Table A-4 is reckoned from the mean, i.e., from the axis of symmetry of the normal curve; this is shown diagrammatically in Fig. 10-5. The relation between the two is simply:

$$\text{Tail area} = 0.5 - F(z)$$

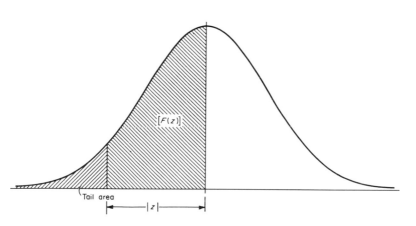

Fɪɢ. 10 5. Diagrammatic representation of tail area used in construction of probability paper and $F(z)$ of Table A-4.

When normal probability paper is used, a normal cumulative frequency plots as a straight line passing through the centroidal point (mean value of variate, 50 percent probability), and the paper is therefore useful in visual testing of normality of a set of observations.

As an example, Fig. 10-6 shows the cumulative frequency distribution for the data of Table 2-3, with the "best" straight line drawn by eye. Since we are interested in strength lower than a given value, the abscissae represent upper class boundaries. The mean is found as the abscissa of the point corresponding to a 50 percent cumulative frequency, in our case 1,000 psi, which agrees exactly with the value obtained by calculation following Eq. 3-3.

Since the area under a normal curve between the mean and a deviation equal to the standard deviation is equal to 34.13 percent of the total

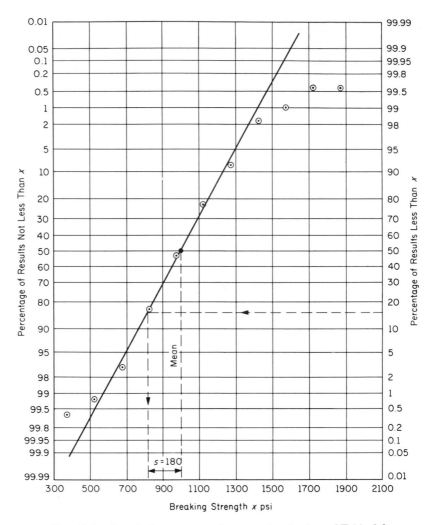

FIG. 10-6.　Cumulative percentage frequency for the data of Table 2-3; abscissae show the upper class boundaries.

area under the curve (see Fig. 9-3), we can read off an estimate of the standard deviation from our graph by finding the difference in abscissae between the mean and a point whose ordinate is $50 - 34.13 \backsimeq 16$ percent. This is illustrated in Fig. 10-6. In our case, the standard deviation is estimated to be 180 psi, compared with 202 psi obtained by calculation following Eq. 4-8.

The agreement between the values read off Fig. 10-6 and the calculated values is good, and indeed the diagram shows that the actual distribution departs only very slightly from normal. We should note that in drawing the "best" line we pay more attention to points near the center of the distribution than to those near the extremes. Tails are bound to show scatter since the actual number of observations in that region is usually very small; for example, the normal distribution may require 0.4 percent of observations to have a strength less than 525 psi. This would correspond to 0.4 × 10^{-2} × 270 = 1.08 observations. The actual number must be an integer, and if 1 it is too low, if 2 it is too high.

To offer general guidance we can say that a line which, even though straight, does not pass through the centroidal point (i.e., a point whose coordinates are the true sample mean and the 50 percent probability) signifies a skewed distribution.

If the points are so distributed that those corresponding to probabilities somewhat below 50 percent "less than" lie below a straight line through the centroidal point, and those corresponding to probabilities above 50 percent "less than" lie above the straight line, the distribution is more peaked than normal. If the deviations are in the opposite direction, the distribution is less peaked than normal. However, to establish the significance for departures from normality not less than about 500 observations are needed.

MEAN DEVIATION IN NORMAL DISTRIBUTION

The use of mean deviation d_m was discouraged in Chapter 4, but in the case of the normal distribution, d_m may be of use when only a very approximate value of standard deviation σ is required. It can be shown that when the variate is normally distributed,

$$\sigma = \sqrt{\frac{\pi}{2}} \, d_m$$

$$\sigma \approx 1.25 \, d_m$$

The mean deviation d_m has of course the advantage of being obtained very rapidly from Eq. 4-9.

CENTRAL LIMIT THEOREM

The importance of the normal distribution lies not only in the fact that numerous variables are actually nearly normally distributed but also in the large body of statistical methods and tables derived for the normal distribution and often applicable approximately even to distributions departing from normal. In particular, numerous statistical techniques concerned with sampling involve the use of normal distribution.

We mentioned in Chapter 6 that sample means follow approximately normal distribution even if the underlying distribution is not normal, and we shall now present this more formally as the central limit theorem. This states that if we draw samples of size n from a population with a mean μ and a finite variance σ^2, with an increase in n the distribution of sample means approaches a normal distribution with a mean μ and variance σ^2/n. We can see that virtually the only limitation on the underlying distribution is that the variance be finite, and this is satisfied in nearly all engineering and scientific problems.

How good the approximation is for a given sample size depends on the shape of the underlying distribution. We can look at the problem another way and say that the further the underlying distribution is removed from normal, the larger the samples need to be for their mean to be nearly normally distributed. However, even if the underlying distribution is rectangular or triangular, the means of samples of four items or more are approximately normally distributed. The approximation is least accurate near the tails, and care is necessary when that part of the distribution is of importance.

We can see thus how the use of normal distribution is extended by the central limit theorem. Furthermore, many statistical tests which have been derived for normal distribution (such as tests of significance and analysis of variance, dealt with in Chapters 13 and 18) remain valid for distributions which depart from normality.

TRANSFORMATION TO A NORMALLY DISTRIBUTED VARIATE

If, however, a distribution is known not to be normal and its shape is known, it would be foolish to disregard this knowledge. But even then it may be possible to transform the data to a form which is normally distributed. For example, in fatigue tests the variation in the number of cycles which metal members survive before failing is such that logarithms of these life values are normally distributed.

The log transformation is applicable in many other cases, especially when the range of observations covers several orders of magnitude. The measurement of acidity by pH is an example of such a transformation in ordinary scientific work.

Transformation of the observed variable x other than by logarithms may be required to achieve a normal distribution relation; the more common transforms are $1/x$, $\sqrt{x}$, $\sqrt[3]{x}$, and so on.

The need for transformation may arise from the method of measurement used. For example, assume that spherical components are manufactured and their size (diameter) is known to be normally distributed. If we measure the components by weight, we shall find that the weights are not normally distributed since they are proportional to a third power of the linear dimension. Changing, therefore, the variable to the cube root of the weight will produce normal distribution. The same would apply in particle grading, where the size of particles is determined by a linear test but is measured by weight.

If we have no prior information as to which transformation should be used, we have to resort to trial and error. The transformation which yields the "best" straight line when the cumulative frequency of the transformed variable is plotted on normal probability paper is considered most suitable.

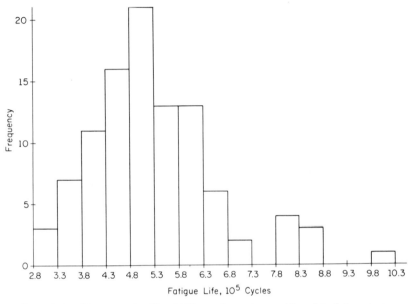

FIG. 10-7.   Histogram for life of 100 metal members subjected to fatigue tests.

As an illustration of rectification by transformation, Fig. 10-7 shows a histogram for fatigue tests on 100 metal members.[2] This is markedly skewed, and the skewness is confirmed by the cumulative frequency plot in Fig. 10-8. Log transformation was applied to the data, and resulted in an approximately normal distribution, as shown in Figs. 10-9 and 10-10.

We may note that the log transformation has to be applied to the original data before grouping; for this reason the number of class intervals and the class frequency after transformation are different from those in the original data.

BINOMIAL APPROXIMATION

Although we have fitted different distributions to different types of sets of data, it is important to be aware of the relation between the various dis-

[2] J. Pope and N. Bloomer, "Statistics as Applied to Fatigue Testing," Metal Fatigue Symposium, Nottingham University, England, 1955.

tributions. In Chapter 8 we saw how a markedly asymmetrical binomial distribution can be approximated by a Poisson distribution. Later we used a symmetrical binomial distribution in obtaining a normal distribution. The agreement between the terms of an expansion of $(q + p)^n$ (where $p =$

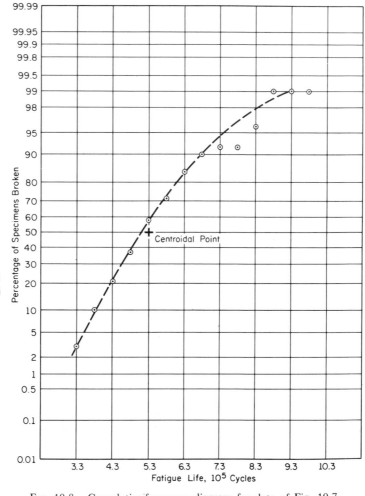

Fig. 10-8.   Cumulative frequency diagram for data of Fig. 10-7
plotted on normal probability paper.

$q = \frac{1}{2}$) and a normal distribution is better the larger the value of n. It is interesting to note that when n is very large the approximation of the bi-nomial distribution by the normal distribution is good, even if p differs considerably from q, as the binomial distribution loses a great deal of its skew-

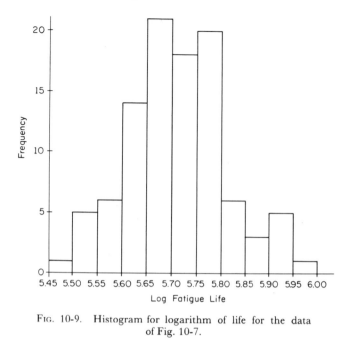

Fɪɢ. 10-9. Histogram for logarithm of life for the data
of Fig. 10-7.

ness. For example, for $q = 0.8$, $p = 0.2$, and $n = 50$ the binomial distribution approximates closely to normal. The greater the difference between p and q, the larger n has to be for a given closeness of approximation.

LEVEL OF SIGNIFICANCE

When observations are normally distributed, it follows that $[1 - 2F(z)]$ represents the probability of a value falling outside the range $\mu \pm z\sigma$. This probability is called the level of significance of a statistical test. Thus, when $z = 1.96$, $[1 - 2F(z)] = 0.05$, and we say that the level of significance is 5 percent. This means that if we obtain an observation that deviates from the mean by at least $\pm 1.96\sigma$, we can say that the observation is *significantly* different from the body of the data described by the given normal distribution, and the probability of our being in error is 5 percent. In other words, if we draw such a conclusion a large number of times, we shall be wrong in 5 percent of all the cases.

The term *significant* is used in the statistical sense of the word and means that the probability of the observed difference being due to chance alone is equal to the level of significance. A difference may be *statistically significant* but quite unimportant and not significant from the practical point of view.

From the fact that there is a 5 percent probability of an observation

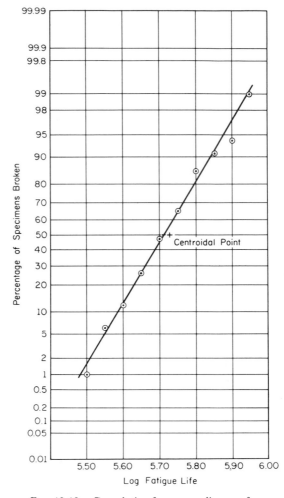

F$_{IG}$. 10-10. Cumulative frequency diagram for data of Fig. 10-9, plotted on a normal probability paper.

having a deviation from the mean greater than $|1.96\sigma|$ it follows that there is a 95 percent probability that an observation will fall within the range $\mu \pm 1.96\sigma$, and this degree of confidence is referred to as the 95 percent confidence level. Thus, the *confidence level* (or confidence coefficient) is described by $2F(z)$ expressed as a percentage (see Fig. 10-5). The limits $(\mu - z\sigma)$ and $(\mu + z\sigma)$ are called *confidence limits*, and they describe between them the *confidence interval*.

The values of z corresponding to the more commonly used values of the level of significance are presented in Table 10-1.

TABLE 10-1
VALUES OF z FOR A SPECIFIED PERCENTAGE OF RESULTS
TO LIE WITHIN THE RANGE $\mu \pm z\sigma$

Level of significance (percentage of results outside the range), percent	z	Confidence level (percentage of results within the range), percent
10	1.645	90
5	1.960	95
2	2.326	98
1	2.576	99
0.1	3.291	99.9
0.01	3.891	99.99

The confidence interval, which can be calculated for any statistic, is of considerable importance as it expresses the reliability of our estimate of a parameter: the narrower the interval, the more precise the estimate.

If we know μ and σ, then we can say that, for example, the 99.74 percent confidence interval for the mean of a sample of size n is $\mu \pm (3\sigma/\sqrt{n})$. In the converse and more common case when μ is unknown, we can express the 99.74 percent confidence interval for μ as $\bar{x} \pm (3\sigma/\sqrt{n})$. This asserts that the true mean lies within the interval with a 99.74 percent probability of our being right.

When σ is not known but only estimated, the confidence limits must perforce be wider. This is discussed in Chapter 13; Chapter 14 deals with the confidence limits for variance.

We should stress the fact that all our statements are in terms of probability, and it is not possible to *prove* whether or not an observation belongs to a population.

Example. Imagine that a coin was tossed 576 times and 256 heads were obtained. Are we justified in suspecting that the coin is biased or the experimenter dishonest?

Since $p = q = \frac{1}{2}$ and n is large, we can use the normal distribution as an approximation to binomial. We have:

$$n = 576$$
$$\mu = np = 288 \text{ (a value obviously expected)}$$
$$\sigma = \sqrt{npq} = 12$$

The observed value is

$$x = 256$$

Hence

$$z = \frac{|x - \mu|}{\sigma} = 2.67$$

From Table 10-1 we find that a deviation of 2.576σ is exceeded only in 1 percent of all cases, and the observed deviation is larger than the tabulated value. We conclude, therefore, at the 1 percent level of significance, that the observed value does not belong to the population (of all the possible sets of 576 throws of a coin); the probability of our making a wrong accusation of dishonesty is 1 percent.

SPECIFYING A MINIMUM VALUE

When material such as concrete is used in construction, it is common to specify a certain minimum strength. Because of the statistical probability of encountering a test result falling below any specified minimum, the word is generally not taken to mean an absolute minimum. We require a specified confidence level; i.e., we stipulate that not less than a prescribed percentage of test results falls above the "minimum." If this is, say, 99 percent, the area of *one* tail[3] is 1 percent, that is, $z = 2.326$.

If the material used, for example, is concrete, the mix is proportioned so as to give a certain *mean* strength. This mean has to be chosen so that with the variance that is characteristic of the process of manufacture, the "minimum" has a value exceeded by 99 percent of the test results.

We can state the problem as follows:

Let x_m = "minimum" strength

   μ = mean strength

   σ = standard deviation, and

   $z_m = \dfrac{x_m - \mu}{\sigma}$

Then,

$$F(z_m) + 0.5 \geq 0.99 \qquad (10\text{-}3)$$

Since x_m is specified by the designer, the value of μ which satisfies Eq. 10-3 depends on σ. This is illustrated in Fig. 10-11 for $x_m = 3{,}000$ psi and three different values of σ. In all cases the area under the normal curve to the left of the abscissa $x_m = 3{,}000$ is the same.

It is clear that the higher the value of σ, the higher the necessary value of μ for the specified x_m, and if the cost of manufacture is related to μ, which is generally the case, then a higher value of σ requires the use of a more expensive material. On the other hand, a reduction in σ demands a closer control of manufacture and, therefore, a higher cost, so that in practice the choice of σ (and therefore μ) is a result of a compromise.

SOLVED PROBLEMS

10-1. Foil strain gages are produced with a mean resistance of 120.0 ohms. If the specification limits are 120 ± 0.5 ohms, what is the maximum allowable stand-

---

[3] Note that Table 10-1 has been prepared for results falling within a range—i.e., with two tails taken into account.

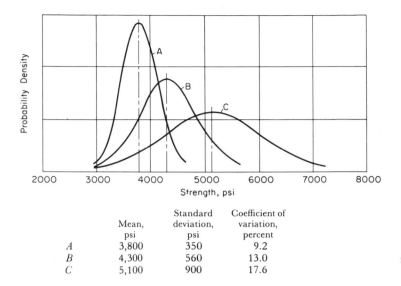

	Mean, psi	Standard deviation, psi	Coefficient of variation, percent
A	3,800	350	9.2
B	4,300	560	13.0
C	5,100	900	17.6

Fig. 10-11. Normal distribution curves for concrete with a minimum strength (exceeded by 99 percent of results) of 3,000 psi and different values of standard deviation. (From A. M. Neville, *Properties of Concrete*. New York: John Wiley & Sons, Inc., 1964.)

ard deviation which will permit no more than one gage in 1000 to be defective? It is assumed that the resistance of the gages is normally distributed.

Solution:

Given $\mu = 120.0$ ohms, $x - \mu = 0.5$ ohm. The area under the normal curve inside the specification limits must be

$$1 - \frac{1}{1,000} = 0.999$$

$$\text{Half this area} = \frac{0.999}{2} = 0.4995$$

For this value of $F(z)$, Table A-4 gives $z = 3.27$. Hence

$$\sigma = \frac{x - \mu}{z} = \frac{0.5}{3.27}$$

$$= 0.153 \text{ ohm}$$

10-2. A certain process of manufacture produces records whose weight is normally distributed with a standard deviation of 0.005 lb. What must be the mean weight, if the probability of obtaining a weight exceeding 0.21 lb is to be 0.01?

Solution:

Given $\sigma = 0.005$ lb and $x = 0.21$. The area under the normal curve is

$$F(z) = 0.5000 - 0.01$$

$$= 0.4900$$

The corresponding z from Table A-4 is

$$z = 2.33$$

But

$$z = \frac{x - \mu}{\sigma}$$

Therefore

$$0.21 - \mu = z\sigma = 2.33 \times 0.005 = 0.01165$$

Hence

$$\mu = 0.198 \text{ lb} \simeq 0.2 \text{ lb}$$

10-3. Results from a tensile test on 36 steel cables chosen at random from a certain mill were grouped as follows:

Tensile strength, kip/in.^{2}....	155–165	165–175	175–185	185–195	195–205	205–215	215–225
Frequency.............	1	4	7	11	9	3	1

(a) Find the mean and standard deviation of the tensile strength of the cable;

(b) Plot on normal probability paper the tensile strength versus fractional cumulative frequency. Draw "by eye" a straight line through the points and obtain the mean and standard deviation from the graph, and observe whether the results appear to follow the normal distribution;

(c) Estimate the probability of obtaining a random measurement which has a deviation from the mean of between -10 kip/in.^{2} and 20 kip/in.^{2};

(d) Calculate the range in which we would expect the mean of the population to fall with a probability of 95 percent.

Solution:

(a) Take origin at 160 kip/in.^{2} and a class width $w = 10$ kip/in.^{2} Then, in tabular form

Class interval kip/in.^{2}	Class midpoint x_i	Frequency f_i	Cumulative frequency F	Fractional cumulative frequency F/n	Deviation from origin in terms of class width X_i'	$f_i X_i'$	$f_i X_i'^2$
155–165	160	1	1	0.028	0	0	0
165–175	170	4	5	0.139	1	4	4
175–185	180	7	12	0.333	2	14	28
185–195	190	11	23	0.639	3	33	99
195–205	200	9	32	0.889	4	36	144
205–215	210	3	35	0.972	5	15	75
215–225	220	1	36	1.000	6	6	36
Totals ..		$\Sigma f_i = 36$				$\Sigma f_i X_i' = 108$	$\Sigma f_i X_i'^2 = 386$

$$\text{Mean} = \bar{x} = 160 + w \times \frac{\Sigma f_i X_i'}{\Sigma f_i} = 160 + 10 \times \frac{108}{36} = 190 \text{ kip/in.}^2$$

Standard deviation $s = w\sqrt{\dfrac{\Sigma f_i X_i'^2 - \dfrac{(\Sigma f_i X_i')^2}{n}}{n-1}} = w\sqrt{\dfrac{386 - \dfrac{(108)^2}{36}}{35}}$

$= 1.33 \times w = 1.33 \times 10$

$= 13.3 \ \text{kip/in.}^2$

(*b*) The cumulative frequency is plotted on normal probability paper in Fig. 10-12, using the upper boundary of each class interval. We find that the mean $= 189.7 \ \text{kip/in.}^2$ and standard deviation $= 12.7 \ \text{kip/in.}^2$. The graph indicates that the results follow a normal distribution very closely.

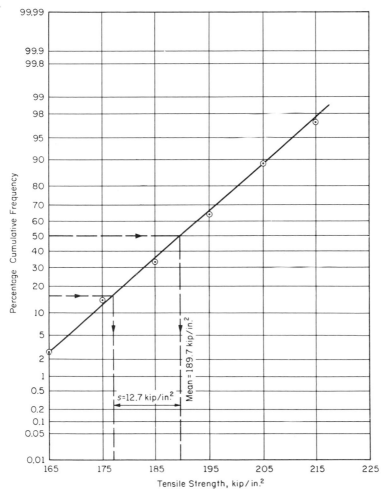

Fɪɢ. 10-12

(c)   Given $\mu - x_1 = 10\,\text{kip/in.}^2$, and $x_2 - \mu = 20\,\text{kip/in.}^2$

μ (est. from the sample mean) $= 190\,\text{kip/in.}^2$
σ (est. from the sample) $= 13.3\,\text{kip/in.}^2$

$$z_1 = \frac{\mu - x_1}{\sigma} = \frac{10}{13.3} = 0.752$$

From Table A-4

$$F(z) = 0.2740$$

Also

$$z_2 = \frac{x_2 - \mu}{\sigma} = \frac{20}{13.3} = 1.504$$

Therefore,

$$F(z_2) = 0.4337$$

The probability that a random measurement will fall within the limits $(190 - 10)\,\text{kip/in.}^2$ and $(190 + 20)\,\text{kip/in.}^2$, i.e., between 180 and 210 kip/in.^2, is:

$$F(z_1) + F(z_2) = 0.2740 + 0.4337 = 0.7077$$
$$= 70.77 \text{ percent}$$

(d)   Table A-4 gives the area under the normal curve on one side of the mean. Thus for a probability of 95 percent the area required $= 0.95/2 = 0.475$. The corresponding z from Table A-4 is $z = 1.96$. The range within which we would expect the population mean to fall is

$$190 \pm z\sigma_{\bar{x}} = 190 \pm 1.96 \times 13.3/\sqrt{36}$$
$$= 190 \pm 4.3 \text{ kip/in.}^2$$

10-4.   A steel company made numerous studies on the life span of their plate products immersed in water of a particular city. The results showed that the life span of such plate products was normally distributed, with a mean $\mu = 2{,}160$ days and standard deviation $\sigma = 252$ days.

(a)   What is the probability that the mean of a sample of 121 plates will not differ from μ by more than 60 days?

(b)   Find the 95 percent confidence limits for the mean of a sample of 121 plates, and for a single plate.

(c)   What should be the size of a sample in future studies if it is required that the probability of the sample mean being in error by more than 90 days is 5 percent?

Solution:

(a)   Given $\mu = 2{,}160$ days and $\sigma = 252$ days, we find:

$$\sigma_{\bar{x}} = \frac{\sigma}{\sqrt{n}} = \frac{252}{\sqrt{121}} = 22.9$$

$$z = \frac{\bar{x} - \mu}{\sigma_{\bar{x}}} = \frac{60}{22.9} = 2.62$$

From Table A-4 for such a value of z, $F(z) = 0.4956$. This is the area to one side of the mean of the normal curve. For a deviation in either direction, the area is $2 \times 0.4956 = 0.9912$. Therefore the probability that the mean life span of 121 plates will not differ from $\mu = 2{,}160$ days by more than 60 days is 99.12 percent.

(b) For 95 percent confidence limits the area under the normal curve is 0.95. Therefore the area to either side of the mean is $0.95/2 = 0.475$, for which (from Table A-4) $z = 1.96$. Hence the deviation of the mean life span of 121 plates is

$$z\sigma_{\bar{x}} = \frac{z\sigma}{\sqrt{n}} = \frac{1.96 \times 252}{\sqrt{121}} = 44.8 \text{ or } 45 \text{ days}$$

Thus the 95 percent confidence limits for the mean life span of 121 plates are

$$\mu \pm z\sigma_{\bar{x}} = 2{,}160 \pm 45 \text{ days}$$

For a single plate, the deviation of its life span from μ is $z\sigma = 1.96 \times 252 = 494$ days. Thus the range in which a single observation will fall with a probability of error of 5 percent is $2{,}160 \pm 494$ days.

(c) Table A-4 uses the area to one side of the mean. Thus

$$\text{Required area} = \frac{1 - 0.05}{2} = 0.475$$

$$\text{Corresponding } z = 1.96$$

The given deviation is $\bar{x} - \mu = 90$ days. From

$$z = \frac{\bar{x} - \mu}{\sigma_{\bar{x}}} = \frac{\bar{x} - \mu}{\sigma/\sqrt{n}} = \frac{90}{252/\sqrt{n}} = 1.96$$

we find

$$\sqrt{n} = 5.49$$

or

$$n = 30$$

Hence the sample size to be used is 30.

10-5. On a construction project the compressive strength of 50 concrete cylinders was measured, and the following values (in psi) were observed:

2,450	3,300	3,400	3,650	3,800
2,650	3,150	3,100	3,500	2,850
3,050	4,300	3,300	3,300	3,150
2,100	3,300	3,650	3,150	3,550
2,900	3,250	3,000	3,400	3,750
3,900	3,600	3,150	3,600	3,000
4,200	3,700	3,050	3,300	2,350
4,150	2,950	3,200	3,900	3,200
3,200	3,450	2,500	3,050	2,650
3,050	2,800	2,700	3,450	3,400

(a) Group these strengths into a frequency distribution with class width $w = 250$ psi starting with 2,000 psi.

(b)   Draw a histogram and a frequency polygon.

(c)   Calculate the mean, an estimate of the standard deviation, and the co-efficient of variation from the grouped data, and indicate the mean on the histogram.

(d)   What is the range of the given data? Find also the mode, and the median of the grouped data.

(e)   By plotting the fractional cumulative frequency on normal probability paper, check whether the distribution of the data is approximately normal.

(f)   Assuming normal distribution, find the minimum cylinder strength which can be used for design, accepting a definite risk that 1 percent of test cylinders will have a strength less than this minimum. Indicate whether any of the 50 cylinders fall below this strength.

(g)   Calculate the standard error of the mean and explain its significance.

(h)   Obtain the equations to the normal probability curve and the normal frequency curve for the given data. Draw the normal probability curve.

(i)   Estimate the probability that a random test result will have a deviation from the mean lying between -200 and $+500$ psi.

(j)   Estimate the probability that a mean of a sample of 36 cylinders from the same concrete mix will exceed 3,500 psi.

(k)   Find the limits for the mean of a sample of 36 cylinders at the 1 percent and 5 percent level of significance.

(l)   What should be the size of a sample in future tests in order that the probability of the sample mean being in error by more than 400 psi be not more than 0.1?

Solution:

(a)   The required grouping of the test results is shown in the table.

Class interval psi	Class midpoint x_i	Frequency f_i	Cumulative frequency F	Fractional cumulative frequency F/n	Deviation from origin in terms of class width X_i'	$f_i X_i'$	$f_i X_i'^2$
2,000–2,250	2,125	1	1	0.02	0	0	0
2,250–2,500	2,375	2	3	0.06	1	2	2
2,500–2,750	2,625	4	7	0.14	2	8	16
2,750–3,000	2,875	4	11	0.22	3	12	36
3,000–3,250	3,125	14	25	0.50	4	56	224
3,250–3,500	3,375	11	36	0.72	5	55	275
3,500–3,750	3,625	7	43	0.86	6	42	252
3,750–4,000	3,875	4	47	0.94	7	28	196
4,000–4,250	4,125	2	49	0.98	8	16	128
4,250–4,500	4,375	1	50	1.00	9	9	81
Totals		$\Sigma f_i = 50$				$\Sigma f_i X_i' = 228$	$\Sigma f_i X_i'^2 = 1,210$

(b)   The histogram and the frequency polygon are shown in Fig. 10-13.

(c)   If the arbitrary origin is taken as 2,125 psi, then the deviation of the class midpoint from this origin, X_i', is calculated as shown in the preceding table, with a class width $w = 250$ psi. Thus from this table we get the mean:

$$\bar{x} = 2{,}125 + \frac{w \Sigma f_i X_i'}{\Sigma f_i} = 2{,}125 + \frac{250 \times 228}{50}$$

$$= 3{,}265 \text{ psi}$$

The estimate of the standard deviation is

$$s = w \sqrt{\frac{\Sigma f_i X_i'^2 - \dfrac{(\Sigma f_i X_i')^2}{\Sigma f_i}}{n - 1}}$$

$$= 250 \sqrt{\frac{1{,}210 - \dfrac{(228)^2}{50}}{49}}$$

$$= 466 \text{ psi}$$

The coefficient of variation $V = \dfrac{s}{\bar{x}} \times 100 = \dfrac{46{,}600}{3{,}265} = 14.27$ percent

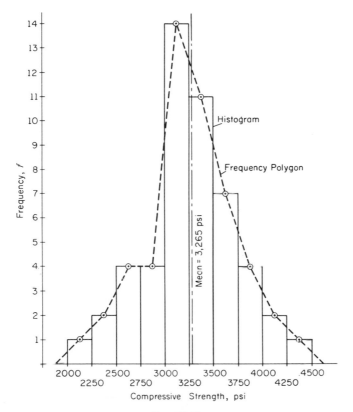

FIG. 10-13

(*d*) Range = 4,300 − 2,100 = 2,200 psi (from the raw data). For the grouped data: MODE is the midpoint of the class interval with the highest frequency = 3,125 psi. MEDIAN is the value that divides the histogram into two equal areas = 3,250 psi (by inspection).

(*e*) The fractional cumulative frequency (in percent) is plotted against the upper-class boundary on normal probability paper, Fig. 10-14. It can be seen that the plotted points closely follow a straight line drawn "by eye." From this graph, the mean is 3,250 psi and the standard deviation *s* = 475 psi. Both these values are close to those calculated from the grouped data, and we conclude that the distribution of the given values is sensibly normal.

(*f*) For a 1 percent risk the tail area of the normal probability curve (and we

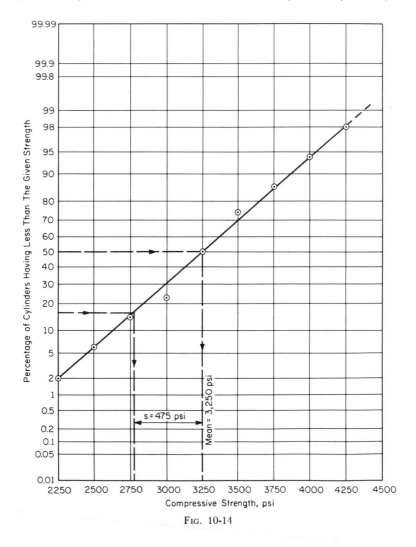

FIG. 10-14

are interested in one tail only) is 0.01. Therefore the area $F(z)$ is $0.50 - 0.01 = 0.49$. For this value of $F(z)$ Table A-4 gives $z = 2.33$. But

$$z = \frac{\text{deviation from the mean}}{s}$$

Hence

$$\text{Deviation from the mean} = zs = 2.33 \times 466$$
$$= 1086 \text{ psi}$$

Therefore the minimum cylinder strength used in design is

$$3{,}265 - 1{,}086 = 2{,}179 \text{ psi}$$

Among the data in hand only 1 cylinder has a strength which falls below this minimum.

(g) The standard error of the mean is $s/\sqrt{n} = 466/\sqrt{50} = 66$ psi. Thus there is a 68.26 percent probability that the mean of the population (i.e., of all the concrete represented by the test cylinders) lies within the range $3{,}265 \pm 66$, that is, between 3,200 and 3,300 psi.

(h) Equation 9-18 gives the normal probability curve as

$$y = \frac{1}{\sqrt{2\pi}} e^{-\frac{z^2}{2}}$$

$$= 0.3989 e^{-\frac{z^2}{2}}$$

where $z = X/\sigma$ is the deviation from the mean of the grouped data in terms of standard deviation.

From Eq. 9-14 the equation to the normal frequency curve is

$$y = \frac{n}{\sigma\sqrt{2\pi}} e^{-\frac{z^2}{2}}$$

where n = area under the histogram
$$= w \, \Sigma f_i = 250 \times 50$$

Hence

$$y = \frac{250 \times 50}{466\sqrt{2\pi}} e^{-\frac{z^2}{2}}$$

$$= 10.7012 \, e^{\frac{z^2}{2}}$$

where z is as defined in Part (f).

To plot the normal *probability* curve, the values of the oridinate y (the probability density) are obtained from Table A-3 for selected deviations $\pm z$ from the mean 3,265 psi. The normal probability curve is shown in Fig. 10-15.

(i) To find the probability that a random measurement will have a deviation from the mean lying between -200 and $+500$ psi, we calculate

$$z_1 = \frac{|\text{ deviation }|}{\sigma} = \frac{200}{466} = 0.43$$

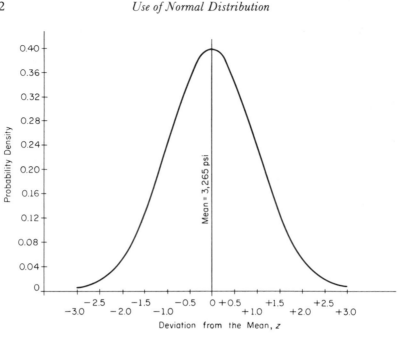

Fig. 10-15

The corresponding area under the normal curve is given in Table A-4 as $A_1 = 0.1664$. Also

$$z_2 = \frac{500}{466} = 1.073$$

From Table A-4, $A_2 = 0.3583$;

Total area under normal probability curve $= A_1 + A_2$

$$= 0.1664 + 0.3583$$

$$= 0.5247$$

Thus there is a 52.47 percent probability that a single test has a deviation from the mean of 3,265 psi falling between -200 and $+500$ psi.

(j) From Eq. 6-7, after taking $s = \sigma$, we obtain

$$\sigma_{\bar{x}} = s \sqrt{\frac{N - n}{n(N - 1)}} = 466 \sqrt{\frac{50 - 36}{36 \times 49}} = 41.5 \text{ psi}$$

Deviation $X = 3,500 - 3,265 = 235$ psi

Therefore,

$$z = \frac{X}{\sigma_{\bar{x}}} = \frac{235}{41.5} = 5.66$$

From Table A-4, the area under the normal curve for such a value of z can be taken as 0.5. Therefore the area under the curve for a value of $z > 5.66$ is considered to be zero. Thus the required probability is zero.

(k) For the 5 percent level of significance the total area under the normal curve outside the appropriate ± deviations from the mean is 0.05. Therefore

$$\text{Area inside the appropriate} \pm \text{deviations} = 1 - 0.05 = 0.95$$

The area on either side of the mean is 0.95/2. Hence, from Table A-4, $z = 1.96$. Therefore

$$\text{Deviation } X = z\sigma_{\bar{x}} = 1.96 \times 41.5 = 81 \text{ psi}$$

Thus the limits of the mean at the 5 percent level of significance, or the 95 percent confidence limits, are $3,265 \pm 81$ psi.

Similarly, for the 1 percent level of significance $z = 2.575$.

$$\text{Deviation } X = z\sigma_{\bar{x}} = 2.575 \times 41.5 = 107 \text{ psi}$$

Thus the limits at the 1 percent levels of significance are $3,265 \pm 107$ psi.

(l) The value of z for a 10 percent probability of the mean $\bar{x}$ being in error by more than 400 psi is the value corresponding to the area under the normal curve of $(1.00 - 0.10)/2 = 0.45$; from Table A-4, $z = 1.645$. To find the size of the sample n, we use Eq. 6-9, where (again assuming $s = \sigma$):

$$\sigma_{\bar{x}} = \frac{s}{\sqrt{n}}$$

Now

$$z = \frac{\text{deviation}}{\sigma_{\bar{x}}} = \frac{400}{466/\sqrt{n}}$$

$$= 1.645$$

Hence

$$\sqrt{n} = 1.916$$

or

$$n = 3.67$$

Therefore use a sample size of $n = 4$.

PROBLEMS

10-1. Tests on 16 tubes drawn at random from a normal population have yielded the mean value of resistance $\bar{y} = 20\,\mu\Omega$ and $\Sigma(y_i - \bar{y})^2 = 260$.
(a) Estimate the population mean and variance;
(b) Calculate the standard deviation of the sample mean;
(c) Find the 99 percent confidence interval for the mean.

10-2. Of 10,000 children entering grade I in a given year, 5,170 are male. Using the approximation of normal distribution, establish whether the figures suggest that the numbers of males and females are not equally distributed.

10-3. In a true-false examination, find the probability that a student can guess the answers to (a) 14 or more out of 27, (b) 22 or more out of 40 questions.

10-4. From past experience, it has been found that a particular machine produces piston rings of which 10 percent are defective. Find the probability that in a random sample of 500 rings (*a*) at most 50, (*b*) between 50 and 60, (*c*) 65 or more of the rings, will be defective.

10-5. The weight in grains of a certain pharmaceutical product is distributed normally with a variance of 0.0025 (grain)^2. Find the size of the sample necessary to estimate, at the 0.5 percent level of significance, the mean weight within 0.025 grain.

10-6. (*a*) The diameter of a certain shaft is normally distributed with a mean of 2.79 in. and a standard deviation of 0.01 in. The specification limits are 2.77 ± 0.03. If 1,000 shafts were produced, how many would be unacceptable? What are the limits for the 1 percent level of significance about the mean. Using these limits, how many of the 1,000 shafts would one expect to be rejects?

(*b*) What is the probability that a diameter measurement would deviate from the true mean by ±0.02 in.?

(*c*) Estimate the size of a sample in future measurements in order that the probability will not be greater than 0.05 of the sample mean being in error by more than ±0.01 in.

10-7. Fit a normal frequency curve to the data given in Prob. 2-1. Draw both the histogram and the fitted curve on the same set of coordinate axes. Compare the two plots and comment.

10-8. Find the equations to the normal probability and frequency curves representing the data in Prob. 2-4. From a plot on normal-probability paper of the cumulative frequency distribution, estimate the mean and standard deviation of the population distribution. Compare these values with those obtained previously and comment.

10-9. From the 64 values of hardness given in the first table of Prob. 4-5,

(*a*) Estimate the 90 percent confidence limits for hardness (estimated by a mean of 10 readings).

(*b*) Fit a normal frequency curve to the data.

(*c*) Test for normality of the distribution of hardness number by means of a plot on normal-probability paper. Comment on the result.

10-10. Fit a normal frequency curve to the data of Prob. 4-6 and calculate what proportion of results will in the long run fall below 2,500 psi.

10-11. The "minimum" strength of concrete on a certain job is specified to be 4,000 psi, the "minimum" being defined as a value exceeded by 9/10 of all tests. If the coefficient of variation is 11.8 percent, find the mean strength of the concrete. What would the mean strength have to be if the coefficient of variation increased to 19.5 percent?

chapter 11

Rejection of Outliers

Probably every engineer or scientist has encountered observations which, he is convinced, are incorrect. Specifically, in a group of readings or in a supposedly homogeneous sample, one of the observations may be very different from all the others. Such an observation is called an *outlier*. The question arises: Is the experimenter justified in discarding the outlier and in treating the data as if the "faulty" observation did not exist?

REASONS FOR OUTLIERS

The cause of a faulty observation may be a mistake, but we generally assume that all mistakes have been eliminated. A second possibility is that an additional variable has entered the picture; for example, an overload of the grid may have appreciably reduced the voltage which had previously been reasonably constant, or a changed direction of wind may have caused an excessive amount of solid matter in the air.

Under such circumstances we may encounter an observation which will not fall within the expected range, i.e., one whose deviation from the mean will be greater than expected. What is it though that we expect, or are justified in expecting? Table 10-1 showed that, when the variate is normally distributed, 95 percent of all observations are expected to fall within $1.96\,\sigma$ of the mean, i.e., the chance of an observation falling outside the range $(\mu - 1.96\,\sigma, \mu + 1.96\,\sigma)$ is 1 in 20. For a deviation of $\pm 2.58\,\sigma$ the chance is 1 in 100, for $\pm 3.29\,\sigma$ it is 1 in 1,000, and for $\pm 4.89\,\sigma$, one in a million.[1]

It is thus reasonable under normal circumstances to reject an observation which differs from the mean by more than a specified $z\sigma$; the value of z depends on size of the sample. Such a rejection is justified either because we were probably wrong to assume that the sample containing the extreme observation came from the specific population which we are testing (as the occurrence of such a large deviation is unlikely in a sample from the population in question), or because we are interested in testing representative samples, and a sample containing such a large deviation is not representative. It is important to appreciate this reasoning and not

---

[1] These are values for both "tails" and should be distinguished from the case where we are interested only in a value smaller *or* greater than the mean by a certain number of standard deviations.

simply to reject indiscriminately observations which appear to be more widely scattered than we would like. In particular, if large deviations occur in a number of samples, we should suspect the presence of additional factors, probably of intermittent character; the experiment must then be carefully examined.

Under industrial conditions it is important to distinguish between the two cases mentioned in the last paragraph, namely, whether the outlier is caused by a real factor or is just an improbable result.

A number of criteria for the rejection of outliers have been proposed, but we shall discuss only two of them here.

REJECTION ON BASIS OF ESTIMATED VARIANCE

In Nair's method the maximum deviation from the sample mean $\bar{x}$ that can be expected for single values in samples of size n is related to the estimated variance of the population; the estimate must be based on a larger sample than the one containing the outlier.

Let x_m be the greatest or smallest value of x that can be expected in a sample of size n at a given significance (probability) level; the levels considered are 10 percent, 5 percent, 1 percent and 0.1 percent, but data for other levels are also available. Let s_e be the estimated standard deviation, the estimate being based on data with ν degrees of freedom. Table A-5 gives the values of $\dfrac{|x_m - \bar{x}|}{s_e}$ which are not normally expected to be exceeded in samples of size n between 3 and 9. If a deviate larger than the tabulated value is observed, then the observation may be rejected as being significantly different from the remainder of the sample. The level of significance at which the rejection is decided upon represents the risk of error, e.g., a 5 percent level of significance means that there is a 5 percent probability that we reject a value which does correctly belong to the sample in question.

Example. Twenty-five observations on the weights of material from a packing machine have given an estimate of standard deviation as 0.40 lb. Assume that weights, in pounds, taken by a customer on five packages from his consignments are

$$100.4, \qquad 100.2, \qquad 100.5, \qquad 100.2, \qquad 99.2$$

The question is whether the value of $x_m = 99.2$ can be discarded.

Since $\bar{x} = 100.1$ and $s_e = 0.40$

$$\frac{|x_m - \bar{x}|}{s_e} = \frac{0.9}{0.40} = 2.25$$

We now enter Table A-5 with the value of 2.25 for $n = 5$ and the number of degrees[2] of freedom $v = 25 - 1 = 24$. The extreme deviates in Table A-5 are 2.23 at the 5 percent level of significance, and 2.85 at the 1 percent level. Thus the value $x_m = 99.2$ can be rejected with a 5 percent risk of error of wrong rejection.

Once the extreme deviate has been rejected the sample mean becomes 100.32 lb and the standard deviation estimated from the sample is $s = \sqrt{0.0225}$; this is based on the number of degrees of freedom $v = 4 - 1 = 3$. It may be of interest to compare the standard deviation from this sample with the value of 0.40 estimated for 24 degrees of freedom. This is done by means of the F test (see Chapter 14). We find

$$F = \frac{(0.4)^2}{0.0225} = 7.11$$

For $v_1 = 24$ and $v_2 = 3$, F at the 5 percent level of significance is 8.64. We conclude, therefore, that the variation in the estimates of variance given by the two samples is due to chance alone.

CHAUVENET'S CRITERION

Another criterion of rejection of outliers is due to Chauvenet: An observation in a sample of size n is rejected if it has a deviation from the mean greater than that corresponding to a $1/(2n)$ probability. The probability is calculated on the assumption of a normal distribution, using an estimate of variance on the basis of the sample considered. For example, if $n = 10$, then $1/(2n) = 0.05$, which is the probability of a deviate of at least 1.96σ. Thus an outlier which deviates from the mean by at least $1.96s$ would be rejected.[3] The mean and standard deviation of the remaining 9 observations are then calculated and used in further work.

To simplify calculations, Table A-6 gives the maximum values of $\dfrac{|x_m - \bar{x}|}{s}$ for different values of n; an outlier exceeding the tabulated value can be rejected.

For example, for the five weights given in the preceding example, $s = 0.52$, and

$$\frac{|x_m - \bar{x}|}{s} = \frac{0.9}{0.52} = 1.73$$

For $n = 5$, Table A-6 gives the maximum value of $\dfrac{|x_m - \bar{x}|}{s}$ as 1.64.

We are therefore justified in rejecting the outlier, and both Chauvenet's and Nair's methods lead to the same conclusion, but this need not always be the case.

[2] See Chapter 4.
[3] We use s because we only estimate σ.

We should also note that the rejection of an outlier decreases s. When Chauvenet's criterion is used, this could easily lead to successive rejection of extreme observations—a procedure that must never be used.

The decision to reject an observation should be based on experience and must not be made lightly. It is important to realize that in rejecting an observation we *may* be in our ignorance, throwing away vital information which *could* lead to the discovery of a hitherto unrecognized factor.

PROBLEMS

11-1. Ten measurements of the diameter of a shaft were as follows:

6.06, 5.92, 6.01, 6.01, 5.99, 5.99, 6.02, 6.03, 6.02, 5.97 (in.)

Using Chauvenet's criterion, determine whether any one of the observations can be considered as an outlier.

11.2. Twenty observations of deflection of similar beams have given an estimate of the standard deviation as 0.5 in. If the deflections of six beams are:

3.4, 3.2, 3.5, 3.2, 4.6, 3.4 in.

determine whether the deflection of any beam can be considered abnormal, using (a) Nair's method; (b) Chauvenet's criterion. After discarding the appropriate measurement, recalculate the mean and compare it with the original mean deflection.

chapter 12

The Chi-Squared Test

We have stated repeatedly that experimental observations are subject to scatter, and all experimental results must be viewed in relation to this scatter. This statement is fundamental to *tests of significance*, which enable us to judge whether any observed differences are real or are due to chance alone. The differences studied may be those between two comparable sets of observations or between an experimental distribution and a hypothetical distribution.

NULL HYPOTHESIS

In this chapter we consider the χ^2 test,[1] which enables us to find whether observed frequencies differ *significantly* from frequencies expected from an assumed model. The test requires, in general, the use of frequencies and not percentages.

The derivation of the χ^2 distribution will not be given here. In the χ^2 test, as in all tests of significance, we always postulate that there is no significant difference between the distributions being compared, i.e., that they are drawn from the same population. This is known as the *null hypothesis*. We measure the probability of the actual difference occurring due to chance alone, and if this probability is very small, we reject the null hypothesis and infer that a real difference exists. However, we can never formally prove the null hypothesis to be correct. This may seem an unsatisfactory state of affairs, but statistical inference is not an end in itself; it is only a tool which enables us to fit a hypothesis to observed physical facts or, alternatively, makes us reject it and seek another pattern.

SIGNIFICANCE OF TEST

To perform the χ^2 test we compare each expected class frequency E with the observed frequency O, and compute for each class the term

$$\frac{(O - E)^2}{E}$$

The statistic χ^2 is then defined as

$$\chi^2 = \sum \frac{(O - E)^2}{E} \tag{12-1}$$

the summation extending over all classes.

---

[1] Sometimes written chi, pronounced *kī* as in kite.

The calculated value is then compared with tabulated values of χ^2; the latter are values which cannot be exceeded by the calculated value *when there is no real difference* at a specified level of significance, i.e., with a given probability. Table A-7 gives values of χ^2 for a range of probabilities from 0.001 to 0.99.

To find the requisite probability, we locate on the table the appropriate number of degrees of freedom (see the following section) and find the highest tabulated value which is exceeded by the calculated value. At the head of the column containing this tabulated value we read off the probability of the null hypothesis not being true. It is usual to reject the null hypothesis at the 5 percent or the 1 percent level of significance (i.e., a probability of 0.05 and 0.01 respectively).

If the level of significance is higher, we generally do not reject the null hypothesis, but this does not necessarily mean that the observed distribution is the same as the hypothetical one. It is possible that we simply do not have adequate data in hand, and further tests should be made before a reliable conclusion can be drawn.

We should note that the χ^2 test determines the probability of obtaining the values of $\mid O - E \mid$ of *at least* the magnitude observed and not of exactly that magnitude.

DEGREES OF FREEDOM

We now have to explain the term degrees of freedom—a concept of great importance in tests of significance, and yet one not easily defined.[2] For the present purposes we take the number of degrees of freedom as the number of classes which can be assigned arbitrarily. Care is necessary in determining this number. For example, if we toss a coin n times and observe a heads, then we can assign only one class (say, heads) arbitrarily, the other class (tails in this case) being perforce $(n - a)$: the number of degrees of freedom is one. If we compare the number of accidents on three days, our hypothesis being, for example, that there is no significant difference between the frequencies on the three days, then, given the total number of accidents, we can assign two classes arbitrarily, the third one being uniquely determined from the mean value; the number of degrees of freedom is thus 2. Great care is necessary in obtaining the correct number of degrees of freedom.

Example. At the end of the first semester the number of failures in three large sections of a class, the sections being chosen at random and being equal in size, was 2, 9, 10. Can we conclude that the three instructors differ in their marking with respect to the proportion of failures?

We adopt the null hypothesis that there is no significant difference be-

_____
[2] See Chapter 4.

tween sections, so that the expected number of failures per section is $\frac{2 + 9 + 10}{3} = 7$. We can set out the data as follows:

Section	O	E	$|O - E|$
A	2	7	5
B	9	7	2
C	10	7	3

Hence

$$\chi^2 = \frac{5^2}{7} + \frac{2^2}{7} + \frac{3^2}{7} = 5.428$$

The number of degrees of freedom is 2 since, given the total number of failures, we can assign arbitrarily only two classes. Table A-7 gives $\chi^2 = 5.991$ at the 5 percent level of significance, and we cannot therefore conclude that there is a difference in severity or leniency between the instructors.

If a student who may consider himself a victim of severe marking is not satisfied with this conclusion, we answer that we do not deny that a difference *may* exist, but the evidence available is inadequate to regard the difference as established.

The suspicious student may therefore collect further evidence, and let us assume that at the end of the second semester, all conditions having remained unaltered, the numbers of failures have increased to 3, 13, and 14. The expected number of failures in each section is $\frac{3 + 13 + 14}{3} = 10$. Hence

$$\chi^2 = \frac{7^2}{10} + \frac{3^2}{10} + \frac{4^2}{10} = 7.4$$

With 2 degrees of freedom this value is significant at the 5 percent level, and we consider our suspicions confirmed: The marking in the three sections is not uniform.

MINIMUM CLASS FREQUENCY

The preceding example illustrates the point that the χ^2 test is sensitive to the size of the samples used. In general, the test should not be used when an *expected* class frequency is less than 5, as the relative frequency for such a class is very small. However, it is usually possible to combine ajdacent classes with a frequency below 5 in order to reach or exceed this value.

Example. Five pressures were used in extruding a difficult shape, and the following numbers of rejects were obtained. Is there a significant difference between the proportion of rejects produced by each pressure?

Pressure, kip/in.^{2}	2.0	2.2	2.4	2.6	2.8
Class	A	B	C	D	E
Number manufactured	3	11	12	11	3
Observed number of rejects O. . . .	2	3	6	6	3
Expected number of rejects E. . . .	1½	5½	6	5½	1½

On the assumption that there is no difference between the classes, we calculate the expected proportion of rejects as

$$\frac{\Sigma \text{ rejects}}{\Sigma \text{ manufactured}} = \frac{20}{40} = 0.5$$

Therefore, the expected number of rejects in each class is 0.5 times the number made, and these values are entered in the last row of the table above.

To satisfy the requirement of an expected class frequency of not less than 5, we combine A and B, and D and E:

Class	A and B	C	D and E
O	5	6	9
E	7	6	7

Hence

$$\chi^2 = \frac{2^2}{7} + 0 + \frac{2^2}{7}$$

That is, $\chi^2 = 1.143$ with 2 degrees of freedom. A value of 1.386 can be obtained with a probability of 50 percent, and we therefore conclude that there is no significant difference between the pressures: (A and B), C, and (D and E). We cannot distinguish between A and B, or D and E until further tests have been made.

CONTINUITY CORRECTION

We should note that χ^2 is a continuous variable and, if the actual distribution is discontinuous, we have to apply a *continuity correction*. This can be done only when the number of degrees of freedom is 1. The correction consists of reducing by 0.5 the values of observed frequency which are greater than the expected frequency, and increasing those which are smaller. Failure to apply the correction leads to too high a value of calculated χ^2. Thus without the correction we may wrongly reject the null hypothesis at a specified level of significance. If, however, the null hypothesis is not rejected without the correction being applied, the correction would not affect our conclusion.

Example. We toss a coin 50 times and obtain 17 heads. Are we justified in suspecting that the coin is biased?

The number of degrees of freedom is 1.

We tabulate the data as follows:

	Heads	Tails
Observed.	17	33
Expected E	25	25
Observed, corrected O	17.5	32.5
$\lvert O - E \rvert$	7.5	7.5

Hence

$$\chi^2 = \frac{7.5^2}{25} + \frac{7.5^2}{25} = 4.5$$

This is significant at the 5 percent level but not at the 1 percent level; we have, therefore, a good, but not an overwhelming, reason to suspect the coin.

CONTINGENCY TABLES

The χ^2 tests can also be written down in a somewhat different form. For example, if we compare two methods of treatment in order to establish whether or not there is a significant difference between them, we can set out the results in the form of a contingency table.

Item	Number of successes	Number of failures	Totals
Method A	A_1	A_2	A_t
Method B	B_1	B_2	B_t
Totals.	T_1	T_2	T_t

Instead of the χ^2 calculations given in Eq. 12-1, we can use a mechanical formula:

$$\chi^2 = \frac{(B_1 A_2 - A_1 B_2)^2 \times T_t}{A_t B_t T_1 T_2} \tag{12-2}$$

The number of degrees of freedom is 1, as only one of the values of A_1, A_2, B_1, and B_2 can be assigned arbitrarily, all the others being governed by the totals T_1, T_2, A_t, and B_t.

It can be easily shown that Eq. 12-2 gives the same result as calculation of χ^2 by Eq. 12-1.

TOO GOOD A FIT

Table A-7 gives the values of χ^2 for probabilities of 0.001 to 0.10, that is, for levels of significance of 0.1 to 10 percent which are the usual levels at which the rejection of the null hypothesis is considered. The table also contains, however, values for probabilities of 0.50 to 0.99. The occurrence of χ^2 corresponding to a probability higher than about 0.99 makes us suspect that the data have been "rigged." This has, for example, been shown to have been the case with some of the test results reported by Mendel's disciples. Too high a value of χ^2 may also occur when, for example, spurious pulses of uniform frequency are mixed with pulses being observed, or, in general, when there is a lack of randomness.

Example. In the statistics laboratory we ask students to draw samples of 4 from a bowl containing red and black balls in equal proportions, the drawn balls being returned into the bowl after each test; 160 samples are drawn and the students report their results. We compare the observed distribution with that expected, i.e., with the binomial distribution. Are the results suspicious?

Number of red balls in sample r	0	1	2	3	4
Number of samples with r red balls observed O . .	9	40	59	41	11
Number of samples with r red balls expected E . .	10	40	60	40	10
$\lvert O - E \rvert$	1	0	1	1	1

Hence,

$$\chi^2 = \frac{1}{10} + \frac{1}{60} + \frac{1}{40} + \frac{1}{10} = 0.24$$

The number of degrees of freedom is 4.

Table A-7 gives $\chi^2 = 0.297$ at the 99 percent level of significance. Therefore, the probability of obtaining χ^2 *as small* as calculated is less than 1 percent, and we are therefore justified in suspecting that the experiment was not performed but that the "results" were arbitrarily written down so as to appear plausible in the students' eyes.

This simple example may be of didactic interest!

χ^2 AS A MEASURE OF GOODNESS OF FIT

As mentioned earlier, the χ^2 test is used to test the goodness of fit; in this case the null hypothesis states that there is no significant difference between the observed distribution and a postulated standard distribution. The preceding example involved the binomial distribution, but perhaps a better illustration is offered by the data in Chapter 8 on the number of deaths caused by a horse-kick. On the assumption of Poisson distribution, we calculated there the expected number of deaths per army corps per annum, and we can now apply the χ^2 test to find how well the observed data fit the assumed distribution. The data for the example are repeated below.

Number of deaths per corps per annum r	0	1	2	3	4
Observed number of corps with r deaths O . .	109	65	22	3	1
Expected number of corps with r deaths E	109	66	20	4	0.6 $\simeq$ 1
$\lvert O - E \rvert$	0	1	2		1

Hence,

$$\chi^2 = \frac{1^2}{66} + \frac{2^2}{20} + \frac{1^2}{5} = 0.415$$

The number of degrees of freedom is 3, and Table A-7 gives $\chi^2 = 0.584$ at the 90 percent level of significance. Thus the goodness of fit is excellent, and we are satisfied that the observed distribution is a Poisson distribution.

SOLVED PROBLEMS

12-1. An experiment was conducted to test the effect of the rate of loading on the type of failure in steel rods. Twenty-four specimens were tested to failure, 12 at a fast-loading rate and the other 12 at a slow rate. It was found that 11 of the "slow" specimens showed a complete cone failure, whereas only 5 of the "fast" specimens showed this type of failure. Establish whether the rate of loading influences the shape of the failure zone for the given steel.

Solution:

There are two criteria here and hence two-way classification. Let a complete cone failure be denoted as *A* failure and all other types of failure as *B*. Then the *observed* 2 × 2 contingency table is as follows:

	Failure A	Failure B	Total
Slow method	11	1	12
Fast method	5	7	12
Total	16	8	24

The *expected* values in tabular form are:

	Failure A	Failure B	Total
Slow method..............	8	4	12
Fast method	8	4	12
Total	16	8	24

The number of degrees of freedom, $\nu = 1$. The value of χ^2 *without the continuity correction* is

$$\chi^2 = \frac{(3)^2}{8} + \frac{(3)^2}{8} + \frac{(3)^2}{4} + \frac{(3)^2}{4} = 6.75$$

The value of χ^2 *with the continuity correction* is

$$\chi^2 = \frac{(2.5)^2}{8} + \frac{(2.5)^2}{8} + \frac{(2.5)^2}{4} + \frac{(2.5)^2}{4} = 4.69$$

This is significant at the 5 percent level, and hence the rate of loading does influence the shape of the failure zone at the above level of significance.

12-2. Five machines, *A*, *B*, *C*, *D*, and *E* are experimentally used to make precision tools. The following are the numbers of tools made by the five machines and the numbers rejected:

Machine	A	B	C	D	E	Total
Number made	20	18	16	24	22	100
Number rejected	12	16	10	14	18	70

Test the hypothesis that there is no difference in the rejection rate among the machines.

Solution:

The observed number of tools in each category is as follows:

Machine	A	B	C	D	E	Total
Rejected................	12	16	10	14	18	70
Accepted	8	2	6	10	4	30
Total	20	18	16	24	22	100

Solution:

Expected number of rejects from any machine = $\dfrac{\text{total number of rejects}}{\text{total number of tools made}} \times \dfrac{\text{number of tools made}}{\text{by that particular machine}}$

In tabular form, the expected numbers are as follows:

Machine	A	B	C	D	E	Total
Rejected................	14.0	12.6	11.2	16.8	15.4	70
Accepted	6.0	5.4	4.8	7.2	6.6	30
Total	20	18	16	24	22	100

$$\chi^2 = \Sigma \frac{(O - E)^2}{E} = \frac{(12 - 14)^2}{14} + \frac{(16 - 12.6)^2}{12.6} + \frac{(10 - 11.2)^2}{11.2}$$
$$+ \frac{(14 - 16.8)^2}{16.8} + \frac{(18 - 15.4)^2}{15.4} + \frac{(8 - 6)^2}{6} + \frac{(2 - 5.4)^2}{5.4}$$
$$+ \frac{(6 - 4.8)^2}{4.8} + \frac{(10 - 7.2)^2}{7.2} + \frac{(4 - 6.6)^2}{6.6} = 7.458$$

For $\nu = n - 1 = 5 - 1 = 4$ degrees of freedom, Table A-7 gives the probability of such a value of χ^2 as between 0.10 and 0.20. We have, therefore, no reason to reject the null hypothesis, and we conclude that there is no difference in the rejection rate of the five machines.

12-3. Test the null hypothesis in Solved Problem 12-2 using the following data:

Machine	A	B	C	D	E	Total
Number made	12	18	24	24	22	100
Number rejected	4	16	18	14	18	70

Solution:

We calculate the observed and expected numbers as before.

Machine	A	B	C	D	E	Total
Observed rejected	4	16	18	14	18	70
Observed accepted	8	2	6	10	4	30
Expected rejected.,,,,,,,	8.4	12.6	16.8	16.8	15.4	70
Expected accepted.......	3.6	5.4	7.2	7.2	6.6	30

Since the expected number in A is smaller than 5, we pool the expected numbers of A and B, and at the same time pool the observed rejects of A and B. Thus

$$\chi^2 = \frac{(20 - 21)^2}{21} + \frac{(18 - 16.8)^2}{16.8} + \frac{(14 - 16.8)^2}{16.8} + \frac{(18 - 15.4)^2}{15.4}$$

$$+ \frac{(10 - 9)^2}{9} + \frac{(6 - 7.2)^2}{7.2} + \frac{(10 - 7.2)^2}{7.2} + \frac{(4 - 6.6)^2}{6.6} = 3.463$$

The number of degrees of freedom is $n - 1$, where $n = 4$, since we pooled the expected numbers in A and B. From Table A-7, for $\nu = 3$, the probability is approximately 50 percent. Therefore, there are no grounds for rejection of the null hypothesis. However, nothing can be said about the difference between the machines A and B until further tests have been made.

12-4. The manufacturer of a particular casting kept the following record of the number of defective units produced in 50 shifts:

Number of defectives per shift r	0	1	2	3	4	5	6	7	8
Shifts with r defectives O	2	6	10	10	7	6	4	3	2

Determine whether the data support the hypothesis that the number of defective castings is completely random, i.e., we are not justified in suspecting that different shifts produce significantly different numbers of defective castings.

Solution:

If the distribution is random, it will not differ significantly from a Poisson distribution. We therefore start by fitting a Poisson distribution to the observed data. In tabular form:

Number of defectives per shift r	Shifts with r defectives O	$r \times O$
0	2	0
1	6	6
2	10	20
3	10	30
4	7	28
5	6	30
6	4	24
7	3	21
8	2	16
Totals............. $\Sigma O = 50$		$\Sigma(r \times O) = 175$

Mean number of defectives per shift $= np = \dfrac{175}{50} = 3.5$.

Using the cumulative Poisson probability graph of Fig. 8-1, we obtain:

r	0	1	2	3	4	5	6	7	8
P cumulative	0.03	0.13	0.32	0.535	0.725	0.86	0.93	0.97	0.99
P_r	0.03	0.10	0.19	0.215	0.19	0.135	0.07	0.04	0.02
E	1.5	5.0	9.5	11.0	9.5	7.0	3.5	2.0	1.0

where $E = 50 \times P_r =$ expected number of shifts with r defective castings.

Since the expected number of shifts producing 0 defectives and those producing 6, 7, and 8 defectives are smaller than 5, we pool the expected numbers of shifts of

0 and 1 defectives, and 6, 7, and 8 defectives respectively; at the same time the corresponding numbers of observed shifts O are pooled. Thus in tabular form:

Number of defectives	0 and 1	2	3	4	5	6, 7, and 8	Σ
Observed numbers of shifts O	8	10	10	7	6	9	50
Expected number of shifts E..........	6.5	9.5	11	9.5	7.0	6.5	50

$$\chi^2 = \Sigma \frac{(O - E)^2}{E} = \frac{(8 - 6.5)^2}{6.5} + \frac{(10 - 9.5)^2}{9.5} + \frac{(10 - 11)^2}{11}$$

$$+ \frac{(7 - 9.5)^2}{9.5} + \frac{(6 - 7)^2}{7} + \frac{(9 - 6.5)^2}{6.5}$$

$$= 0.346 + 0.026 + 0.091 + 0.658 + 0.143 + 0.961$$

$$= 2.225$$

The number of degrees of freedom $\nu = n - 1$ where $n = 6$ after pooling. Thus from Table A-7, for $\nu = 5$ the probability of such a value of χ^2 is between 0.80 and 0.90. Therefore there is no justification in claiming that the identity of the shift affects the number of defective castings produced.

PROBLEMS

12-1. A product is supposed to contain 5 percent of defective items. We take a sample of 100 items and find it to contain 12 defectives. Are we justified in suspecting that the consignment is not up to specification?

12-2. For the data given in Prob. 8-1, use the χ^2 test to determine whether the distribution differs significantly from a Poisson distribution.

12-3. For the data given in Prob. 8-3, use the χ^2 test to check on the goodness of fit of the assumed Poisson distribution.

12-4. A course is taught in two classes. In class A there are 27 failures out of 202 students taking the course. In class B there are 9 failures out of 199 students. Can we conclude that class B receives better instruction?

12-5. A number of machines of two types were used over a period of time, and the records of their serviceability are as follows:

Type	Broken down	Temporarily out of order	Always serviceable
A	11	132	212
B	58	29	13

Can we conclude that type A is superior in so far as it leads to "less trouble"?

12-6. Of 10,000 children entering grade I in a given year, 5,170 are male. Use the χ^2 test to determine whether the figures suggest that the numbers of males and females differ significantly.

12-7. Samples of 100 items each were taken from two machines producing the same product. Among those from machine A there were 17 defectives, but there were only 3 defectives among those from machine B. Should we conclude that there is a significant difference between the two machines?

chapter 13

Comparison of Means

In the present chapter we are concerned with comparing means of samples for the purpose of determining whether the observed difference is due to chance only, or whether we should suspect some real cause to be responsible and hence consider the difference to be statistically significant.

Suppose that we have determined the compressive strength of concrete supplied by two ready-mix concrete manufacturers, and found that the mean strength of the concrete from supplier *A* was 7,000 psi and the standard deviation was 400 psi, the corresponding values for the concrete from supplier *B* being 9,200 and 400 psi respectively. In each case the result was obtained from a sample of 10 specimens. We have no doubt that the latter concrete has a higher strength as the difference between the means (2,200 psi) is more than five times the value of the standard deviation of the values in either sample. It is therefore highly improbable that the two samples have been drawn from the same population and that their difference is due to chance. This conclusion is intuitively obvious and statistical proof is not necessary.

INFERENCE ERRORS

When, however, the difference is smaller—e.g., if concrete *B* has a mean strength of 7,300 psi with the standard deviation remaining at 400 psi—it is far from obvious that this concrete is *really* superior to concrete *A*. We can use statistical methods in an attempt to infer whether or not there is a real difference between the strengths of the two concretes; however, our answer cannot be *guaranteed* to be correct, but it has only a specified probability of being correct. It is important at this stage to know the type of inference error that we may commit. The usual nomenclature is as follows.

A Type I error is said to have been made if we infer that there is a real difference between the two samples while in fact the observed difference is due to chance only. To reduce the risk of a Type I error we may insist on a higher level of significance of the difference being studied before we accept the difference as real; for example, we may require a 1 percent level of significance, rather than 5 percent, i.e., a probability of only 1 percent that such a difference may occur by chance and not be due to real causes. (The choice in a practical case depends on judgment and experience.)

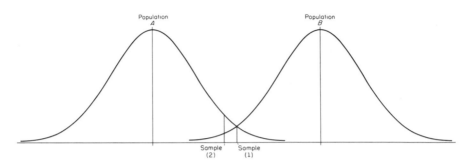

Fig. 13-1. Normal distribution curves for two populations. Which population does sample (1) belong to? If we infer that it does not belong to A while, in fact, it does, we have committed a Type I error. If we infer that (1) does belong to A while, in fact, it does not, we have committed a Type II error. (In the diagram, the area under the normal distribution curve for population A to the right of sample (1) represents 2.5 percent of the total area under the curve.)

However, a decrease in the risk of a Type I error increases the chances of committing a Type II error. This occurs if we conclude that there is no real difference between two samples while the difference does in fact exist.

The situation is illustrated in Fig. 13-1. Sample (1) may belong to the same population as Sample (2). Conversely, it is possible that the two samples belong to two distinct populations which overlap at their tail ends, so that there is always a small chance that a Sample (1) belonging to population B is so near the mean of population A that Sample (1) can be erroneously believed to belong to A.

It is not possible to reduce both errors simultaneously in a single test. Usually, the tests of significance are arranged so that there is a specified risk of committing a Type I error (this risk is expressed as the level of significance of the test) without a provision for controlling the risk of a Type II error, which depends on the true unknown value of the parameter in question. The probability of committing a Type II error is decreased, however, by increasing the sample size. The choice of sample size for specified risks of committing errors of both types is discussed in Chapter 20.

NORMAL DISTRIBUTION TEST

We frequently want to determine whether a set of observations (i.e., a sample) accords with the hypothesis that the population mean has a specific value. The standard deviation of the population may be known (as in quality control work when a large amount of previous data is available) or may have to be estimated from the standard deviation of the actual observations (as is usually the case in experimental work). In the latter case the sample must be sufficiently large (say, $n \geq 30$) for a close estimate of the population standard deviation σ to be possible.

To answer our question we apply the normal distribution test, pro-vided of course that the underlying distribution is normal. The test con-sists of calculating

$$u = \frac{|\mu - \bar{x}|}{\dfrac{\sigma}{\sqrt{n}}} \tag{13-1}$$

where μ = population mean
  $\bar{x}$ = sample mean
  n = sample size
  $\dfrac{\sigma}{\sqrt{n}}$ = standard deviation of the mean (from Eq. 6-8)

We can now find from Table A-4 the probability of obtaining a value of u at least this large. (u is essentially the same as z but the variate is now the mean; for this reason the standard deviation of the variate is $\sigma/\sqrt{n}$.) This probability is represented by $1 - 2 \times F(z)$. The factor 2 is appropriate here since we are generally interested in testing the significance of the dif-ference $|\mu - \bar{x}|$, and are not concerned with whether $\mu > \bar{x}$ or $\mu < \bar{x}$. When the probability given by Table A-4 is small (below a specified mini-mum), we reject the hypothesis.

If the underlying population is not infinite but consists of N items, then u is modified to:

$$u = \frac{|\mu - \bar{x}|}{\dfrac{\sigma}{\sqrt{n}} \sqrt{\dfrac{N - n}{N - 1}}} \tag{13-2}$$

Example. The mean ultimate strength of a certain prestressing wire is stated by the manufacturer to be 250 kip/in.² A contractor buys a con-signment of wire and tests specimens from 35 coils. The mean value from these tests is 247.4 kip/in.² with a standard deviation of 11.2 kip/in.² Is the contractor justified in concluding that the consignment does not ac-cord with the manufacturer's statement?

We have

$$\mu = 250$$
$$\bar{x} = 247.4$$
$$s = 11.2$$

Because the sample size is large ($n = 35$), we can use the normal distribu-tion test and take the standard deviation of the mean as

$$\frac{11.2}{\sqrt{35}} = 1.89$$

From Eq. 13-1,

$$u = \frac{250 - 247.4}{1.89} = 1.37$$

From Table A-4 the probability of obtaining a value at least this large is greater than 5 percent. We conclude, therefore, that the consignment belongs to the manufacturer's stated population and advise the contractor to accept the wire.

The normal distribution test can also be used to compare the means of two samples, provided that they are *independent* quantities. The variance of the difference of the means σ_d^2 of two such quantities is the sum of variances of the two sample means (Eq. 14-14), that is,

$$\sigma_d^2 \simeq \frac{s_1^2}{n_1} + \frac{s_2^2}{n_2} \tag{13-3}$$

where s_1^2 and s_2^2 are the variance estimates from the two samples of size n_1 and n_2 respectively. As in Eq. 13-1, the significance of the difference of means is measured by the ratio of the difference to its standard deviation, namely:

$$u = \frac{|\bar{x}_1 - \bar{x}_2|}{\sigma_d} \tag{13-4}$$

or

$$u = \frac{|\bar{x}_1 - \bar{x}_2|}{\sqrt{\dfrac{\Sigma(x_1 - \bar{x}_1)^2}{n_1(n_1 - 1)} + \dfrac{\Sigma(x_2 - \bar{x}_2)^2}{n_2(n_2 - 1)}}} \tag{13-5}$$

where x = sample mean

n = sample size

and the subscripts 1 and 2 refer to the two samples being compared.

The probability of $|\bar{x}_1 - \bar{x}_2|$ being smaller than $u\sigma_d$ (if drawn by chance from the same population) is given by the area under the normal curve between the limits $\mu \pm u\sigma_d$. Since we are testing the difference between the two means regardless of sign (i.e., the absolute value of $\bar{x}_1 - \bar{x}_2$), we require double the area given in Table A-4; this is the so-called two-sided (or two-tail) test. For convenience the more common values of the areas between $\mu - u\sigma_d$ and $\mu + u\sigma_d$ are given in Table 13-1. It should be

TABLE 13-1

PROBABILITY FOR NORMAL DISTRIBUTION

u	Probability of $\|\bar{x}_1 - \bar{x}_2\|$ being smaller than $u\sigma_d$, percent
0.524	40
0.674	50
1.036	70
1.282	80
1.645	90
1.960	95
2.326	98
2.576	99
3.291	99.9

stressed that the test is applicable only if the standard deviation σ_d is closely estimated and if the distribution within samples is approximately normal. The normal distribution test is thus a particular case of the t test (see below) when the sample size is large. This can be seen from a comparison of Table 13-1 and the last line of Table A-8.

Example. Traffic studies before and after traffic control improvements were made at a certain intersection in a city. The condensed data are as follows:

Time	Mean speed $\bar{x}$, mph	Number of speed observations n	Standard deviation s, mph
Before	18.2	140	3.51
After.........	19.2	160	3.15

Does the difference between the two mean speeds represent a significant increase?

The standard deviations of the two means are:

$$\frac{s_1}{\sqrt{n_1}} = \frac{3.51}{\sqrt{140}} = 0.297 \quad \text{and} \quad \frac{s_2}{\sqrt{n_2}} = \frac{3.15}{\sqrt{160}} = 0.249$$

From Eq. 13-3 the standard deviation of the difference of means is:

$$\sigma_d = \sqrt{(0.297)^2 + (0.249)^2} = 0.388$$

We now calculate u (given by Eq. 13-4):

$$u = \frac{|\bar{x}_1 - \bar{x}_2|}{\sigma_d} = \frac{19.2 - 18.2}{0.388} = 2.58$$

From Table A-4 we find the probability of obtaining by chance a value of u of at least this magnitude as $(0.5000 - 0.4951) = 0.0049 = 0.49$ percent.

We conclude, therefore, that the observed increase in the mean speed is significant, and not due to chance error.

THE *t* TEST

When the conditions stated at the end of the preceding section are not satisfied, we apply Student's t test. (Student is the pseudonym of W. S. Gosset.) The test is applied to the null hypothesis that the two samples being compared are drawn from the same population, and we calculate the probability of the difference $|\bar{x}_1 - \bar{x}_2|$ having a value as large, or greater than observed. If the samples belong to the same population, then the sample means (being means of random samples) are normally distributed about the population mean, even if the distribution within the samples is not normal. The combined (population) variance s_c^2 is estimated by pooling the sums of squares of the residuals $(x - \bar{x})$ of both samples and dividing by the total number of degrees of freedom. Thus

$$s_c^2 = \frac{\Sigma(x_1 - \bar{x}_1)^2 + \Sigma(x_2 - \bar{x}_2)^2}{(n_1 - 1) + (n_2 - 1)} \qquad (13\text{-}6)$$

If the data in hand give estimates of the standard deviation of the two samples, s_1 and s_2, rather than the sums of squares, Eq. 13-6 can be written as

$$s_c^2 = \frac{s_1^2(n_1 - 1) + s_2^2(n_2 - 1)}{(n_1 - 1) + (n_2 - 1)} \qquad (13\text{-}7)$$

Thus each estimated variance is weighted by the number of degrees of freedom available for its calculation. This is the only method of obtaining a combined variance. Averaging of variances without considering the numbers of degrees of freedom involved is incorrect. Averaging of standard deviations is also incorrect.

The standard deviations of the two means are given in the usual manner by $s_c/\sqrt{n_1}$ and $s_c/\sqrt{n_2}$ respectively. The standard deviation of the difference of means is thus:

$$s_d = \sqrt{\frac{s_c^2}{n_1} + \frac{s_c^2}{n_2}}$$

or

$$s_d = s_c \sqrt{\frac{n_1 + n_2}{n_1 n_2}} \qquad (13\text{-}8)$$

The significance of the difference is measured by the ratio of the difference to its standard deviation, and is denoted by t, so that:

$$t = \frac{|\bar{x}_1 - \bar{x}_2|}{s_d} \qquad (13\text{-}9)$$

i.e.

$$t = \frac{|\bar{x}_1 - \bar{x}_2|}{\sqrt{\dfrac{\Sigma(x_1 - \bar{x}_1)^2 + \Sigma(x_2 - \bar{x}_2)^2}{(n_1 - 1) + (n_2 - 1)} \times \left(\dfrac{n_1 + n_2}{n_1 n_2}\right)}} \qquad (13\text{-}10)$$

the number of degrees of freedom being the number of observations less two (which were used in determining the means), that is, $(n_1 - 1) + (n_2 - 1)$.

Since the null hypothesis being examined by the t test assumes that the two samples belong to the same population, the two variance estimates must be consistent with this hypothesis, i.e., the two variances must not be significantly different. This should be verified by means of the F test (see Chapter 14) before the t test is applied. When $n_1 = n_2 = n$, Eq. 13-10 is simplified to:

$$t = \frac{|\bar{x}_1 - \bar{x}_2|}{\sqrt{\dfrac{\Sigma(x_1 - \bar{x}_1)^2 + \Sigma(x_2 - \bar{x}_2)^2}{n(n-1)}}} \tag{13-11}$$

The probability of $\bar{x}_1 - \bar{x}_2$ exceeding ts_d, if drawn by chance from the same population, represents the odds *against* the null hypothesis and, similarly to the case in Chapter 10, is known as the level of significance. Values of t for various levels of significance and degrees of freedom are given in Table A-8.

We usually specify the level of significance at which we are prepared to reject the null hypothesis as 5 percent or 1 percent. If the calculated t is greater than the tabulated value at the specified level of significance, we reject the null hypothesis and conclude that the difference is significant. If the calculated t is not greater than the tabulated t at, say, the 5 percent level of significance, the null hypothesis is accepted, but we cannot tell whether there is no difference between the means being compared or whether the data are inadequate to establish whether or not there is a difference. As previously stated, there is no question of ever proving the null hypothesis. We must remember also that statistical considerations are not the sole basis for drawing inferences; a physical appreciation of the problem, judgment, and experience should also be brought into the picture.

We can now answer the question posed at the beginning of this chapter. The difference between the mean strengths of the two concretes is $7,300 - 7,000 = 300$ psi; and

$$s_d = 400 \sqrt{\frac{20}{100}} = 179 \text{ psi}$$

Hence

$$t = \frac{300}{179} = 1.68$$

For $20 - 2 = 18$ degrees of freedom, Table A-8 gives $t = 1.734$ at the 10 percent level of significance, and we conclude, therefore, that there is no significant difference between the strengths of the two concretes.

We should note that for a given probability (i.e., a specified level of significance) the size of the sample required to make a decision possible increases as the difference between the means decreases.

Example. The slopes of two types of valley walls were measured. Sample A comprised slopes at whose base talus and slope wash have accumulated, indicating that considerable time has elapsed since stream erosion was active against the slope base. Sample B comprised slopes at whose base stream erosion has recently been active. We wish to determine whether the slopes of Sample A differ significantly from those of B. In other words, do the data indicate that a slope, if left to weather and waste without basal cutting, tends to decline in angle rather than retreat in parallel planes?[1]

Sample	Mean slope $\bar{x}$	Standard deviation s	Sample size n
A	38.23°	2.70°	34
B	44.82°	3.27°	172

The *F* test (see Chapter 14) shows that the variances of the two samples do not differ significantly, and of course the two samples are independent of one another.

From Eq. 13-7 the pooled estimate of variance is

$$s_c^2 = \frac{33 \times 2.7^2 + 171 \times 3.27^2}{33 + 171} = 10.142$$

and

$$s_c = 3.2°$$

Using Eq. 13-8,

$$s_d = 3.2 \sqrt{\frac{1}{34} + \frac{1}{172}} = 0.60$$

and from Eq. 13-10:

$$t = \frac{44.82 - 38.23}{0.60} = 10.98$$

The number of degrees of freedom is $172 + 34 - 2 = 204$, and Table A-8 gives the probability of less than 0.1 percent of obtaining a value of *t* equal to or greater than 10.98. The null hypothesis can therefore be rejected, and we conclude that absence of erosion at the base of a slope leads to a decline in the angle of the slope, but when erosion takes place, the slope retreats parallel to itself.

ONE-SIDED AND TWO-SIDED TESTS

There are two general questions which we may seek to answer by means of the *t* test. The first one is: Is $\bar{x}_1$ significantly different from $\bar{x}_2$? Here we are not interested in whether $\bar{x}_1 > \bar{x}_2$ or $\bar{x}_1 < \bar{x}_2$; the null hypothesis can be wrongly rejected in favor of either of these possibilities, and the test is therefore two-sided. The null hypothesis is rejected if the proportional area under *two* tails is greater than that corresponding to the specified level of significance, i.e., when calculated $|t|$ > tabulated *t*.

The second question is of the type: Is $\bar{x}_1 \geq \bar{x}_2$? If $\bar{x}_1 \ngtr \bar{x}_2$, we accept the null hypothesis regardless of how much smaller $\bar{x}_1$ is than $\bar{x}_2$. This is a one-sided test, and the sign of $\bar{x}_1 - \bar{x}_2$ is material. In a one-sided test

[1]A. N. Strahler, "Statistical Analysis in Geomorphic Research," *Journal of Geology* (January 1954), p. 12.

we are interested in one tail of the distribution only, and the probability given at the top of Table A-8 should therefore be halved. This follows from the fact that the distribution of t is symmetrical, and, for example, a 5 percent level of significance means that there is a $2\frac{1}{2}$ percent probability of obtaining t greater than tabulated and a $2\frac{1}{2}$ percent probability of obtaining t smaller than the negative tabulated value [i.e., the tabulated value times (-1)].

It is advisable to decide whether we should apply a one-sided or a two-sided test before commencing the calculations so as to avoid the tendency to lean toward the test which will give a more "convenient" result. As a general rule, a one-sided test is appropriate if a deviation in a direction opposite to that postulated would have no practical significance. For example, if we require fuel with a certain minimum octane rating level, we would test whether the actual rating is significantly lower than that specified, but we would not be concerned if it were higher.

An example of a one-sided test is afforded by the traffic speed problem, considered earlier in this chapter, since the question asked concerned an increase in speed.

We should stress the fact, mentioned earlier, that the t test can be used for any underlying distribution while the "normal distribution test" of Eq. 13-5 is limited to normal distribution with a close estimate of population variance available. Thus, although Eq. 13-4 and 13-9 are similar, they are applied in different cases. We may note that t itself is not normally distributed but becomes so when the number of degrees of freedom ν approaches infinity. This can be seen from a comparison of the values of t for $\nu = \infty$ (Table A-8) and the values of z for the corresponding $2F(z)$ (Table A-4). For example, at the 10 percent level of significance $t = 1.645$. Now for $z = 1.645$, $2F(z) = 0.90$ which corresponds to the 10 percent level of significance.

t TEST FOR PAIRED DATA

The comparison of means discussed in the preceding pages is applicable when the two samples have been drawn independently of one another; for example, they may represent products of two factories, and we may want to compare these products in order to determine whether there is a significant difference between them. If, however, the samples are drawn from one source and then subjected to two different treatments whose effects are being studied, we can use a somewhat different technique, although the t test on the difference of means is still permissible.

In the case of paired variables we consider the mean difference between two samples as the variate and compare it with *its* standard deviation, i.e., we apply the t test to the paired data. In this manner, the effect of the test-to-test variation is eliminated, but this advantage is offset by a loss in precision due to the standard deviation being based on fewer degrees of freedom (the number of *pairs* less one, instead of the total number of observations less two).

It should be stressed that this technique can be used only when the pairs of samples are truly correlated; pairing by random choice or by arrangement of samples in each group by rank is not permitted. Because of the somewhat confusing terminology, it is important to distinguish between a test for the difference between means, and a test for the mean difference between pairs of observations.

INTERPRETATION OF RESULTS

When the data are truly paired we can apply either form of the *t* test. Which one is more convenient to use will depend on whether the variation between tests, which may be made under different conditions, obscures the difference between two members of a pair forming one test. This is illustrated by the next example.

Having a choice of tests of significance, the reader may wonder what to do when one test indicates a significant difference between two sets of values while the other does not. We should remember that failure to detect a significant difference does not mean that there is none, but only that we cannot say with a sufficiently high probability of being right that a difference is present. Thus if *any* method of test shows a definitely significant difference, its testimony is vital, even though another method fails to show a similar result.

Example. The influence of the size of the test specimen on the strength of concrete was tested as follows. Seven mixes were made and from each one large and one small concrete specimen were prepared and tested.

Test whether there is a significant difference between the strengths of the two types of specimens.

Strength of specimen, psi		Difference, psi $x_2 - x_1$
small x_2	large x_1	
4,404	4,140	264
4,326	3,984	342
3,788	3,842	− 54
3,475	3,053	422
3,418	3,145	273
2,262	1,813	449
7,415	6,867	548
$\Sigma x_2 = 29{,}088$	$\Sigma x_1 = 26{,}844$	$\Sigma (x_2 - x_1) = 2{,}244$

Hence

$$\bar{x}_2 = \frac{\Sigma x_2}{n_2} = \frac{29{,}088}{7} = 4{,}155.43 \text{ psi}$$

and

$$\bar{x}_1 = \frac{26{,}844}{7} = 3{,}834.86 \text{ psi}$$

Since the data are paired, we consider $x_2 - x_1$ as the variable. Let $y = x_2 - x_1$. Then

$$\bar{y} = \frac{\Sigma y}{n} = \frac{2{,}244}{7} = 320.57 \text{ psi}$$

Now the standard deviation of y is

$$s = \sqrt{\frac{\Sigma (y - \bar{y})^2}{n - 1}}$$

$$= \sqrt{\frac{224{,}731.71}{6}} = 193.53 \text{ psi}$$

The standard deviation of $\bar{y}$ is

$$s_{\bar{y}} = \frac{s}{\sqrt{n}}$$

$$= \frac{193.53}{\sqrt{7}} = 73.17 \text{ psi}$$

We now apply the t test to $\bar{y}$ by comparing it to a zero mean difference:

$$t = \frac{|\bar{y} - 0|}{s_{\bar{y}}} = 4.38$$

The number of degrees of freedom is 6, and Table A-8 gives $t = 3.707$ at the 1 percent level of significance. The difference in strength is thus significant.

Let us now ignore the pairing and apply the t test to the mean difference of strengths.

Using Eq. 13-6, we compute the combined population variance s_c^2:

$$s_c^2 = \frac{\Sigma (x_1 - \bar{x}_1)^2 + \Sigma (x_2 - \bar{x}_2)^2}{2n - 2}$$

$$= \frac{14{,}484{,}406.90 + 15{,}442{,}547.80}{12}$$

$$= 2{,}493{,}912.89$$

The standard deviation of the difference of means is given by Eq. 13-8:

$$s_d = s_c \sqrt{\frac{2}{n}}$$

$$= 1579.21 \sqrt{\frac{2}{7}} = 844.12 \text{ psi}$$

The mean difference of strengths is

$$\bar{x}_2 - \bar{x}_1 = 4155.43 - 3834.86 = 320.57 \text{ psi}$$

We now apply the t test:

$$t = \frac{|\bar{x}_2 - \bar{x}_1|}{s_d}$$

$$= \frac{320.57}{844.12} = 0.380$$

The number of degrees of freedom is $(2n - 2) = 12$. Table A-8 gives $t = 2.179$ at the 5 percent level. The difference appears thus to be not significant.

It is clear that the conclusion from the last test is due to the considerable difference in the level of strength of the different mixes. The paired test is more discriminating, and we conclude that there is a significant difference between the strengths of the specimens of the two sizes.

CASE OF NONHOMOGENEOUS VARIANCES

Equation 13-10 was obtained on the assumption that the variances of the two samples being compared are not significantly different (i.e., are homogeneous), this being implicit in the hypothesis that the two samples belong to the same population. The homogeneity of variances is examined by the F test (see Chapter 14).

However, in some cases the condition of homogeneity of variances may not be satisfied, but we may still want to test the significance of the difference of two means. This is the case, for example, when errors of measurement in the two samples are due to different causes so that the estimates of variance cannot correctly be pooled. The t test cannot therefore be applied, and we use a test in which the ratio of the standard deviations of the two sample means, $\dfrac{s_{\bar{x}_1}}{s_{\bar{x}_2}} = \tan \theta$, is considered in determining the significance of the difference of the means. The difference $\bar{x}_1 - \bar{x}_2$ is considered significant if

$$\frac{|\bar{x}_1 - \bar{x}_2|}{\sqrt{s_{\bar{x}_1}^2 + s_{\bar{x}_2}^2}} > d \tag{13-12}$$

where d is given in Table A-9 for two levels of significance and for different values of θ, ν_1, and ν_2. The numbers of degrees of freedom in the two samples, ν_1 and ν_2, are equal to $n_1 - 1$ and $n_2 - 1$ respectively (n_1 and n_2 are the sample sizes).

Example. Imagine that we have used two different methods to determine a physical constant. Each method yields a mean value, and we want to determine whether or not there is a real discrepancy between the two results. Because different methods have been used, the variances may differ and cannot be pooled. Let the results be:

$$\bar{x}_1 = 5.289 \qquad \bar{x}_2 = 5.261$$

$$s_{\bar{x}_1}^2 = 0.00008 \qquad s_{\bar{x}_2}^2 = 0.00001$$

for $\qquad n_1 = 13 \qquad$ and $n_2 = 60$

We may check that the F test yields

$$F = \frac{s_{\bar{x}_1}^2}{s_{\bar{x}_2}^2} = 8$$

which, for the degrees of freedom $\nu_1 = 12$ and $\nu_2 = 59$, shows a significant difference at the 1 percent level (F from Table A-10 is 2.50). We calculate

$$\tan \theta = \sqrt{\frac{0.00008}{0.00001}} = 2.828$$

whence $\theta = 70.5°$. Now

$$\sqrt{s_{\bar{x}_1}^2 + s_{\bar{x}_2}^2} = 0.0095$$

Therefore

$$d = \frac{|\bar{x}_1 - \bar{x}_2|}{\sqrt{s_{\bar{x}_1}^2 + s_{\bar{x}_2}^2}} = \frac{0.028}{0.0095} = 2.95$$

Table A-9 gives the values of θ of 60° and 75°, and we have therefore to interpolate. For the 5 percent level of significance the values of d are for $\nu_1 = 12$:

$$\nu_2 = 24 \quad \begin{cases} \theta = 60° & d = 2.142 \\ \theta = 75° & d = 2.168 \end{cases}$$

$$\nu_2 = \infty \quad \begin{cases} \theta = 60° & d = 2.120 \\ \theta = 75° & d = 2.163 \end{cases}$$

As all these values are close to one another, we shall take simply the arithmetic mean of the four values of d given above; this is $d = 2.15$.

For the 1 percent level of significance the four values of d at the same points are: 2.938, 3.020, 2.909, 3.014. The arithmetic mean is thus 2.97.

We can, therefore, conclude that the difference between the means $\bar{x}_1$ and $\bar{x}_2$ is significant at the 5 percent level but not quite at the 1 percent level.

A special case arises where the standard deviation is not constant for either group but varies with the level of x, the variation being the same in both groups. For example, in testing the strength of concrete it has been found[2] that the standard deviation is proportional to strength. In such a case logarithmic transformation has to be applied to the variate. The variance of the natural logarithm of the original variate is approximately

---

[2] A. M. Neville, "The Relation Between Standard Deviation and Mean Strength of Concrete Test Cubes," *Magazine of Concrete Research*, vol. 10, no. 31 (July, 1959).

equal to the square of the coefficient of variation V^2. We can, therefore, use Eq. 13-9, substituting $\log_e x$ for x, and V^2 for s_c^2. Then

$$t = \frac{|\log_e \bar{x}_1 - \log_e \bar{x}_2|}{\sqrt{\dfrac{V_1^2(n_1 - 1) + V_2^2(n_2 - 1)}{n_1 + n_2 - 2} \times \dfrac{n_1 + n_2}{n_1 n_2}}} \qquad (13\text{-}13)$$

where $\bar{x}_1$ and $\bar{x}_2$ = sample means
n_1 and n_2 = sample
V_1 and V_2 = coefficients of variation

Note that t has $(n_1 + n_2 - 2)$ degrees of freedom.

If n is large, we can consider V^2 to be the variance of $\log_e \bar{x}$ and not an estimate, and Eq. 13-13 reduces to

$$t = \frac{|\log_e \bar{x}_1 - \log_e \bar{x}_2|}{\sqrt{\left(\dfrac{V_1^2}{n_2} + \dfrac{V_2^2}{n_1}\right) \times \dfrac{n_1 + n_2}{n_1 + n_2 - 2}}} \qquad (13\text{-}14)$$

SOLVED PROBLEM

13-1. It is suspected that the state of stress in a steel wire affects the percentage loss in the ultimate tensile strength in the wire when such a wire has been immersed in a calcium chloride solution. Twelve lengths of wire were obtained, and each one was cut into four specimens. Two of these were stressed, one in solution, one in air; the other two were unstressed, likewise one in solution, one in air.

The table below gives the percentage loss in the ultimate tensile strength for the appropriate pairs.

Test number	Stressed	Unstressed
1	10.4	7.1
2	8.1	8.4
3	8.5·	7.2
4	9.7	8.3
5	8.2	6.8
6	10.1	8.5
7	7.9	7.9
8	9.8	8.2
9	8.4	8.4
10	8.7	6.5
11	9.3	7.0
12	8.6	8.8

Establish whether stressing affects the percentage loss in strength caused by immersion in the solution.

Solution:

Since the samples are paired, we shall apply the t test to find the significance of the mean difference between the unstressed and stressed specimens. In tabular form:

Test number	Stressed	Unstressed	Difference d	d^2
1	10.4	7.1	3.3	10.89
2	8.1	8.4	−0.3	0.09
3	8.5	7.2	1.3	1.69
4	9.7	8.3	1.4	1.96
5	8.2	6.8	1.4	1.96
6	10.1	8.5	1.6	2.56
7	7.9	7.9	0	0
8	9.8	8.2	1.6	2.56
9	8.4	8.4	0	0
10	8.7	6.5	2.2	4.84
11	9.3	7.0	2.3	5.29
12	8.6	8.8	−0.2	0.04
Totals............................		$\Sigma d = 15.1 - 0.5 = 14.6$	Σ	.88

$$\text{Mean difference } \bar{d} = \frac{14.6}{12} = 1.217$$

$$\text{Estimated standard deviation } s = \sqrt{\frac{\Sigma d^2 - \frac{(\Sigma d)^2}{n}}{n-1}} = \sqrt{\frac{31.88 - \frac{(14.6)^2}{12}}{11}} = \sqrt{1.283}$$

$$= 1.13$$

Therefore

$$s_{\bar{d}} = \frac{s}{\sqrt{n}} = \frac{1.13}{\sqrt{12}}$$

Hence

$$t = \frac{|\bar{d} - 0|}{s_{\bar{d}}} = \frac{1.217}{1.13} \times \sqrt{12} = 3.731$$

For $v = n - 1 = 12 - 1 = 11$, Table A-8 gives for the 1 percent level of significance $t = 3.106$. Since the calculated $t > 3.106$, the difference is significant at the 1 percent level. In other words, there is strong evidence to support the contention that the state of stress affects the percentage loss in ultimate strength after immersion in a calcium chloride solution.

The χ^2 test can be used to give a quick, albeit rough, check on the significance of the difference. We calculate the expected numbers of positive and negative signs of the difference on the basis of the null hypothesis and compare these with the observed numbers of positive and negative signs. In tabular form:

	+ ve sign	− ve sign
Observed number of signs O	8	2
Expected number of signs E	5	5

$$\chi^2 = \Sigma \frac{(O-E)^2}{E} = \frac{(8-5)^2}{5} + \frac{(2-5)^2}{5} = \frac{9}{5} + \frac{9}{5} = 3.6$$

For $v = 1$, from Table A-7, the probability of obtaining such a value of χ^2 by chance is between 0.10 and 0.05. Therefore, we suspect the null hypothesis and should test the significance by the t test (as already done).

As a somewhat more accurate alternative, the binomial distribution can be used to calculate the possibility of obtaining the distribution of positive and negative signs actually observed.

If the specimens had not been paired, i.e., if we had measured the loss in strength on immersion in the solution for 12 consignments of wire using stressed specimens and for another 12 consignments using unstressed specimens, pairing would have not been possible. In such a case the t test must be applied to the difference of means, but the procedure is permissible even when the data are paired. Thus we have

(a) for stressed specimens:

Strength loss x_1	Deviation, $x_1 - \bar{x}_1$		$(x_1 - \bar{x}_1)^2$
10.4	1.425		2.031
8.1		−0.875	0.766
8.5		−0.475	0.226
9.7	0.725		0.526
8.2		−0.775	0.601
10.1	1.125		1.266
7.9		−1.075	1.156
9.8	0.825		0.681
8.4		−0.575	0.331
8.7		−0.275	0.076
9.3	0.325		0.106
8.6		−0.375	0.141
$\Sigma x_1 = 107.7$	$\Sigma(x_1 - \bar{x}_1) = +4.425$	$-4.425 = 0$	$\Sigma(x_1 - \bar{x}_1)^2 = 7.907$

$$\bar{x}_1 = \frac{107.7}{12} = 8.975$$

(b) for unstressed specimens:

Strength loss x_2	Deviation, $(x_2 - \bar{x}_2)$		$(x_2 - \bar{x}_2)^2$
7.1		−0.6583	0.433
8.4	0.6417		0.412
7.2		−0.5583	0.312
8.3	0.5417		0.293
6.8		−0.9583	0.918
8.5	0.7417		0.550
7.9	0.1417		0.020
8.2	0.4417		0.195
8.4	0.6417		0.412
6.5		−1.2583	1.583
7.0		−0.7583	0.575
8.8	1.0417		1.085
$\Sigma x_2 = 93.1$	$\Sigma(x_2 - \bar{x}_2) = +4.1916$	$-4.1915 \simeq 0$	$\Sigma(x_2 - \bar{x}_2)^2 = 6.788$

$$x_2 = \frac{\Sigma x_2}{n} = \frac{93.1}{12} = 7.758$$

Pooled estimate of variance is

$$s_c^2 = \frac{\Sigma(x_1 - \bar{x}_1)^2 + \Sigma(x_2 - \bar{x}_2)^2}{(n_1 - 1) + (n_2 - 1)}$$

$$= \frac{7.907 + 6.788}{11 + 11} = \frac{14.695}{22} = 0.668$$

Standard deviation of the difference of means is

$$s_d = s_c \sqrt{\frac{n_1 + n_2}{n_1 n_2}}$$

$$= \sqrt{\frac{0.668}{6}} = 0.3337$$

Difference of means $= \bar{x}_1 - \bar{x}_2 = 8.975 - 7.758 = 1.217$. Hence

$$t = \frac{1.217}{0.3337} = 3.647$$

Number of degrees of freedom $= 24 - 2 = 22$.

From Table A-8, $t = 2.819$ at the 1 percent level of significance and 3.792 at the 0.1 percent level. The difference is, therefore, highly significant.

PROBLEMS

13-1. A special brand of cement is sold in bags containing 50 lb. We choose 11 bags at random and find their weights in pounds:

49.2, 50.1, 49.8, 49.7, 50.1, 50.5, 49.6, 49.9, 50.4, 50.2, 49.7

Are these results consistent with the assumption that the bags belong to a population with a mean of 50 lb?

13-2. To check two weighing machines, 8 samples were weighed on each machine. Do the results suggest that there is a significant difference between the two machines?

Machine A	10.063	8.051	9.036	9.067	3.056	5.076	5.074	2.006
Machine B	10.063	8.050	9.033	9.062	3.060	5.070	5.070	2.000

13-3. To test his laboratory a manufacturer took 13 samples of his product, halved each of them, and had one-half tested in his laboratory (A) and the other in an independent laboratory (B). Is there a significant difference between the test results of the two laboratories?

Sample No.	1	2	3	4	5	6	7	8	9	10	11	12	13
Laboratory A	17.2	17.0	17.4	18.0	18.3	15.2	13.2	18.7	16.7	19.4	14.7	17.7	16.9
Laboratory B	19.1	19.8	17.9	18.0	18.3	15.0	14.3	18.2	17.7	19.3	16.7	16.8	16.7

13-4. The mean resistance of a box has been established by the manufacturer to be $250\,\Omega$. A purchaser tests 10 boxes and finds the following values:

246, 261, 249, 254, 235, 242, 235, 231, 266, 239

Does the consignment meet the specification if values within the 10 percent level of significance are tolerated?

13-5. In a laboratory it was suspected that the measurements of viscosity obtained in the morning were lower than in the afternoon. Ten samples were therefore split in half, one-half of each being tested in the morning, the other in the afternoon. Do the data suggest that the "afternoon viscosity" is higher?

Sample No.	Viscosity (coded)	
	Morning	Afternoon
1	43	45
2	48	48
3	48	50
4	50	53
5	55	54
6	50	52
7	72	73
8	75	75
9	73	72
10	54	56

13-6. Results of chemical analyses for the content of A in materials from two sources are as follows:

	Content of A, percent					
Source 1	93.12	93.57	92.81	94.32	93.77	93.52
Source 2	92.54	92.38	93.21	92.06	92.55	

Test the hypothesis that there is no difference in the content of A between the two sources.

13-7. The strength of two alloys was compared, 10 samples of each being tested. Alloy A had a mean strength of 31,400 psi with a coefficient of variation of 19 percent; the corresponding values for alloy B were 27,100 psi and 15 percent. Can we conclude that the strengths of the two alloys do not differ at the 1 percent level of significance?

13-8. Measurements of a certain angle in castings over two periods yielded the following data:

$$n_1 = 154 \qquad n_2 = 149$$
$$\theta_1 = 90.0° \qquad \theta_2 = 89.7°$$
$$s_1 = 3.6° \qquad s_2 = 3.5°$$

Does this mean that the angle is becoming smaller? (If the angle were increasing, we would not worry.)

13-9. In order to determine whether the use of rubber packing between the concrete specimen and the platen of the testing machine affects the observed strength, two specimens were made from each of six batches of concrete.[3] Of each pair of specimens one was tested with the packing, the other without. Is there a significant difference between the strengths obtained by the two test methods?

---

[3] P. J. F. Wright, "Statistical Methods in Concrete Research," *Magazine of Concrete Research*, Vol. 5, No. 15 (March 1954) p. 143.

Batch No.	Tensile strength, psi	
	with packing	without packing
1	400	360
2	395	290
3	385	330
4	380	305
5	430	345
6	360	310

13-10. To compare the strength of two cements, six mortar cubes were made with each cement, and the following strengths (psi) were recorded:

Cement A 4600, 4710, 4820, 4670, 4760, 4480
Cement B 4400, 4450, 4700, 4400, 4170, 4100

Is there a significant difference between the strengths of the two cements?

13-11. The resistance (in Ω) of 40 boxes supplied from each of three manufacturers was found to be as listed below. Test whether there is a significant difference between the mean values of Groups A and B, and Groups B and C.

GROUP A:

6,040	7,240	6,160	7,000	7,160	8,000	7,360	6,800
6,040	5,680	6,320	6,120	8,240	8,040	7,760	7,040
6,720	6,920	7,600	6,600	6,920	7,280	6,400	6,200
8,120	8,120	8,000	7,800	7,320	7,560	7,200	7,280
7,560	7,520	7,520	6,840	6,640	7,160	7,280	6,680

GROUP B:

7,040	7,640	6,480	6,000	6,640	6,880	6,200	6,480
6,160	6,480	7,320	6,680	6,440	6,600	6,280	7,480
7,320	6,320	7,880	7,520	8,760	8,280	7,880	7,040
6,720	6,600	8,080	7,120	6,600	7,960	6,440	5,960
6,680	6,600	6,600	6,040	6,080	6,720	6,640	6,600

GROUP C:

7,240	7,240	6,840	7,240	7,320	7,080	7,320	7,720
7,280	7,360	7,320	7,440	7,240	7,240	8,400	8,440
7,800	7,720	7,640	7,640	7,520	7,720	7,640	7,600
8,600	8,520	8,880	8,800	8,440	8,400	7,320	8,800
7,520	7,520	6,320	5,680	7,440	7,640	6,960	8,920

13-12. Apply the t test to the differences in strength of Prob. 7-8, and hence establish whether there is a real difference between the strengths of the 10 and 20 cm cubes.

chapter 14

Comparison of Variances and Their Properties

In the tests on the significance of means we either assumed that the two samples whose means were being compared had the same standard deviation (or, strictly speaking, deviations belonging to the same population of standard deviations) or we allowed for the inequality of the standard deviations (as in the text on page 150). However, it is often important to know with some degree of certainty whether the standard deviations of two samples are the same, i.e., they do not differ significantly; such standard deviations are said to be *homogeneous*. For example, if we want to establish that two samples belong to the same population, we should test their means and determine that they do not differ significantly, and also test their standard deviations and determine that they do not differ significantly. It is, of course, possible for one of these conditions to be satisfied but not the other.

Although we refer to standard deviations, it is really variances that are the statistic being studied.

F TEST

If there are only two variances, we apply the variance ratio test, known as the F test. As in other tests of significance, we adopt a null hypothesis, which in this case is that the variances of the two samples belong to the same population. The F value is calculated as:

$$F = \frac{s_1^2}{s_2^2} \qquad (14\text{-}1)$$

where $s_1 > s_2$. This condition must be satisfied as the F test is a one-sided test when the alternative to the null hypothesis is $s_1^2 > s_2^2$. If the alternative is simply $s_1^2 \neq s_2^2$, the test is two-sided and the probabilities in Table A-10 are doubled.

The variances s_1^2 and s_2^2 are really estimates of the population variance obtained from the two samples.

Table A-10 gives values of F for various degrees of freedom of the two samples, and if the calculated F exceeds the tabulated value, the probability that the difference between the two variances is due to chance alone is smaller than the specified probability (5, 1, or 0.1 percent), and we are justified in rejecting the null hypothesis (with the given probability of committing a Type I error).

If the two samples are of size n_1 and n_2, the numbers of degrees of freedom are $\nu_1 = n_1 - 1$ and $\nu_2 = n_2 - 1$ respectively, since, given the value of variance and $n - 1$ observations, the nth observation is uniquely determined.

It has been shown that the larger the sample the more accurately the variance is determined. For this reason, the larger the samples being compared, the lower the value of F at which the null hypothesis is rejected with a given probability of a correct decision. This is illustrated by Table A-10.

Example. In tests on a plastic the following data were obtained for two samples from two sources.

Source	Sample size n	Estimate of standard deviation s
A	11	300
B	21	200

Can we say that the standard deviations of the plastics produced by the two sources differ significantly? We have:

$$s_1 = 300 \qquad \nu_1 = 11 - 1 = 10$$
$$s_2 = 200 \qquad \nu_2 = 21 - 1 = 20$$

From Eq. 14-1,

$$F = \left(\frac{300}{200}\right)^2 = 2.25$$

From Table A-10, $F = 2.35$ at the 5 percent level of significance. The difference between the variances is therefore not significant, but we would be wise to take further specimens and repeat the F test for the enlarged samples.

It may be of interest to mention that F at 1 degree of freedom is equal to t^2.

If variance is a function of the level of the mean and the populations whose variability is being compared have different means, the F test cannot be applied directly to the variances. For example, if the standard deviation is directly proportional to the mean strength of the population,[1] then it is the squares of the coefficients of variations that have to be tested

---

[1] See Chapter 13.

for homogeneity. The square of the coefficient of variation is approximately equal to the variance of the natural logarithm of the original variate; we can imagine thus that we are dealing with the variance of a log-transformed variable.

BARTLETT'S TEST

The F test can be used to compare two variances only. If more than two variances are involved, then a test of homogeneity of the variances, known as Bartlett's test, may be applied. This is a special application of the χ^2 test, in which we compare the difference between the total number of degrees of freedom times the natural logarithm of the pooled estimate of variance and the sum, extended over all samples, of the product of the degrees of freedom and the natural logarithm of the estimate of variance. Thus, if n_i is the sample size, s_i^2 is the estimate of variance from sample i, and $\bar{s}^2$ is the pooled estimate of variance, then Bartlett's test requires the calculation of

$$\chi^2 = 2.3026 \{\log \bar{s}^2 \times \Sigma(n_i - 1) - \Sigma[(n_i - 1)\log s_i^2]\} \quad (14\text{-}2)$$

The coefficient 2.3026 is introduced by conversion of natural logarithms to those to base 10, since

$$\log_e a = 2.3026 \log_{10} a$$

When all samples are of the same size n, Eq. 14-2 reduces to:

$$\chi^2 = 2.3026(n - 1)[k \log \bar{s}^2 - \Sigma \log s_i^2] \quad (14\text{-}3)$$

where k is the number of samples whose variances are being compared.

The computations are conveniently set out in tabular form:

Sample number	Sample size	Sum of squares of deviations	Degrees of freedom ν	Estimated variance s_i^2	Logarithm of variance	Product	Reciprocal of ν
1	.	.	.	.	.	.	.
.	.	.	.	.	.	.	.
i	n_i	$\sum\limits_1^{n_i}(x - \bar{x}_i)^2$	$n_i - 1$	$\dfrac{\Sigma(x - \bar{x}_i)^2}{n_i - 1}$	$\log s_i^2$	$(n_i - 1)\log s_i^2$	$\dfrac{1}{n_i - 1}$
.	.	.	.	.	.	.	.
.	.	.	.	.	.	.	.
k	.	.	.	.	.	.	.
		$\sum\limits_1^k\sum\limits_1^{n_i}(x - \bar{x}_i)^2$	$\Sigma(n_i - 1)$		$\Sigma \log s_i^2$	$\Sigma[(n_i - 1)\log s_i^2]$	$\Sigma\dfrac{1}{n_i - 1}$

Now

$$\bar{s}^2 = \frac{\Sigma\Sigma(x - \bar{x}_i)^2}{\Sigma(n_i - 1)}$$

and, substituting the other summations in Eq. 14-2, χ^2 can be calculated. This enables us to test the hypothesis that all the variances are homogeneous, using Table A-7 with $(k - 1)$ degrees of freedom. If the calculated value of χ^2 is greater than the tabulated value at a specified level of significance, we conclude that the variances are not homogeneous. The level of significance represents, as always, the probability of our having reached the wrong conclusion.

The value of χ^2 as calculated from Eq. 14-2 is biased towards the high side so that we may wrongly reject the null hypothesis. If χ^2 indicates acceptance, then, after correction for bias, the hypothesis would be even more likely to be correct so that we need not worry about the bias. However, rejection at the 5 percent level has to be checked by calculating a corrected value of χ^2, say χ_c^2. This is given by

$$\chi_c^2 = \frac{\chi^2}{C} \tag{14-4}$$

where

$$C = 1 + \frac{1}{3(k - 1)}\left[\sum\left(\frac{1}{n_i - 1}\right) - \frac{1}{\sum(n_i - 1)}\right] \tag{14-5}$$

Often a considerable computational effort can be saved by applying an F test to the largest and smallest variances before Bartlett's test. If the F test indicates that the largest variance is not significantly different from the smallest one, then one can reasonably assume that the variances lying in between do not differ significantly, and all the variances can be regarded as homogeneous.

Example. The performance of five testing machines was compared by testing four specimens, all from the same source, in each machine. Does the variability of the different machines differ significantly?

Machine	Coded results[2] x_i	$\bar{x}_i$	$\sum(x_i - \bar{x})^2$	s_i^2	$\log s_i^2$
1	2, 3, 5, 2,	3.0	6.00	2.00	0.30103
2	3, 4, 4, 1	3.0	6.00	2.00	0.30103
3	3, 3, 3, 4	3.25	0.75	0.25	−0.60206
4	2, 1, 3, 4	2.5	5.00	1.67	0.22272
5	5, 2, 2, 5	3.5	9.00	3.00	0.47712
Totals				$\sum s_i^2 = 8.92$	$\sum \log s_i^2 = 0.69984$

Hence

$$\bar{s}^2 = \frac{3 \times 8.92}{5 \times 3} = 1.784$$

$$\log \bar{s}^2 = 0.25139$$

[2]"Coding" or simplifying the computations is explained in Chapters 3 and 18.

From Eq. 14-3

$$\chi^2 = 2.3026 \times 3(5 \times 0.25139 - 0.69984)$$
$$= 3.85$$

The number of degrees of freedom is 4 and Table A-7 gives $\chi^2 = 7.779$ at the 10 percent level of significance. Since the test indicates an acceptance of the null hypothesis, there is no need to apply the correction of Eq. 14-5, and we conclude that there is no significant difference between the variances of the test results of the five machines.

STANDARD DEVIATIONS OF VARIOUS STATISTICS

It may be appropriate here to list the standard deviations of various statistics for a sample of size n and an estimate of variance of s^2. Equation 6-8 showed that:

$$\text{Standard deviation}^3 \text{ of the mean} = \frac{s}{\sqrt{n}} \tag{14-6}$$

We can now list the following without proof:

$$\text{Standard deviation of variance} = s^2 \sqrt{\frac{2}{n}} \tag{14-7}$$

$$\text{Standard deviation of standard deviation} = \frac{s}{\sqrt{2n}} \tag{14-8}$$

$$\text{Standard deviation of the coefficient of variation } V = \frac{V}{\sqrt{2n}} \tag{14-9}$$

Equations 14-6 to 14-9 are valid only when the underlying distribution is normal, but even then the standard deviations of variance, of standard deviation, or of the coefficient of variation are not normally distributed.[4] These standard deviations are useful as only an approximate guide to the precision of the estimate of the appropriate statistic and are not greatly used.

PROPAGATION OF ERRORS

Suppose we want to determine a quantity Q which is determined from two measured quantities x_1 and x_2; for example, let

$$Q = ax_1 \pm bx_2 \tag{14-10}$$

Assume that we have a large number of observations of x_1 and x_2, and hence of Q. We can compute the standard deviations of x_1 and x_2, and we want to determine the standard deviation of Q.

---

[3] This standard deviation and those that follow are known as standard errors (see Chapter 10).

[4] Variance has a distribution close to χ^2 but as n increases, the distribution tends to normal.

Let μ_Q, μ_1, and μ_2 be the true mean values of the three quantities. Then

$$\mu_Q = a\mu_1 \pm b\mu_2 \tag{14-11}$$

If ΔQ, Δx_1, and Δx_2 denote the deviations of observations from the appropriate means, then

$$\Delta Q = a\,\Delta x_1 \pm b\,\Delta x_2$$

and

$$(\Delta Q)^2 = a^2\,(\Delta x_1)^2 + b^2(\Delta x_2)^2 \pm 2ab\,\Delta x_1\,\Delta x_2 \tag{14-12}$$

We can write Eq. 14-12 for each set of observations. The mean value of $(\Delta Q)^2$ then represents the variance of Q, σ_Q^2. Similarly, the mean value of $(\Delta x_1)^2$ is the variance of x_1, $\sigma_{x_1}^2$, and the mean value of $(\Delta x_2)^2$ is the variance of x_2, $\sigma_{x_2}^2$.

The mean value of $\Delta x_1\,\Delta x_2$ is the *covariance* of x_1 and x_2, and is a measure of correlation between x_1 and x_2.

If the variables x_1 and x_2 are independent, i.e., not correlated, the covariance is zero. Under such circumstances, the mean values of the various terms of Eq. 14-12 yield the relation

$$\sigma_Q^2 = a^2\sigma_{x_1}^2 + b^2\sigma_{x_2}^2 \tag{14-13}[5]$$

When $a = b = 1$, that is, for $Q = x_1 \pm x_2$, we have

$$\sigma_Q^2 = \sigma_{x_1}^2 + \sigma_{x_2}^2 \tag{14-14}$$

Thus the variance of a sum or of a difference of two *independent* variables is equal to the sum of the variances of the variables. The argument can be extended to any number of variables.

Equation 14-14 is of great importance in apportioning errors to various causes and forms the basis of the analysis of variance, which is the subject of Chapter 18.

In a more general way, Eq. 14-13 depicts the propagation of errors. For example, if

$$Q = \text{perimeter of an isosceles triangle}$$
$$x_1 = \text{length of the base}$$

and $\qquad x_2 = \text{length of the side}$

then $\qquad Q = x_1 + 2x_2$

From Eq. 14-13, the variance of the perimeter is

$$\sigma_Q^2 = \sigma_{x_1}^2 + 4\sigma_{x_2}^2$$

and the standard deviation of the perimeter is

$$\sigma_Q = \sqrt{\sigma_{x_1}^2 + 4\sigma_{x_2}^2}$$

---

[5] Equation 14-13 is a particular case of the general equation

$$\sigma_Q^2 = \left(\frac{\partial Q}{\partial x_1}\right)^2\sigma_{x_1}^2 + \left(\frac{\partial Q}{\partial x_2}\right)^2\sigma_{x_2}^2 + \left(\frac{\partial Q}{\partial x_3}\right)^2\sigma_{x_3}^2 + \cdots$$

where $Q = f(x_1, x_2, x_3, \ldots)$

CONFIDENCE LIMITS FOR VARIANCE

By analogy to the confidence limits of the mean, the confidence limits of variance give the limits within which the true population variance lies with a specified probability.

If s^2 is the variance calculated from a sample with ν degrees of freedom, then the limits are given by

$$\frac{\nu}{\chi^2} s^2 \qquad (14\text{-}15)$$

where χ^2 has a value corresponding to ν degrees of freedom and to the 5 percent level of significance for the lower limit, and to the 95 percent level of significance for the upper limit.

Thus we have a 5 percent probability of σ^2 falling below the lower limit and a 5 percent probability of σ^2 falling above the upper limit. The confidence limits thus contain the true value of σ^2 with a 90 percent probability. Similarly, if we take χ^2 at the 1 percent level of significance, the confidence limits contain the true value of σ^2 with a 98 percent probability.

Example. Tests on 10 concrete compression specimens yielded an estimate of the population variance of 40,000 (standard deviation of 200 psi). Find the 90 percent confidence limits.

For $\nu = 9$, we find from Table A-7:

$$\chi^2 = 16.919 \text{ at the 5 percent level of significance}$$

and $\qquad \chi^2 = 3.325$ at the 95 percent level of significance

Thus the lower limit of σ^2 is

$$\frac{9}{16.919} \times 40,000 = 21,300$$

and the upper limit is

$$\frac{9}{3.325} \times 40,000 = 108,500$$

Hence we conclude, with a 90 percent probability of being correct, that:

$$21,300 \leq \sigma^2 \leq 108,500$$

or

$$146 \leq \sigma \leq 329$$

In the case of large samples, say $n > 30$, we can take advantage of Eq. 14-8 for the standard deviation of the standard deviation; this is $\sigma_s = \sigma/\sqrt{2n}$.

For instance, if in the previous example we tested 50 specimens, the standard deviation remaining at 200 psi, we find the standard deviation of the standard deviation:

$$\sigma_s = \frac{200}{\sqrt{2 \times 50}} = 20 \text{ psi}$$

Since the standard deviation is not normally distributed, we have to use the t distribution. At the 5 percent level of significance and $\nu = 49$, $t \simeq 2.010$ (from Table A-8). Thus, the confidence limits are

$$200 \pm 2.010 \times 20$$

that is,

$$160 \leq \sigma \leq 240$$

It is apparent how an increase in sample size decreases the width of the confidence interval at a given level of significance.

COMPARISON OF STANDARD DEVIATIONS OF LARGE SAMPLES

In the case of very large samples (say, $n > 120$) we can test the significance of a difference between two *standard deviations* by the normal distribution test of Chapter 13 instead of by the F test. This will not seem strange if we are quite clear about the fact that we treat the standard deviation as the variate.

The procedure is as follows: We compute a pooled estimate of the assumed common variance s_c. This is similar to the value given by Eq. 13-7, except that Bessel's correction can be ignored because the samples are large. Thus

$$s_c^2 = \frac{n_1 s_1^2 + n_2 s_2^2}{n_1 + n_2} \tag{14-16}$$

where s_1^2, and s_2^2 are variances of the two samples, and n_1 and n_2 are the respective sample sizes.

We now use Eq. 14-8 to write the variance of the distribution of sample standard deviations s_c as:

$$\frac{s_c^2}{2n_1} \quad \text{and} \quad \frac{s_c^2}{2n_2}$$

for the two distributions, respectively.

Since the variance of a difference is equal to the sum of variances (Eq. 14-14), the standard deviation of the difference s_d is given by:

$$s_d = s_c \sqrt{\frac{1}{2n_1} + \frac{1}{2n_2}} \tag{14-17}$$

We can now apply the normal distribution test of Eq. 13-4, i.e., compare the difference of the observed standard deviations s_1 and s_2 with s_d:

$$z = \frac{|s_1 - s_2|}{s_d}$$

The probability of encountering z at least this large is given in Table A-4.

Example. Concrete test specimens were obtained on two sites, as follows:

Site	Number of specimens	Standard deviation, psi
1	120	300
2	150	150

Is there a significant difference between the variabilities on the two sites, i.e., are the two standard deviations significantly different?
We have:

$$s_c^2 = \frac{120 \times 300^2 + 150 \times 150^2}{120 + 150}$$

$$= 52,500$$

Now

$$s_d = \sqrt{52,500\left(\frac{1}{2 \times 120} + \frac{1}{2 \times 150}\right)} = 19.8 \text{ psi}$$

Hence

$$z = \frac{300 - 150}{19.8} = 7.58$$

The probability of obtaining such a value of z by chance is extremely low, and we conclude that the difference between the standard deviations is highly significant.

SOLVED PROBLEMS

14-1. The water hardness of two samples taken from separate outlets in a power plant was checked. The coded results (parts per million) are shown below. Determine whether the variance of water hardness from location 1 is greater than from location 2.

Location 1	Location 2
$\Sigma x_1 = 504$	$\Sigma x_2 = 868$
$\Sigma x_1^2 = 29,101$	$\Sigma x_2^2 = 54,201$
$n_1 = 9$	$n_2 = 14$

Solution:
Estimate of variance

$$s_1^2 = \frac{\Sigma x_1^2 - \dfrac{(\Sigma x_1)^2}{n_1}}{n_1 - 1} = \frac{29,101 - \dfrac{(504)^2}{9}}{8} = 109.6$$

Estimate of variance

$$s_2^2 = \frac{\Sigma x_2^2 - \dfrac{(\Sigma x_2)^2}{n_2}}{n_2 - 1} = \frac{54,201 - \dfrac{(868)^2}{14}}{13} = 29.6$$

$$F = \frac{\text{greater variance}}{\text{smaller variance}} = \frac{109.6}{29.6} = 3.71$$

Using Table A-10 for $v_1 = n_1 - 1 = 9 - 1 = 8$, and $v_2 = n_2 - 1 = 14 - 1 = 13$, $F = 2.77$ at the 5 percent level of significance. Since the calculated $F > 2.77$, the difference in the water hardness of the two samples is significant at the 5 percent level.

14-2. A car manufacturing company carried out a series of tests on the rate of crack growth in tires under four different conditions. The summary of the results is as follows:

Condition k	Sample size n	Variance of the rate of crack growth σ_i^2
1	20	0.0349
2	25	0.0875
3	20	0.0652
4	15	0.0445

We want to determine whether the variability of the measurements under the four conditions is the same, i.e., whether the variances are homogeneous.

Solution:

k	$v_i = n_i - 1$	s_i^2	Sum of squares $v_i s_i^2$	$\log s_i^2$	$v_i \log s_i^2$	$\frac{1}{v_i}$
1	19	0.0349	0.663	0.542825 − 2	10.313675 − 38	0.05263
2	24	0.0875	2.100	0.942008 − 2	22.608192 − 48	0.04167
3	19	0.0652	1.239	0.814248 − 2	15.470712 − 38	0.05263
4	14	0.0445	0.623	0.648360 − 2	9.077040 − 28	0.07143
Σ	76		4.625	2.947441 − 8	57.469619 − 152 = −94.530381	0.21836

$$\bar{s}^2 = \frac{\Sigma v_i s_i^2}{\Sigma v_i} = \frac{4.625}{76} = 0.060855$$

$$\log \bar{s}^2 = 0.784296 - 2 = -1.215704$$

From Eq. 14-2,

$$\chi^2 = 2.3026[76 \times (-1.215704) - (-94.530381)]$$

$$= 2.3026 \times 2.136877$$

$$= 4.920$$

From Eq. 14-5, the correction factor is

$$C = 1 + \frac{1}{3(k-1)} \left[\Sigma\left(\frac{1}{v_i}\right) - \frac{1}{\Sigma v_i} \right]$$

$$= 1 + \frac{1}{3(4-1)}(0.21836 - 0.01316)$$

$$= 1.0228$$

Thus

$$\chi_c^2 = \frac{\chi^2}{C} = \frac{4.920}{1.0228} = 4.810$$

with $(k - 1) = 4 - 1 = 3$ degrees of freedom.

Table A-7 gives $\chi^2 = 4.642$ at the 20 percent level of significance, and $\chi^2 = 6.251$ at the 10 percent level. We conclude, therefore, that there is no significant difference in the variances of the different tests. We would, however, be wise to apply Bartlett's test again when more test results are available.

NOTE: The correction C is not necessary since the uncorrected χ^2 indicates that the difference is not significant; the computation of χ_c^2 is given solely as an illustration of the method of applying the correction.

14-3. The following data were calculated from compression tests on two samples of concrete cylinders; we can assume that the observations within each sample are normally distributed:

$$\text{Sample size } n_1 = 11 \qquad \sum_1^{11} x_1 = 33{,}000 \text{ psi} \qquad \sum_1^{11} x_i^2 = 100.6 \times 10^6$$

$$\text{Sample size } n_2 = 6 \qquad \sum_1^{6} x_2 = 16{,}800 \text{ psi} \qquad \sum_1^{6} x_2^2 = 48.84 \times 10^6$$

(a) Test the hypothesis that $s_1 = s_2$ against the alternative $s_1 \neq s_2$ at the 10 percent level of significance.

(b) Assuming that the sample sizes are $n_1 = n_2 = 144$ and that the standard deviations of the two samples are $s_1 = 300$ psi and $s_2 = 320$ psi, apply an appropriate test to the null hypothesis that $s_1 = s_2$.

Solution:

$$(a) \quad s_1 = \sqrt{\frac{\sum x_i^2 - \dfrac{(\sum x_1)^2}{n_1}}{n_1 - 1}} = 10^3 \times \sqrt{\frac{100.6 - \dfrac{(33)^2}{11}}{10}} = 400 \text{ psi}$$

$$s_2 = 10^3 \times \sqrt{\frac{48.84 - \dfrac{(16.8)^2}{6}}{5}} = 600 \text{ psi}$$

Hence

$$F = \frac{s_2^2}{s_1^2} = \left[\frac{600}{400}\right]^2 = 2.25$$

We enter Table A-10 with $\nu_1 = 11 - 1 = 10$, and $\nu_2 = 6 - 1 = 5$, as ν, has to correspond to the larger variance. Then $F = 4.74$ at the 5 percent level of significance. As this is a two-sided test, we double this probability. Thus, since the calculated $F < 4.74$, the difference in the sample variances is not significant at the 10 percent level.

(b) The samples can be considered large ($n > 30$), and we can therefore use the normal distribution test.

The pooled estimate of the variance is

$$s_c^2 = \frac{300^2 + 320^2}{2} = 9.62 \times (100)^2$$

The standard deviation of the difference is

$$s_d = s_c \sqrt{\frac{1}{n}} = 100 \times \sqrt{\frac{9.62}{144}} = 25.85 \text{ psi}$$

Hence

$$z = \frac{|s_1 - s_2|}{s_d} = \frac{|300 - 320|}{25.85} = 0.774$$

Table A-4 gives the probability of obtaining at least this value of z by chance as about $0.5 - 0.28 = 0.22$. The difference cannot therefore be deemed significant.

PROBLEMS

14-1. Two different precision instruments were compared, 20 measurements being taken with instrument A and 30 with instrument B. The errors of instrument A had a variance of 15; those of B had a variance of 10. Assuming that the population of errors is normally distributed, test the hypothesis that

(a) $\sigma_A^2 = \sigma_B^2$

(b) $\sigma_A^2 = 1.75 \, \sigma_B^2$

(c) $\sigma_A^2 \ne \sigma_B^2$

14-2. In Prob. 13-2 verify the assumption of equal variances of the two machines, A and B. Use a 1 percent level of significance.

14-3. From numerous tests (which can be considered infinite) on a certain type of light bulb, it was found that the variance in burning time was 9,000 hours. A sample of 25 new type light bulbs is found to have a variance of 13,000. Determine at the 5 percent level of significance whether or not the two variances are different.

14-4. The variability of six planimeters is to be tested. Six observations are taken on each planimeter, and the sample variances are computed. The coded results are as follows:

$$6.5, \quad 9.4, \quad 8.7, \quad 12.4, \quad 10.5, \quad 7.7$$

Determine at the 1 percent level of significance whether all the planimeters have the same variance.

14-5. Verify the assumption of equal variances in content of A from the two sources 1 and 2 in Prob. 13-6, using a 5 percent level of significance.

14-6. The variance of error of tests in five laboratories is given below. Establish whether there are any significant differences among them.

Laboratory	Sample size	Estimate of variance
A	91	267
B	92	388
C	89	552
D	90	860
E	90	480

14-7. Twenty-six shipments of cement were obtained from each of five plants. From each shipment 15 test specimens were made, their average strengths being given on page 170.[6] A "control" supply of cement was also obtained, and on every

[6] S. Walker and D. L. Bloem, "Tests of Uniformity of Mortar Strengths of Cement Samples from Same Source," National Ready Mixed Concrete Assn., (Washington D.C.: Jan. 1957).

occasion when tests were made on the shipped-in cement, similar tests were made on the control cement (which, of course, did not vary).

Comment on the suggestion that the shipment-to-shipment variability is no greater than the variability within the control cement. (HINT: The standard deviation of control represents the testing error. Is the standard deviation for shipments from a given plant significantly greater?)

| Sample number | Compressive strength, psi, for cement source number | | | | | |
	Control	1	2	3	4	5
1	2,651	2,959	1,965	1,899	2,709	1,598
2	2,581	2,851	2,156	1,892	3,005	2,143
3	2,385	2,755	--	2,030	2,588	1,731
4	2,575	2,295	--	2,421	2,680	2,061
5	2,394	2,196	2,159	1,907	2,759	1,699
6	2,432	2,454	2,048	2,099	2,673	2,082
7	2,382	2,514	2,254	1,756	2,889	1,925
8	2,369	2,716	2,143	2,215	2,538	1,670
9	2,322	2,366	1,995	2,323	2,783	1,591
10	2,440	2,778	2,306	2,120	2,906	1,966
11	2,478	2,637	2,385	1,925	2,696	2,165
12	2,518	2,511	2,331	2,055	2,726	2,072
13	2,535	3,035	2,061	2,314	2,576	2,215
14	2,451	3,363	1,980	1,841	2,500	1,570
15	2,528	3,339	1,868	2,525	2,666	1,998
16	2,481	2,818	1,961	1.744	2,642	2,023
17	2,477	3,198	1,963	2,081	2,541	1,740
18	2,443	2,889	1,854	2,003	2,459	1,960
19	2,484	2,899	2,124	1,910	2,130	1,968
20	2,465	--	--	2,026	2,342	2,035
21	2,446	--	1,852	2,091	2,615	1,982
22	2,585	3,043	1,735	2,050	2,814	2,060
23	2,368	2,721	1,977	2,067	2,875	2,074
24	2,475	3,105	1,820	2,270	2,553	2,036
25	2,360	2,450	1,679	2,109	1,801	2,019
26	2,280	2,887	1,556	1,874	1,596	--

14-8. For the data of Prob. 13-11 test the homogeneity of standard deviations.

14-9. The standard deviation of the strength of beams of four different sizes was obtained using three series of tests, each test consisting of two specimens.[7] Are the standard deviations homogeneous?

| Beam size, in. | Number of tests | | | Standard deviation, psi | | |
	Series A	Series B	Series C	Series A	Series B	Series C
6	17	10	6	73	36	19
9	24	8	2	71	20	11
12	16	10	4	78	47	12
18	8	3	2	56	33	32

[7]A. M. Neville, "Some Aspects of the Strength of Concrete," Part I, *Civil Engineering* (London) Vol. 54 (Oct. 1959) p. 1156.

chapter 15

Method of
Least Squares and
Regression

In elementary work we often establish numerical relations by determining the values of the variables at a number of points equal to the total number of variables. For example, if a linear relation $y = a + bx$ is postulated, two pairs of values (x_1, y_1) and (x_2, y_2) determine the constants in the equation. This is satisfactory provided that the observed quantities are free from error.

In practice, error enters all our observations, and if we take further observations, say (x_3, y_3), we may obtain a point which does not fit exactly on the straight line through the original two points. This also applies, of course, to curves involving powers of x and y. Statistical methods help us to fit the "best" line to a given set of data, instead of simply drawing a line "by eye."

Our main interest is in studying association between two variables, rather than estimating one variable from the other.

METHOD OF LEAST SQUARES

The principle underlying the fitting of the "best" line is that of least squares; this states that if y is a linear function of an independent variable x, the most probable position of a line $y = a + bx$ is such that the sum of squares of deviations of all points (x_i, y_i) from the line is a minimum; the deviations are measured *in the direction of the y-axis*. It should be stressed that the underlying assumption is that x is either free from error (being assigned) or subject to negligible error only, while y is the observed or measured quantity, subject to errors which have to be "eliminated" by the method of least squares. The observed y is thus a random value from the population of values of y corresponding to a given x. Such a situation exists in controlled experiments, where we are interested in finding a mean value of $\bar{y}_i$ for each given value of x_i.

Suppose our observations consist of n pairs of values:

$$\begin{cases} x_1, x_2, \ldots, x_n \\ y_1, y_2, \ldots, y_n \end{cases}$$

and imagine that the various pairs plot as points shown in Fig. 15-1. Assume further that from the physical nature of the relation between y and x we know that the relation is linear, or alternatively expect or suspect it to be linear. We postulate therefore the relation as

$$y = a + bx \qquad (15\text{-}1)$$

Our problem is to find the values of a and b for the line of "best fit."

For a point i *on* this line:

$$y_i - (a + bx_i) = 0 \qquad (15\text{-}2)$$

but if there is error in the measurement, there will be a residual ϵ_i such that

$$y_i - (a + bx_i) = \epsilon_i \qquad (15\text{-}3)$$

With n observations we have n equations:

$$y_1 - (a + bx_1) = \epsilon_1$$
$$y_2 - (a + bx_2) = \epsilon_2$$
$$\vdots \qquad \vdots \qquad \vdots$$
$$y_n - (a + bx_n) = \epsilon_n$$

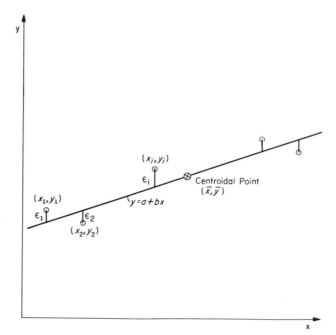

FIG. 15-1. Regression line

Using the summation notation, we can write the sum of squares of residuals as

$$P = \Sigma \epsilon_i^2 \qquad (15\text{-}4)$$

or

$$P = \Sigma [y_i - (a + bx_i)]^2 \qquad (15\text{-}5)$$

the summation extending from $i = 1$ to $i = n$.

As stated before, we have to satisfy the condition that the sum of squares of residuals is a minimum, that is, P is a minimum. This occurs when

$$\left.\begin{array}{c} \dfrac{\partial P}{\partial a} = 0 \\[2ex] \text{and} \\[2ex] \dfrac{\partial P}{\partial b} = 0 \end{array}\right\} \qquad (15\text{-}6)$$

or

$$\Sigma [y_i - (a + bx_i)] = 0 \qquad (15\text{-}7)$$

and

$$\Sigma x_i [y_i - (a + bx_i)] = 0 \qquad (15\text{-}8)$$

Omitting the subscripts we can write Eq. 15-7 as:

$$\Sigma y - \Sigma a - b\Sigma x = 0$$

Since a is a constant, we have:

$$\Sigma y = na + b\Sigma x \qquad (15\text{-}9)$$

or

$$\frac{\Sigma y}{n} = a + b \frac{\Sigma x}{n}$$

Thus

$$\bar{y} = a + b\bar{x} \qquad (15\text{-}10)$$

Equation 15-10 states that the line passes through the point $(\bar{x}, \bar{y})$, that is, through the point whose coordinates are the appropriate means of all observations; we can call this point the centroidal point of all observations. From the fact that the point $(\bar{x}, \bar{y})$ lies on the line, it follows that Eq. 15-1 can be written also as

$$y \quad \bar{y} - b(x - \bar{x}) \qquad [15\text{-}1a]$$

Returning now to Eq. 15-8 we have:

$$\Sigma xy = a\Sigma x + b\Sigma x^2 \qquad (15\text{-}11)$$

Equations 15-9 and 15-11 are called the *normal equations*.

REGRESSION LINE

Solving the normal equations

$$\Sigma y = na + b\Sigma x \qquad [15\text{-}9]$$
$$\Sigma xy = a\Sigma x + b\Sigma x^2 \qquad [15\text{-}11]$$

we obtain

$$a = \frac{\Sigma x^2 \, \Sigma y - \Sigma x \, \Sigma xy}{n \Sigma x^2 - (\Sigma x)^2} \qquad (15\text{-}12)$$

and[1]

$$b = \frac{n \Sigma xy - \Sigma x \, \Sigma y}{n \Sigma x^2 - (\Sigma x)^2} \qquad (15\text{-}13)$$

Hence the equation to the line of best fit can be written as

$$y = \frac{\Sigma x^2 \, \Sigma y - \Sigma x \, \Sigma xy}{n \Sigma x^2 - (\Sigma x)^2} + \frac{n \Sigma xy - \Sigma x \, \Sigma y}{n \Sigma x^2 - (\Sigma x)^2} x \qquad (15\text{-}14)$$

In practice, it is more convenient to compute a and b separately (using Eqs. 15-12 and 15-13), and to use the numerical values of a and b directly in writing $y = a + bx$.

The line given by Eq. 15-14 is called the line of *regression of y on x*. In deriving the line we assumed that x is the assigned variable (i.e., sensibly free from error) and that y is the observed quantity.

If, however, the properties of the variables are reversed, i.e., if y is the assigned variable and x is the observed quantity, we find the constants in the equation to the line

$$x = a' + b'y \qquad (15\text{-}15)$$

by minimizing the sum of squares of the x *residuals*. The equation to the line, known as the line of *regression of x on y*, is

$$x = \frac{\Sigma y^2 \, \Sigma x - \Sigma y \, \Sigma xy}{n \Sigma y^2 - (\Sigma y)^2} + \frac{n \Sigma xy - \Sigma x \, \Sigma y}{n \Sigma y^2 - (\Sigma y)^2} y \qquad (15\text{-}16)$$

In general,

$$a \neq -\frac{a'}{b'}$$

and

$$b \neq \frac{1}{b'}$$

but both lines intersect at $(\bar{x}, \bar{y})$. An example of the two regression lines is shown in Fig. 15-2. We may note here that it is possible to calculate regression when both variables are subject to error.

The computation of a and b is best performed by arranging the values of x, y, x^2, and xy in a tabular form. Tables of squares or logarithmic tables are of course useful. If a calculating machine is available, the values of Σx^2

[1] Note that

$$n \Sigma xy - \Sigma x \, \Sigma y = n \Sigma (x - \bar{x})(y - \bar{y})$$

since

$$n \Sigma (x - \bar{x})(y - \bar{y}) = n(\Sigma xy - \bar{x} \Sigma y + \bar{x} \Sigma y - \bar{y} \Sigma x)$$

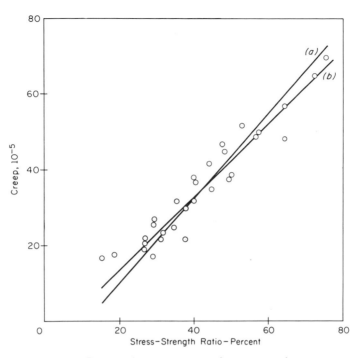

FIG. 15-2. Relation between creep of mortar and stress-strength ratio: (*a*) line of regression of stress-strength ratio upon creep; (*b*) line of regression of creep upon stress-strength ratio.

and Σxy can be found by one series of operations: x and y are set at the two extremes of the calculator keyboard; a multiplication by x then yields x^2 and xy respectively at the two ends of the carriage. The operation is repeated for all values of (x_i, y_i), the sum being carried, so that at the end Σx^2 and Σxy are obtained.

The computation of a and b may be rather laborious and may involve large numbers. The effort can be reduced by taking advantage of the fact that $(\bar{x}, \bar{y})$ is a point on the line. We can, therefore, transform the axes of coordinates to a new origin $(\bar{x}, \bar{y})$. The new coordinates (X, Y) are then:

$$\left. \begin{array}{l} X = x - \bar{x} \\ Y = y - \bar{y} \end{array} \right\} \tag{15-17}$$

Since the origin of coordinates (X, Y) is at the centroidal point, it follows that

$$\Sigma X = \Sigma Y = 0$$

Therefore, from Eq. 15-12

$$a = 0$$

and from Eq. 15-13

$$b = \frac{\Sigma XY}{\Sigma X^2} \qquad (15\text{-}18)$$

This is equivalent to writing Eq. 15-13 in the form:

$$b = \frac{\Sigma(x - \bar{x})(y - \bar{y})}{\Sigma(x - \bar{x})^2} \qquad (15\text{-}19)$$

which is of more theoretical interest.

Using Eq. 15-18, the equation to the line of regression of y on x (or Y on X) becomes

$$Y = \frac{\Sigma XY}{\Sigma X^2} X \qquad (15\text{-}20)$$

The use of (X, Y) requires of course computing $(x - \bar{x})$ and $(y - \bar{y})$ for all the observations. This may be tedious if $\bar{x}$ or $\bar{y}$ involve several decimal places, and the computation of products and squares may in consequence be more laborious than operation on (x, y) directly when the latter are integers. As an example, computation by both methods is given below.

Example. To determine the relation between the normal stress and the shear resistance of soil, a shear-box experiment was performed, giving the following results:

Normal stress x, psi	11	13	15	17	19	21
Shear resistance y, psi......	15.2	17.7	19.3	21.5	23.9	25.4

In the test the value of x is assigned, and y is the derived quantity. The relation between the two is of the form

$$y = a + bx$$

where a = cohesion of soil
$b = \tan \phi$
ϕ = angle of friction

Tabular arrangement is most convenient.

x	y	x^2	xy	$X = x - \bar{x}$	$Y = y - \bar{y}$	XY	X^2
11	15.2	121	167.2	-5	-5.3	26.5	25
13	17.7	169	230.1	-3	-2.8	8.4	9
15	19.3	225	289.5	-1	-1.2	1.2	1
17	21.5	289	365.5	1	1.0	1.0	1
19	23.9	361	454.1	3	3.4	10.2	9
21	25.4	441	533.4	5	4.9	24.5	25
$\Sigma = 96$	123.0	1,606	2,039.8	$8 - 8 = 0$	$9.3 - 9.3 = 0$	71.8	70

$$\bar{x} = \frac{\Sigma x}{n} = \frac{96}{6} = 16.0 \text{ psi} \qquad \bar{y} = \frac{\Sigma y}{n} = \frac{123.0}{6} = 20.5 \text{ psi}$$

From Eq. 15-12,

$$a = \frac{\Sigma x^2\, \Sigma y - \Sigma x\, \Sigma xy}{n\Sigma x^2 - (\Sigma x)^2}$$

$$= \frac{1{,}606 \times 123 - 96 \times 2{,}039.8}{6 \times 1{,}606 - 96 \times 96}$$

$$= 4.089$$

From Eq. 15-13,

$$b = \frac{n\Sigma xy - \Sigma x\, \Sigma y}{n\Sigma x^2 - (\Sigma x)^2}$$

$$= \frac{6 \times 2{,}039.8 - 96 \times 123}{6 \times 1{,}606 - 96 \times 96}$$

$$= 1.026$$

Hence the relation between the normal stress x and the shear resistance y is given by

$$y = 4.089 + 1.026x$$

We can solve the same problem using coordinates (X, Y) referred to the centroidal point; the appropriate values are computed in the right-hand part of the preceding table. From Eq. 15-18,

$$b = \frac{\Sigma XY}{\Sigma X^2} = \frac{71.8}{70} = 1.026$$

Substituting in Eq. 15-20,

$$Y = 1.026X$$

Transforming to the original coordinates,

$$y - 20.5 = 1.026\,(x - 16.0)$$

whence

$$y = 4.089 + 1.026x \quad \text{(as before)}$$

The line of regression of y on x, as well as the experimental points, is shown in Fig. 15-3.

LIMITATIONS OF METHOD

It may be worth stating explicitly that the method of least squares is applicable only when the observed values of y_i correspond to assigned (or error-free) values of x_i; furthermore, the error in y (expressed as variance of y) must be independent of the level of x. (Of course, x and y may be reversed.)

For inferences and estimates to be made about regression (but not for the method of least squares), it is also necessary that the values of y_i corresponding to a given x_i be normally distributed, with the mean of the

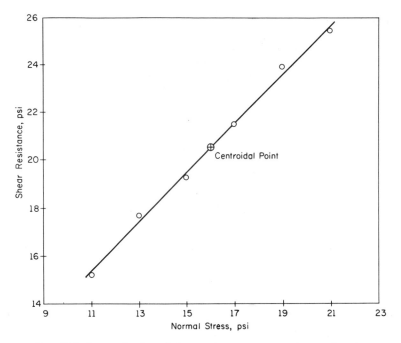

FIG. 15-3. Regression line of shear resistance on normal stress for the
data of the example on page 176.

distribution satisfying the regression equation. Furthermore, the variance
of the values of *y* for a given value of *x* should be independent of the magnitude of *x*. In many practical problems this is not the case,[2] and transformation is then necessary; the usual transformations are by taking logarithms, square roots, etc. The transformation stabilizes the variance of *y*
and makes the distribution closer to normal. This procedure is discussed
in Chapters 10 and 13.

CONFIDENCE LIMITS OF REGRESSION ESTIMATES

When we write the equation to the regression line

$$y = a + bx \qquad\qquad [15\text{-}1]$$

y should, strictly speaking, be written as $\hat{y}$, to denote that it is an estimate.
To reduce the complexity of symbols, the circumflex will be omitted in what
follows, except where required for clarity.

An estimate of *y* is given by Eq. 15-1 for any value of *x*, not necessarily one at which *y* was observed, but within the range of values for which

[2] For example, the scatter of values of temperature determined by the pyrometer is smaller
the higher the temperature, since the source of light is brighter. Contrariwise, the scatter of
values of strength of concrete is greater the higher the mean strength.

Eq. 15-14 was established. The question arises: What confidence can we have in our estimate of the "true" equation to the line?

The variance of an estimate enables us to form confidence limits of the estimate. In a manner similar to the variance of a sample, we shall consider variance about a regression line; in this case the deviations are reckoned from the line instead of from the mean. Thus the variance of y, estimated by the regression line, is the sum of squares of deviations divided by the number of degrees of freedom ν available for calculating the regression line, that is,

$$s_y^2 = \frac{\Sigma \epsilon_i^2}{\nu} \tag{15-21}$$

where ϵ_i is defined by Eq. 15-3.

Two constraints determine the regression line: the centroidal point $(\bar{x}, \bar{y})$ and either slope b or intercept a. Therefore, if n is the number of observations (readings of x_i, y_i), the number of degrees of freedom is

$$\nu = n - 2$$

Hence

$$s_y^2 = \frac{\Sigma \epsilon_i^2}{n - 2} \tag{15-22}$$

The variance of the mean value of y, that is $\bar{y}$, is given in a manner similar to Eq. 6-7 by

$$s_{\bar{y}}^2 = \frac{s_y^2}{n} \tag{15-23}$$

We can now write the confidence limits for $\bar{y}$. As in the case of the sample mean, we find the value of t for the desired level of significance and the appropriate number of degrees of freedom (Table A-8). We can then state that the true value of $\bar{y}$ lies within the interval

$$\bar{y} \pm t s_{\bar{y}}$$

The probability of our being wrong is equal to the level of significance of the value of t.

Since the regression line must pass through the centroidal point, an error in the value of $\bar{y}$ leads to a constant error in y for all points on the line, the line being translated up or down without a change in slope (Fig. 15-4a).

Without derivation, we shall give the variance of the slope b as

$$s_b^2 = \frac{s_y^2}{\Sigma (x - \bar{x})^2} \tag{15-24}$$

The confidence band for the slope is represented by a double fan-shaped area with slopes of $b \pm t s_b$ and apex at $(\bar{x}, \bar{y})$ (Fig. 15-4b).

The confidence area of the regression can be approximated by smooth curves asymptotic to the confidence interval of the slope near the ends of

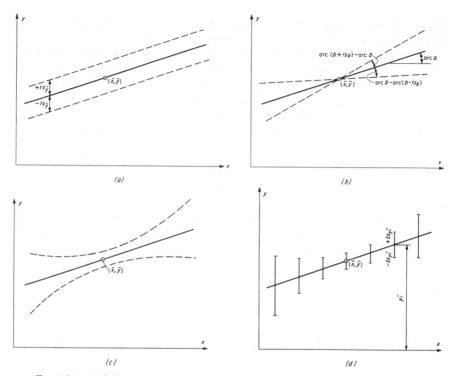

Fig. 15-4. (*a*) Influence of the confidence limits of $\hat{y}$ on the confidence limits of the regression line. (*b*) Confidence band for slope. (*c*) Approximate confidence area of the regression line. (*d*) Confidence limits of an estimate of $y_{\bar{i}}$.

the range of observations and including the confidence limits of $\bar{y}$. This is illustrated by Fig. 15-4*c*.

If we require a closer estimate of the confidence limits, we can calculate the limits for $\hat{y}_i$ corresponding to a specified value of x_i. To do this we need the variance of $\hat{y}_i$, denoted further by y.

If the limits are for the *mean* estimated value for y_i, that is $y_{\bar{i}}$, we require the variance of this mean value. The variance is:

$$s_{\bar{y}_i}^2 = s_y^2 \left[\frac{1}{n} + \frac{(x_i - \bar{x})^2}{\Sigma(x - \bar{x})^2} \right] \tag{15-25}$$

The confidence interval for the mean estimated value of $y_{\bar{i}}$ is then

$$y_{\bar{i}} \pm t s_{y_{\bar{i}}}$$

For a specified level of significance we can thus predict the limits within which a future *mean* estimated value of $y_{\bar{i}}$ will lie with the appropriate probability of error. The limits are wider the larger the value of $(x_i - \bar{x})$, that is, the further x_i is removed from the centroidal point. This is shown in Fig. 15-4*d*.

If we are interested in predicting the confidence interval of a *single* estimated value of $\hat{y}_i$, we have to use the variance of such a single value; this variance is:

$$s_{y_i}^2 = s_y^2 \left[1 + \frac{1}{n} + \frac{(x_i - \bar{x})^2}{\Sigma(x - \bar{x})^2} \right] \qquad (15\text{-}26)$$

This variance is larger than $s_{y_i}^2$ because the variance of the single value is equal to the variance of the mean plus the variance of $\hat{y}$ estimated by the line, that is,

$$s_{y_i}^2 = s_{y_i}^2 + s_y^2 \qquad (15\text{-}27)$$

The confidence interval for a single value is correspondingly greater, namely,

$$y \pm t s_{y_i} \qquad (15\text{-}28)$$

A diagram representing this would be similar to Fig. 15-4d.

If we want to use the intercept a to define the regression line, we find the variance of a as a particular case of the variance of any mean estimated value $\hat{y}_{\bar{x}}$. We substitute, therefore, $x_i = 0$ in Eq. 15-25, and the variance of a is given by

$$s_a^2 = s_y^2 \left[\frac{1}{n} + \frac{\bar{x}^2}{\Sigma(x - \bar{x})^2} \right] \qquad (15\text{-}29)$$

For all the confidence intervals of this section the number of degrees of freedom used in determining t is $\nu = n - 2$, for the reasons stated on page 179.

SIGNIFICANCE TEST FOR SLOPE

In some cases we have a theoretical value b_0 of the slope b in Eq. 15-1, and we want to determine whether there is a significant difference between b_0 and the value of b given by the regression line. This is done by means of the t test applied to $|b - b_0|$.

The standard deviation of $|b - b_0|$ is equal to the standard deviation of b, s_b, because the theoretical value of b is free from error. We find

$$t = \frac{|b - b_0|}{s_b} \qquad (15\text{-}30)$$

and if the calculated t is greater than t given in Table A-8 for a required level of significance, we conclude that there is a significant difference between b and b_0. The level of significance represents the probability of our drawing an erroneous conclusion.

The number of degrees of freedom for which t is found is equal to $(n - 2)$, where n is the number of observations used in deriving the regression line.

A similar test can be applied to the intercept a. The difference between the value given by regression and a theoretical value a_0 is tested by

$$t = \frac{|a - a_0|}{s_a} \qquad (15\text{-}31)$$

The number of degrees of freedom is the same as before.

Sometimes it is useful to test whether the slope differs significantly from zero. We then find

$$t = \frac{b}{s_b} \qquad (15\text{-}32)$$

and proceed as before. If b does not differ significantly from zero, y is independent of x, and the computation of the regression line is pointless.

Example. Referring to the preceding example on the relation between normal stress x and shear resistance of soil y:

- (a) Check whether the intercept a and slope b are significantly different from zero;
- (b) Find whether the slope differs significantly from a theoretically predicted slope $b = 1.000$;
- (c) Find the 95 percent confidence interval for the estimates of a and b;
- (d) Assuming that the regression line can be extrapolated to $x = 25$ psi, find the estimate of the mean value of shear resistance $\hat{y}_i$ for $x = 25$ psi and also the 90 percent confidence interval for this estimate;
- (e) Find the 95 percent confidence interval for a single estimated value of the shear resistance corresponding to $x = 25$ psi.

The regression line of the preceding examples gives $y = 4.089 + 1.026x$. From this we compute the estimates $\hat{y}$, and the deviations $(y_i - \hat{y}_i)$ for all assigned values of x.

In tabular form:

x	$\hat{y}$	$\epsilon_i = y_i - \hat{y}_i$	ϵ_i^2
11	15.375	−0.175	0.0306
13	17.427	+0.273	0.0745
15	19.479	−0.179	0.0320
17	21.531	−0.031	0.0010
19	23.583	+0.317	0.1005
21	25.635	−0.235	0.0552
$n = 6$			$\Sigma \epsilon_i^2 = 0.2938$

(a) From Eq. 15-22

$$s_y = \sqrt{\frac{\Sigma \epsilon_i^2}{n - 2}} = \sqrt{\frac{0.2938}{6 - 2}} = 0.271$$

From Eq. 15-24 and using the value of $\Sigma X^2 = \Sigma(x - \bar{x})^2 = 70$, we have

$$s_b = \frac{s_y}{\sqrt{\Sigma(x - \bar{x})^2}} = \frac{0.271}{\sqrt{70}} = 0.0324$$

From Eq. 15-29:

$$s_a = s_y \sqrt{\frac{1}{n} + \frac{\bar{x}^2}{\Sigma(x - \bar{x})^2}} = 0.271 \sqrt{\frac{1}{6} + \frac{16^2}{70}}$$

$$= 0.5298$$

To test the significance of b, we use Eq. 15-32 and find:

$$t = \frac{b}{s_b} = \frac{1.026}{0.0324} = 31.667$$

For $\nu = 4$, Table A-8 shows this value of t as significant at better than 0.1 percent. For a,

$$t = \frac{a}{s_a} = \frac{4.089}{0.5298} = 7.718$$

and this is significant at the 1 percent level.

(b)   From Eq. 15-30

$$t = \frac{|b - b_0|}{s_b} = \frac{1.026 - 1}{0.0324} = 0.8025$$

From Table A-8 for $\nu = 4$, this value of t is not significant, and we conclude that the observed value of b accords with the predicted value $b_0 = 1.000$.

(c)   The 95 percent confidence intervals for the estimates of a and b are $a \pm t s_a$ and $b \pm t s_b$ respectively. For $\nu = 4$, and a 5 percent level of significance, $t = 2.776$. Hence the required estimates are for a:

$$4.089 \pm 2.776 \times 0.5298 = (2.618,\ 5.560)\ \text{psi}$$

and for b:

$$1.026 \pm 2.776 \times 0.0324 = (0.936,\ 1.116)$$

(d)   From the regression equation $y = a + bx$, for $x = 25$ psi the estimate of the mean value of y_i is:

$$y_{\bar{\imath}} = 4.089 + 1.026 \times 25 = 29.739\ \text{psi}$$

The 90 percent confidence interval for this estimate is

$$y_{\bar{\imath}} \pm t s_{y_{\bar{\imath}}}$$

where $s_{y_i^-}$ is given by Eq. 15-25:

$$s_{y_i^-} = s_y \sqrt{\frac{1}{n} + \frac{(x_i - \bar{x})^2}{\Sigma(x - \bar{x})^2}}$$

$$= 0.271 \sqrt{\frac{1}{6} + \frac{(25 - 16)^2}{70}}$$

$$= 0.312$$

and for $\nu = 4$ and a 10 percent level of significance, $t = 2.132$. The confidence interval is therefore

$$29.739 \pm 2.132 \times 0.312 = (29.074, 30.404) \text{ psi}$$

(e) For a single estimated value of y_i, the standard deviation is given by Eq. 15-26:

$$s_{y_i} = 0.271 \sqrt{1 + \frac{1}{6} + \frac{(25 - 16)^2}{70}} = 0.413$$

For the 5 percent level of significance, $t = 2.776$. Hence, the confidence interval is

$$29.739 \pm 2.776 \times 0.413 = (28.593, 30.885) \text{ psi}$$

USE OF THE METHOD OF LEAST SQUARES IN SURVEYING

It may be of interest to mention that the principle of minimizing errors by the method of least squares can be used also in computing most probable values where these have to satisfy a condition different from that of linearity. For example, in surveying operations we measure angles, lengths, or levels, and these may have to satisfy a condition equation of the type Σ angles $= 360°$ or Σ differences in level $= 0$. The procedure is illustrated by the following example.

Example. Bench marks at three locations A, B, and C were required. Precise leveling was carried from a known bench mark R as shown in Fig. 15-5. Due to differences in lengths of lines, number of instruments settings, etc., the observations were weighted[3] as shown below. Find the most probable values of the elevations of A, B, and C with respect to R.

Leg	Observed difference in elevation, ft	Most probable value	Error	Weight w
R to A	$\alpha_1 = 94.775$	θ_1	$\epsilon_1 = \alpha_1 - \theta_1$	4
A to B	$\alpha_2 = -21.739$	θ_2	$\epsilon_2 = \alpha_2 - \theta_2$	2
B to C	$\alpha_3 = 18.631$	θ_3	$\epsilon_3 = \alpha_3 - \theta_3$	3
C to R	$\alpha_4 = -91.317$	θ_4	$\epsilon_4 = \alpha_4 - \theta_4$	4

[3] The "weight" is proportional to our confidence in the observed value

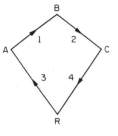

FIG. 15-5

We denote the most probable value of an elevation by θ. Because of the closed circuit of observations, the most probable values must satisfy the condition equation:

$$\theta_1 + \theta_2 + \theta_3 + \theta_4 = 0$$

Hence we can write

$$\epsilon_4 = \alpha_4 + \theta_1 + \theta_2 + \theta_3$$

We now apply the principle of least squares to the circuit by minimizing the *weighted* sum of squares of errors, $\Sigma w \epsilon^2$.
Now

$$\Sigma w \epsilon^2 = w_1 \epsilon_1^2 + w_2 \epsilon_2^2 + w_3 \epsilon_3^2 + w_4 \epsilon_4^2 = P$$

or

$$P = w_1(\alpha_1 - \theta_1)^2 + w_2(\alpha_2 - \theta_2)^2$$
$$+ w_3(\alpha_3 - \theta_3)^2 + w_4(\alpha_4 + \theta_1 + \theta_2 + \theta_3)^2$$

This has a minimum value when

$$\frac{\partial P}{\partial \theta_1} = \frac{\partial P}{\partial \theta_2} = \frac{\partial P}{\partial \theta_3} = 0$$

i.e., when

$$-2w_1(\alpha_1 - \theta_1) + 2w_4(\alpha_4 + \theta_1 + \theta_2 + \theta_3) = 0$$
$$-2w_2(\alpha_2 - \theta_2) + 2w_4(\alpha_4 + \theta_1 + \theta_2 + \theta_3) = 0$$
$$-2w_3(\alpha_3 - \theta_3) + 2w_4(\alpha_4 + \theta_1 + \theta_2 + \theta_3) = 0$$

These are the normal equations. Substituting the values of w and α and simplifying, we get:

$$8\theta_1 + 4\theta_2 + 4\theta_3 = 744.368$$
$$4\theta_1 + 6\theta_2 + 4\theta_3 = 321.790$$
$$4\theta_1 + 4\theta_2 + 7\theta_3 = 421.161$$

Solving these three equations by elimination, we obtain

$$\theta_1 = +94.709, \quad \theta_2 = -21.870, \quad \theta_3 = +18.543, \quad \theta_4 = -91.382$$

Hence, the most probable values of elevation with respect to R are:

$$R = \quad 0 \quad \text{ft}$$
$$A = 94.709 \text{ ft}$$
$$B = 72.839 \text{ ft}$$
$$C = 91.382 \text{ ft}$$

NONLINEAR RELATIONS

The method of fitting a regression line can be extended to the case where the known, expected, or suspected relation is not in the form of a straight line. The procedure is to write the equation to the curve in its general form, tabulate the deviations of y from the assumed curve, and to find the constants in the equation which satisfy the condition that the sum of the squares of deviations is a minimum.

Example. Suppose we observed the values of y for four values of x, x being the assigned variable. (For example, x can be time, and y the measured distance). Assume further that the general relation between y and x is of the form

$$y = a + bx^2$$

We can tabulate the results as follows:

x	0	1	2	3
Observed value y_i........	0.5	6.5	21.3	48.6
Most probable value $\hat{y}$ ...	a	$a + b$	$a + 4b$	$a + 9b$
Deviation $(y_i - \hat{y})$	$0.5 - a$	$6.5 - (a + b)$	$21.3 - (a + 4b)$	$48.6 - (a + 9b)$

Hence the sum of squares of deviations is

$$P = (0.5 - a)^2 + (6.5 - a - b)^2 + (21.3 - a - 4b)^2$$
$$+ (48.6 - a - 9b)^2$$

For P to be a minimum we have to satisfy the conditions:

$$\frac{\partial P}{\partial a} = 0 \quad \text{and} \quad \frac{\partial P}{\partial b} = 0$$

or

$$(0.5 - a) + (6.5 - a - b) + (21.3 - a - 4b) + (48.6 - a - 9b) = 0$$

and

$$(6.5 - a - b) + 4(21.3 - a - 4b) + 9(48.6 - a - 9b) = 0$$

These reduce to the normal equations:

$$4a + 14b = 76.9$$
$$14a + 98b = 529.1$$

Hence $a = 0.219$ and $b = 5.430$.

Thus the equation to the best line of the general form of $y = a + bx^2$ is:

$$y = 0.219 + 5.430x^2$$

It should be stressed, however, that a better fit may be obtained with an equation of a different form, for example, $y = a + bx + cx^2$. This can be determined only by trial and error, the procedure depending on the problem in hand, and of course in many cases the search for a "better fit" may not be warranted.

RECTIFICATION

The application of the method of least squares to nonlinear relations usually requires a great deal of computational effort. However, in many cases, a nonlinear relation can be transformed to a straight-line relation— i.e., rectified. This not only simplifies the handling of the data, but also results in a graphical presentation which is more revealing as far as assessment of scatter is concerned. Extrapolation, if this is warranted (and often it is not), is also easier, and so is computation of various statistics, such as standard deviation or confidence limits. Several simple cases will be illustrated.

The exponential function $y = ab^x$ can be rectified by log transformation, i.e., by taking logarithms of both sides of the equation:

$$\log y = \log a + x \log b$$

This will plot as a straight line if the ordinates give $\log y$ (that is, are to a logarithmic scale) while the abscissae are to a linear scale. Log a and log b are the fitting constants of the equation. In other words, $\log y$ and x are treated as new (and linear) variables to which the principle of least squares is applied.

The power function $y = ax^b$ can be rectified even more simply, again by taking logarithms:

$$\log y = \log a + b \log x$$

The fitting constants are now log a and b, and the new variables log x and log y are linearly related.

The hyperbola $y = a + b/x$ can be rectified by treating $1/x = u$ as the new variable. Then y and u are linearly related.

If the equation is in the form

$$y = \frac{x}{a + bx}$$

we can invert it to

$$\frac{1}{y} = \frac{a}{x} + b$$

Then $1/x$ and $1/y$ are linearly related. Alternatively, we can multiply both sides of the above equation by x, obtaining thus:

$$\frac{x}{y} = a + bx$$

We then plot x/y versus x. The choice depends on the nature of the case considered.

The polynomial function of the form $y = a + bx + cx^2$ is concave up or down, depending on the signs of the coefficients. We differentiate both sides of the equation with respect to x:

$$\frac{dy}{dx} = b + 2cx$$

A straight-line relation is given by plotting $\frac{dy}{dx}$ versus x.

If no advance information on the shape of the curve fitting the experimental data is available, trial-and-error methods may be necessary. As a first step, the data should be plotted using linear x and y coordinates; a smooth curve is then drawn, and a function likely to fit is chosen from the knowledge of the shapes of curves corresponding to simple algebraic functions.

It is important to note that when transformation is used, the deviation minimized is not in y but in the transformed variable. We should remember this when drawing conclusions from an experiment.

Standard computer programs for fitting of various least square curves are available.

SOLVED PROBLEMS

15-1. In an experiment the volume of a gas was measured at different pressures, the temperature remaining constant. The results were as follows:

Pressure p, lb/ft^2	20	25	30	35	40
Volume v, ft^3	0.31	0.22	0.18	0.15	0.13

The assumed relation is given by $p = A/v + B$ where A and B are constants. (B can be considered as instrument error.) Assuming that only v contains errors,

 (*a*) find the best values of A and of B, and

 (*b*) plot the relation between p and $1/v$.

Solution:

 (*a*) The problem is to determine the best value for the constant A, and is best approached by employing a change of variable:

$$v' = \frac{1}{v}$$

then $p = Av' + B$, and we have:

Pressure p, lb/ft^2	20	25	30	35	40
v'	3.226	4.545	5.556	6.667	7.692

This approach implies that the error of all $1/v$ values is the same, which may or may not be the case in practice. The centroidal point of the five observations (p, v') is $(30, 5.537)$. When the pressure is, say p_1, the estimated value for v'_1 from the equation is

$$\hat{v}'_1 = \frac{p_1 - B}{A}$$

Therefore the deviation in v' is

$$\epsilon = \frac{p_1 - B}{A} - v'_1$$

Then

$$\Sigma\epsilon^2 = \left(\frac{p_1 - B}{A} - v'_1\right)^2 + \left(\frac{p_2 - B}{A} - v'_2\right)^2 + \left(\frac{p_3 - B}{A} - v'_3\right)^2$$
$$+ \left(\frac{p_4 - B}{A} - v'_4\right)^2 + \left(\frac{p_5 - B}{A} - v'_5\right)^2$$

To obtain the regression line $\Sigma\epsilon^2$ is to be a minimum, that is,

$$\frac{\partial(\Sigma\epsilon^2)}{\partial A} = 2\left(\frac{p_1 - B}{A} - v'_1\right)\left(\frac{-(p_1 - B)}{A^2}\right) + \cdots$$
$$+ 2\left(\frac{p_5 - B}{A} - v'_5\right)\left(\frac{-(p_5 - B)}{A^2}\right) = 0$$

Hence

$$A = \frac{(p_1 - B)^2 + (p_2 - B)^2 + (p_3 - B)^2 + (p_4 - B)^2 + (p_5 - B)^2}{v'_1(p_1 - B) + v'_2(p_2 - B) + v'_3(p_3 - B) + v'_4(p_4 - B) + v'_5(p_5 - B)}$$
$$= \frac{p_1^2 + p_2^2 + p_3^2 + p_4^2 + p_5^2 - 2B(p_1 + p_2 + p_3 + p_4 + p_5) + 5B^2}{v'_1 p_1 + v'_2 p_2 + v'_3 p_3 + v'_4 p_4 + v'_5 p_5 - B(v'_1 + v'_2 + v'_3 + v'_4 + v'_5)}$$

By substituting we find

$$A = \frac{4{,}750 - 300B + 5B^2}{885.85 - 27.686B}$$

Now, since the regression line must pass through the centroid (30, 5.537), we can write

$$5.537 = \frac{30 - B}{A}$$

Eliminating A,

$$\frac{30 - B}{5.537} = \frac{4{,}750 - 300B + 5B^2}{885.85 - 27.686B}$$

whence

$$55.3B = 274.7$$

$$B = \frac{274.7}{55.3} = 4.967$$

and

$$A = \frac{30 - 4.967}{5.537} = \frac{25.033}{5.537} = 4.521$$

Thus

$$p = 4.967 + 4.521v'$$

Hence

$$p = 4.967 + 4.521\left(\frac{1}{v}\right)$$

is the equation of the "best" line.

(*b*) Figure 15-6 shows the plot of p versus $1/v$.

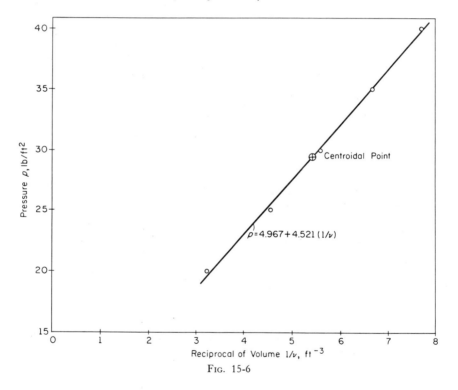

Fig. 15-6

15-2. The following table gives experimental data obtained from measuring plate current versus plate voltage from a triode with grid voltage held at a certain constant level.

Plate voltage $\times \dfrac{1}{10} = x$, volts	1	2	3	4	5
Plate current $\times \dfrac{1}{10} = y$, mA	1.7	5.2	8.9	14.2	19.9

It is assumed that y only is subject to error. Find a polynomial of the form $y = Ax + Bx^2$ to fit best the above data.

Solution:

The values of y for $x = 1, 2, \ldots, 5$ from the formula are respectively

$$A + B, \quad 2A + 4B, \quad 3A + 9B, \quad 4A + 16B, \quad 5A + 25B$$

The deviations ϵ of the experimental values of y from the above are respectively

$$A + B - 1.7, \quad 2A + 4B - 5.2, \quad 3A + 9B - 8.9,$$
$$4A + 16B - 14.2, \quad 5A + 25B - 19.9$$

Therefore

$$\Sigma \epsilon^2 = (A + B - 1.7)^2 + (2A + 4B - 5.2)^2 + (3A + 9B - 8.9)^2$$
$$+ (4A + 16B - 14.2)^2 + (5A + 25B - 19.9)^2$$

Making $\Sigma \epsilon^2$ a minimum with respect to A and B:

$$\frac{\partial (\Sigma \epsilon^2)}{\partial A} = 2[(A + B - 1.7) + 2(2A + 4B - 5.2) + 3(3A + 9B - 8.9)$$
$$+ 4(4A + 16B - 14.2) + 5(5A + 25B - 19.9)] = 0$$

and

$$\frac{\partial (\Sigma \epsilon^2)}{\partial B} = 2[(A + B - 1.7) + 4(2A + 4B - 5.2) + 9(3A + 9B - 8.9)$$
$$+ 16(4A + 16B - 14.2) + 25(5A + 25B - 19.9)] = 0$$

From these two equations we get the normal equations:

$$55A + 225B = 195.1$$
$$225A + 979B = 827.3$$

Solving for A and B we find

$$A = 1.509, \quad B = 0.498$$

Therefore the "best" second degree polynomial is of the form:

$$y = 1.509x + 0.498x^2$$

It is now possible to calculate the "true" current y for the given voltages x from the above formula.

15-3. A round of angles α_1, α_2, α_3, and α_4 was observed at a station R. The sum of the four angles was less than $360°$ by $4''$. The angles were measured several times. The average readings and their weights are shown below.

		Weight, w
$\alpha_1 =$	$75°\ 44'\ 30''$	2
$\alpha_2 =$	$89°\ 15'\ 40''$	3
$\alpha_3 =$	$110°\ 27'\ 35''$	2
$\alpha_4 =$	$84°\ 32'\ 11''$	4

Find the most probable values of the angles θ_1, θ_2, θ_3, and θ_4.

Solution:

Let ϵ_1, ϵ_2, ϵ_3, and ϵ_4 be the errors in the four angles respectively. Then

$$\epsilon_1 = \alpha_1 - \theta_1, \quad \epsilon_2 = \alpha_2 - \theta_2, \quad \epsilon_3 = \alpha_3 - \theta_3, \quad \epsilon_4 = \alpha_4 - \theta_4$$

The sum of the squares of the weighted errors is

$$\Sigma w \epsilon^2 = w_1 \epsilon_1^2 + w_2 \epsilon_2^2 + w_3 \epsilon_3^2 + w_4 \epsilon_4^2$$

$$= w_1 (\alpha_1 - \theta_1)^2 + w_2 (\alpha_2 - \theta_2)^2 + w_3 (\alpha_3 - \theta_3)^2 + w_4 (\alpha_4 - \theta_4)^2$$

Since

$$\theta_4 = 360° - (\theta_1 + \theta_2 + \theta_3)$$

we have only three unknowns. By the principle of least squares, $\Sigma \epsilon^2$ is a minimum when the differential coefficients with respect to θ_1, θ_2, and θ_3 are zero. Thus

$$\frac{\partial (\Sigma \epsilon^2)}{\partial \theta_1} = \frac{\partial (\Sigma \epsilon^2)}{\partial \theta_2} = \frac{\partial (\Sigma \epsilon^2)}{\partial \theta_3} = 0$$

or

$$\frac{\partial (\Sigma w \epsilon^2)}{\partial \theta_1} = -2w_1 (\alpha_1 - \theta_1) + 2w_4 (\alpha_4 - 360° + \theta_1 + \theta_2 + \theta_3) = 0$$

$$\frac{\partial (\Sigma w \epsilon^2)}{\partial \theta_2} = -2w_2 (\alpha_2 - \theta_2) + 2w_4 (\alpha_4 - 360° + \theta_1 + \theta_2 + \theta_3) = 0$$

$$\frac{\partial (\Sigma w \epsilon^2)}{\partial \theta_2} = -2w_3 (\alpha_3 - \theta_3) + 2w_4 (\alpha_4 - 360° + \theta_1 + \theta_2 + \theta_3) = 0$$

After substituting the numerical values of w_1, w_2, w_3, w_4, α_1, α_2, α_3, and α_4, the preceding equations reduce to the following normal equations:

$$6\theta_1 + 4\theta_2 + 4\theta_3 = 1253.337778$$
$$4\theta_1 + 7\theta_2 + 4\theta_3 = 1369.637777$$
$$4\theta_1 + 4\theta_2 + 6\theta_3 = 1322.773888$$

Solving these equations by elimination, we obtain:

$$\theta_1 = 75° \ 44' \ 31.26''$$
$$\theta_2 = 89° \ 15' \ 40.84''$$
$$\theta_3 = 110° \ 27' \ 36.27''$$

and

$$\theta_4 = 360° - (\theta_1 + \theta_2 + \theta_3) = 84° \ 32' \ 11.63''$$

15-4. To determine the effects of rising and falling stages on a particular stage discharge curve the following measurements for falling and rising stages were taken at a constant value of rate of stage change. The instrument used for the falling stage was new and, therefore, assumed subject to error, while the values for the rising stage are believed to be sensibly free from error.

Measured discharge for falling stage in cfs, y	350	770	1,240	1,640	1,980	2,430	3,000	3,430	4,020	4,370
Measured discharge for rising stage in cfs, x	400	800	1,300	1,680	2,010	2,500	3,050	3,510	4,050	4,450

(a) Determine the regression line of discharge for the falling stage upon discharge for the rising stage;

(b) Test the hypothesis that the slope of the regression line is 1.00;

(c) If the true slope = 1.01, what is the probability of accepting the hypothesis in (b)?

(d) Estimate the discharge for the falling stage when the measured discharge for rising stage is 2,010 cfs;

(e) Find the 95 percent confidence limits for a single value of discharge for falling stage corresponding to a rising stage discharge of 2,010 cfs.

Solution:

(a) The constants in the regression line $y = a + bx$ will be found using the tabular arrangement below:

x	y	$x^2 \times 10^{-4}$	$xy \times 10^{-4}$	$X = x - \bar{x}$	$Y = y - \bar{y}$	$XY \times 10^{-4}$	$X^2 \times 10^{-4}$	$Y^2 \times 10^{-4}$
400	350	16.00	14.00	−1.975	−1,973	389.668	390.062	389.273
800	770	64.00	61.60	−1,575	−1,553	244.598	248.063	241.181
1,300	1,240	169.00	161.20	−1,075	−1,083	116.423	115.562	117.289
1,680	1,640	282.24	275.52	−695	−683	47.468	48.303	46.649
2,010	1,980	404.01	397.98	−365	−343	12.519	13.322	11.765
2,500	2,430	625.00	607.50	125	107	1.338	1.563	1.145
3,050	3,000	930.25	915.00	675	677	45.698	45.562	45.833
3,510	3,430	1,232.01	1,203.93	1,135	1,107	125.644	128.823	122.545
4,050	4,020	1,640.25	1,628.10	1,675	1,697	284.247	280.562	287.981
4,450	4,370	1,980.25	1,944.65	2,075	2,047	424.752	430.563	419.021
$\Sigma =$ 23,750	23,230	7,343.01	7,209.48	5,685 − 5,685 = 0	5,635 − 5,635 = 0	1,692.355	1,702.385	1,682.682

$$\bar{x} = \frac{\Sigma x}{n} = \frac{23,750}{10} = 2,375 \text{ cfs}$$

$$\bar{y} = \frac{\Sigma y}{n} = \frac{23,230}{10} = 2,323 \text{ cfs}$$

From Eqs. 15-12 and 15-13

$$a = \frac{\Sigma x^2 \Sigma y - \Sigma x \Sigma xy}{n \Sigma x^2 - (\Sigma x)^2}$$

$$= \frac{7,343.01 \times 23,230 - 23,750 \times 7,209.48}{10 \times 7,343.01 - (237.5)^2}$$

$$= -38.007$$

and

$$b = \frac{n\Sigma xy - \Sigma x\Sigma y}{n\Sigma x^2 - (\Sigma x)^2}$$

$$= \frac{10 \times 7,209.48 - 237.5 \times 232.3}{10 \times 7,343.01 - (237.5)^2}$$

$$= 0.994$$

Therefore

$$y = -38.007 + 0.994x \text{ [with respect to origin (0,0)]}$$

Using the XY method

$$B = \frac{\Sigma XY}{\Sigma X^2} = \frac{1,692.355}{1,702.385} = 0.994$$

or

$$Y = 0.994X \text{ [with respect to centroid}$$
$$(2,375, 2,323) \text{ as origin]}$$

(*b*)   The sum of the squares of the y residuals $\Sigma\epsilon^2$ is obtained from the following table:

x	$\hat{y}$	$\epsilon = \hat{y} - y_{observed}$	ϵ^2
400	359.593	9.593	92.026
800	757.193	−12.807	164.019
1,300	1,254.193	14.193	201.441
1,680	1,631.913	−8.087	65.340
2,010	1,959.933	−20.067	402.684
2,500	2,446.993	16.993	288.762
3,050	2,993.693	−6.307	39.778
3,510	3,450.933	20.933	438.190
4,050	3,987.693	−32.307	1,043.742
4,450	4,385.293	15.293	233.876
Total			$\Sigma\epsilon^2 = 2,969.858$

$$s_y = \sqrt{\frac{\Sigma\epsilon^2}{n-2}} = \sqrt{\frac{2,969.858}{8}} = 19.267$$

To test the hypothesis that $b_0 = 1.00$ calculate:

$$s_b = s_y \sqrt{\frac{1}{\Sigma X^2}} = \frac{19.267}{100} \sqrt{\frac{1}{1,702.385}}$$

$$= 0.00467$$

Then

$$t = \frac{|b - b_0|}{s_b} = \frac{1.00 - 0.994}{0.00467} = 1.285$$

From statistical tables, for $\nu = n - 2 = 10 - 2 = 8$, $t = 1.108$ at a probability level of 30 percent and 1.397 at 20 percent. The difference in slope is, therefore, not significant and the null hypothesis can be considered valid.

(*c*) Calculate

$$t = \frac{1.01 - 1.00}{s_b} = \frac{0.01}{0.00467} = 2.141$$

For $\nu = 8$, Table A-8 gives $t = 2.306$ at the 5 percent level of significance. Therefore, the probability of correctly accepting the hypothesis $b_0 = 1.00$ is a little more than 5 percent.

(*d*) From the equation of the regression line for $x = 2,010$ cfs

$$y = 1,959.933 \text{ cfs}$$

(*e*) The 95 percent confidence limits are

$$1,959.933 \pm t s_{y_i}$$

where t is the value at the 5 percent level of significance for 8 degrees of freedom, and

$$s_{y_i} = s_y \sqrt{1 + \frac{1}{n} + \frac{(x_i - \bar{x})^2}{\Sigma X^2}}$$

Thus the limits are

$$1,959.933 \pm 2.306 \times 19.267 \sqrt{1 + \frac{1}{10} + \frac{(2,010 - 2,375)^2}{17,023,850}}$$

$$= 1,959.933 \pm 46.784$$

$$= (1,913.1, 2,006.7) \text{ cfs} \qquad \text{(say)}$$

15-5. In order to establish bench marks, precise leveling was carried out between four stations A, B, C, and D, as shown in Fig. 15-7. Due to various factors, the results were weighted as indicated below.

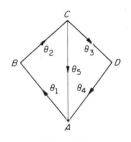

Fig. 15-7

Leg	Observed difference in elevation α, ft	Weight w
A to B	4.912 (rise)	2
B to C	2.638 (rise)	1
C to D	−6.382 (fall)	2
D to A	−1.075 (fall)	3
C to A	−7.450 (fall)	2

Using the method of least squares, find the most probable values of the differences in level between the various points.

Solution:

Let the most probable values of the differences in levels be θ_1, θ_2, θ_3, θ_4, and θ_5 for the legs numbered in Fig. 15-7. Considering the two closed circuits $ABCA$ and $ACDA$, with a common link AC, we have:

$$\theta_1 + \theta_2 + \theta_5 = 0$$

and $\hspace{10cm}$ (1)

$$\theta_3 + \theta_4 - \theta_5 = 0$$

If ϵ_1, ϵ_2, ϵ_3, ϵ_4, and ϵ_5 are the errors in levels, then $\epsilon_1 = \alpha_1 - \theta_1$, $\epsilon_2 = \alpha_2 - \theta_2$, etc. These errors are not all independent, since they are related by means of Eq. (1). Thus only three errors are independent. Let us assume that ϵ_1 and ϵ_3 are dependent errors on ϵ_2, ϵ_4, and ϵ_5. Then using Eq. (1) we have:

$$\epsilon_1 = \alpha_1 + \theta_2 + \theta_5$$

and $\hspace{10cm}$ (2)

$$\epsilon_3 = \alpha_3 + \theta_4 - \theta_5$$

The method of least squares requires that the sum of weighted squares of the errors is a minimum, with respect to the independent most probable differences in levels, θ_2, θ_4, and θ_5. Thus if

$$P = w_1 \epsilon_1^2 + w_2 \epsilon_2^2 + w_3 \epsilon_3^2 + w_4 \epsilon_4^2 + w_5 \epsilon_5^2$$

then

$$\frac{\partial P}{\partial \theta_2} = \frac{\partial P}{\partial \theta_4} = \frac{\partial P}{\partial \theta_5} = 0$$

Writing these in full yields

$$w_1 \epsilon_1 \frac{\partial \epsilon_1}{\partial \theta_2} + w_2 \epsilon_2 \frac{\partial \epsilon_2}{\partial \theta_2} + w_3 \epsilon_3 \frac{\partial \epsilon_3}{\partial \theta_2} + w_4 \epsilon_4 \frac{\partial \epsilon_4}{\partial \theta_2} + w_5 \epsilon_5 \frac{\partial \epsilon_5}{\partial \theta_2} = 0$$

$$w_1 \epsilon_1 \frac{\partial \epsilon_1}{\partial \theta_4} + w_2 \epsilon_2 \frac{\partial \epsilon_2}{\partial \theta_4} + w_3 \epsilon_3 \frac{\partial \epsilon_3}{\partial \theta_4} + w_4 \epsilon_4 \frac{\partial \epsilon_4}{\partial \theta_4} + w_5 \epsilon_5 \frac{\partial \epsilon_5}{\partial \theta_4} = 0$$

$$w_1 \epsilon_1 \frac{\partial \epsilon_1}{\partial \theta_5} + w_2 \epsilon_2 \frac{\partial \epsilon_2}{\partial \theta_5} + w_3 \epsilon_3 \frac{\partial \epsilon_3}{\partial \theta_5} + w_4 \epsilon_4 \frac{\partial \epsilon_4}{\partial \theta_5} + w_5 \epsilon_5 \frac{\partial \epsilon_5}{\partial \theta_5} = 0$$

Hence we obtain the following three normal equations:

$$w_1 \epsilon_1 - w_2 \epsilon_2 = 0$$
$$w_3 \epsilon_3 - w_4 \epsilon_4 = 0$$
$$w_1 \epsilon_1 - w_3 \epsilon_3 - w_5 \epsilon_5 = 0$$

Substituting the numerical values of w and expressing ϵ in terms of α and the unknowns θ_2, θ_4, and θ_5, we obtain

$$3\theta_2 + 2\theta_5 = -7.186$$
$$5\theta_4 - 2\theta_5 = +9.539$$
$$\theta_2 - \theta_4 + 3\theta_5 = -18.744$$

Solution of these three simultaneous equations yields

$$\theta_2 = 2.584 \text{ ft}, \quad \theta_4 = -1.080 \text{ ft}, \quad \theta_5 = -7.469 \text{ ft}$$

and from Eqs. (1):

$$\theta_1 = 4.885 \text{ ft}, \quad \theta_3 = -6.389 \text{ ft}$$

15-6. Design of certain metallic alloys for high temperature is usually based on stress-rupture curves. In many cases the deformation involved is intolerable, and to ensure a life of a given number of hours it is necessary to keep the applied stress below the value that would produce rupture in the same number of hours. An experiment on one such alloy was run at 1200°F, and the following data were obtained relating applied stress to rupture time:

Stress f, ksi	Rupture time T, hr
80	22
70	57
60	205
50	1,324

(a) Estimate the constants in the relation $\log T = a + bf$.
(b) Estimate the rupture time by a point estimate corresponding to a stress $f = 65 \text{ kip/in.}^2$
(c) Estimate the predicted rupture time by a 95 percent confidence interval for the stress given in (b).

Solution:

(a) Let $y = \log T$ and $x = f$. Then in tabular form:

T	y	x	x^2	xy
22	1.3424	80	6,400	107.392
57	1.7559	70	4,900	122.913
205	2.3118	60	3,600	138.708
1324	3.1219	50	2,500	156.095
$\Sigma =$	8.5320	260	17,400	525.108

From Eqs. 15-12 and 15-13,

$$a = \frac{\Sigma x^2 \Sigma y - \Sigma x \Sigma xy}{n\Sigma x^2 - (\Sigma x)^2} = \frac{17,400 \times 8.5320 - 260 \times 525.108}{4 \times 17,400 - 260 \times 260}$$

$$= 5.96436$$

and

$$b = \frac{n\Sigma xy - \Sigma x \Sigma y}{n\Sigma x^2 - (\Sigma x)^2} = \frac{4 \times 525.108 - 260 \times 8.5320}{4 \times 17,400 - 260 \times 260}$$

$$= -0.058944$$

Hence

$$\log T = 5.96436 - 0.058944 f$$

(b)   For $f = 65$ kip/in.^{2}, the above equation for T gives:

$$\log T = 5.96436 - 0.058944 \times 65 = 2.1330$$
$$T = 135.8 \text{ hr}$$

(c)   In order to predict the required confidence interval, the variance of log T, as estimated from the regression line, must be first computed.   In tabular form:

f, kip/in.^{2}	$y\ (= \log T)$	$\hat{y}\ (= \log T$ computed$)$	$\epsilon_i = y_i - \hat{y}_i$	ϵ_i^2
80	1.3424	1.24884	+0.09356	0.00875347
70	1.7559	1.83828	−0.08238	0.00678646
60	2.3118	2.42772	−0.11592	0.01343745
50	3.1219	3.01716	+0.10474	0.01097047
Total....				$\Sigma\epsilon_i^2 = 0.03994785$

From Eq. 15-22,

$$s_y^2 = \frac{\Sigma\epsilon_i^2}{n-2} = \frac{0.03994785}{2} = 0.0199739$$

or

$$s_y = 0.14133$$

Since the confidence interval is required for $x = 65$, and $\bar{x} = 65$, we have from Eq. 15-26:

$$s_{y_i} = 0.14133 \sqrt{1 + \tfrac{1}{4}}$$
$$= 0.15799$$

Hence the confidence interval for a single value

$$= 2.1330 \pm t \times 0.15799$$
$$= 2.1330 \pm 4.303 \times 0.15799$$

since $t = 4.303$ for $\nu = 4 - 2$ at the 5 percent probability level.   Thus the limits for log T are 2.8128 and 1.4531, and for T, 649.8 and 28.4 hr.

PROBLEMS

15-1.   In a laboratory experiment the lateral pressure and failure load were measured, with the following (coded) results:

Pressure x..........	0	1	2	3	4	5	8
Failure load y.......	10	10.7	12.1	12.6	13.8	16.2	18.9

Obtain the regression equation of y on x, and x on y, and plot these together with the experimental data.

15-2.   Tests on the fuel consumption of a vehicle traveling at different speeds yielded the following (coded) results:

Speed x	20	30	40	50	60	70	80	90
Consumption y	18.3	18.8	19.1	19.3	19.5	19.7	19.8	20.0

It is believed that the relation between the two variables is of the type $y = a + b/x$. Obtain the equation to the regression line.

15-3. An experimental determination of the relation between x and y yielded the following results:

x	4	5	6	7	8	9	10	11
y	4	6	8	13	18	23	26	31

(a) Find the equation to the regression line of y on x;

(b) Estimate the 99 percent confidence limits of a predicted single observation of y when $x = 8.5$.

15-4. In a study of the relation between y and x (believed to be free from error), the following data were obtained:

$$n = 18; \quad \Sigma(y - \bar{y})^2 = 720; \quad \Sigma(x - \bar{x})^2 = 144;$$

$$\Sigma(x - \bar{x})(y - \bar{y}) = 288; \quad \bar{x} = 5; \quad a = 10$$

(a) Obtain the equation to the regression line.

(b) Test the hypothesis: $b = 0$.

(c) Test the hypothesis: $a = 8$.

(d) Obtain the 95 percent confidence interval for b.

$$\left[\text{Use the expression: } (n - 2) s_y^2 = \Sigma(y - \bar{y})^2 - \frac{[\Sigma(x - \bar{x})(y - \bar{y})]^2}{\Sigma(x - \bar{x})^2}. \text{ See Appendix E.} \right]$$

15-5. Obtain the equation to the regression line of the modulus of elasticity (y) on content of a certain compound (x) in a plastic:

x	55.8	55.0	54.3	49.9	53.0	50.6	58.3	63.7
y	83.9	66.4	73.1	30.1	36.2	66.7	87.3	135.0
x	67.0	65.0	58.8	57.6	57.5	54.4	54.2	55.8
y	153.1	158.2	65.8	72.1	83.1	72.1	71.3	58.0

Hence calculate the standard deviation of the regression line s_y. If $x = 60$, estimate the expected modulus of elasticity and determine a 95 percent confidence range for the expected modulus at this value of x. Find a prediction interval such that the probability is 95 percent that the value of the modulus of elasticity corresponding to $x = 60$ will lie within the interval.

15-6. Leveling was carried out from a station P at a known elevation of 234.15 ft above datum, the weights of the different legs being given below. Find the most probable values of the levels of points Q, R, and S.

Leg	Difference in level, ft	Weight
P to Q	6.32 rise	1
Q to S	5.68 rise	2
Q to R	3.15 rise	1
R to S	2.59 rise	1
S to P	12.04 fall	2

15-7. A, B, C, and D form a round of angles at a station such that they add up to $360°$. The observed values are:

$$A = 82° \ 15' \ 35'' \qquad C = 66° \ 24' \ 40''$$

$$B = 110° \ 37' \ 45'' \qquad D = 100° \ 42' \ 10''$$

The angle $(A + B)$ was measured separately twice, and the average value was found to be 192° 53′ 25″. If each of the six measurements is of equal reliability (weight), find the most probable values of all the angles.

15-8. The number of bacteria per unit volume found in a tillage after x hours is given in the table below:

Number of hours x	0	1	2	3	4	5	6	7
Number of bacteria y	47	64	81	107	151	209	298	841

(a)   Estimate the constants in the relation $\log y = a + bx$.

(b)   Estimate the number of bacteria per unit volume by a point estimate corresponding to $x = 4.5$ hours.

(c)   Estimate the 99 percent confidence interval for the predicted number of bacteria per unit volume for $x = 4.5$ hours.

(d)   Plot the data on semilogarithmic graph paper.

15-9. The strengths of concrete cylinders of the same proportions but different size were recorded as follows.[4] Obtain an equation to the curvilinear regression line relating the strength (y) and diameter (x).

Diameter, in.	2	3	6	8	12	18	24	36
Strength (coded)	108	106	100	96	92	86	84	84

15-10. The compressive strengths of concrete specimens of three types are as follows:[5]

Test	Strength, psi		
No.	6 in. cubes	5 in. × 5 in. cylinders	6 in. × 12 in. cylinders
1	7,600 7,590 7,530	7,150 7,400 7,450	6,430 6,320 6,290
2	6,490 6,410 6,440	6,250 6,600 6,300	5,240 5,380 5,240
3	8,020 8,090 7,680	8,050 8,050 7,800	6,710 6,440 6,450
4	6,320 6,370 6,420	6,150 6,200 6,550	5,450 5,480 5,660
5	6,110 6,690 6,410	6,250 6,600 6,300	5,590 5,590 5,550
6	5,970 6,410 6,550	6,400 5,800 5,900	5,480 5,550 5,620

(continued)

[4] A. M. Neville, "Some Aspects of the Strength of Concrete," Part II, *Civil Engineering* (London) Vol. 54 (Nov. 1959) p. 1309.

[5] M. W. Cormack, "Note on Cubes v. Cylinders," *New Zealand Engineering*, Vol. 11, No. 3 (March 1956) p. 99.

Test No.	Strength, psi		
	6 in. cubes	5 in. × 5 in. cylinders	6 in. × 12 in. cylinders
7	6,750 6,600 6,550	6,900 6,550 6,550	5,910 5,910 5,680
8	7,150 7,080 7,080	6,900 6,950 6,650	6,120 6,220 6,050
9	6,150 6,300 6,330	5,750 5,650 5,850	5,380 5,310 5,270
10	7,350 —— ——	7,250 7,500 7,600	6,300 6,350 6,400
11	5,500 6,200 6,250	5,800 6,500 6,600	5,200 5,400 5,510
12	6,450 6,325 6,325	6,550 6,550 6,600	5,610 5,590 5,590
13	5,950 6,060 6,160	6,000 6,100 6,200	5,050 5,110 5,160
14	4,720 4,720 4,700	4,550 4,500 4,900	4,020 3,950 4,130
15	3,280 3,240 3,360	3,850 3,900 3,900	3,210 3,250 3,450

Using the means of each test, obtain equations to the regression lines of (*a*) 6 in. cubes and 5 in. cylinders, and (*b*) 6 in. cubes and 6 in. cylinders. Test the significance of these relations. Test also the hypotheses that the slopes are: for (*a*) 1.00; for (*b*) 0.85.

15-11. Experimental measurements of y and x are given below. It is expected that the relation is in the form $y = ax^b$. Fit the constants of the regression line.

x	y	x	y
667	54	3,619	106
727	42	3,865	98
823	34	4,266	261
1,086	75	4,299	197
1,529	103	4,382	106
1,941	87	5,560	216
2,266	53	5,955	251
2,515	113	6,358	347
3,187	137	7,165	339
3,218	114	7,910	282

15-12. From a certain station, angles A, B, and C are observed a number of times by the method of repetition, with the results, all of equal weight, given below:

$$3A = 172°\ 45'\ 50''$$
$$3A + 3B = 400°\ 25'\ 30''$$
$$A + B + C = 225°\ 46'\ 30''$$
$$2B + 2C = 336°\ 22'\ 10''$$
$$3C = 276°\ 52'\ 50''$$
$$3A + 3C = 449°\ 38'\ 50''$$
$$3B = 227°\ 40'\ 10''$$

Find to the nearest second the most probable values of A, B, and C.

15-13. In establishing levels of B, C, and D from an ordnance bench mark at A, precise leveling was carried out from A to each point B, C, and D and in addition between B and C and between C and D with the following results:

	Approx. mileage between stations
B 10.714 ft higher than A	2.0
A 51.762 ” ” ” C	1.5
D 32.840 ” ” ” A	1.0
B 62.463 ” ” ” C	1.5
D 84.624 ” ” ” C	1.5

Assuming that measurement errors are proportional to the square root of the mileage, "weight" the observations and find the most probable values of the heights of B, C, and D with respect to A.

chapter 16

Correlation

We should stress the fact that just because we have fitted a straight-line relation to a number of observations, it does not mean that the physical data really follow a straight line. For example, there may be a cyclic (or any other) relation with a general rise of y with x which could be represented by a straight line. An example of this is shown in Fig. 16-1, and it is clear that although we have fitted a line satisfying the minimum value of the sum of squares of deviations their sum is large. We can distinguish thus between the deviations of the y observations from the regression line (this representing variation about the regression) and the total variation of the y observations about their mean. The difference between the two variations, expressed in an appropriate mathematical form, gives the amount of variation accounted for by regression, and the higher this amount the better the fit.

It is clear, therefore, that the operation of fitting the best line must be followed by a test of the goodness of fit.

CORRELATION COEFFICIENT

Referring to Eq. 15-14, we can observe that, if there is no correlation between y and x, that is, if y is independent of x, the coefficient of x (that is, the slope b) is zero and the line plots as a horizontal line, that is,

$$\frac{n\Sigma xy - \Sigma x\Sigma y}{n\Sigma x^2 - (\Sigma x)^2} = 0 \qquad (16\text{-}1)$$

Considering now the regression of x on y, there is no correlation if x is independent of y, that is, if the line described by Eq. 15-16 is vertical. Thus, referring the slope to a vertical axis,

$$\frac{n\Sigma xy - \Sigma x\Sigma y}{n\Sigma y^2 - (\Sigma y)^2} = 0 \qquad (16\text{-}2)$$

and expressing slope in the usual way (y vertical and x horizontal):

$$\frac{n\Sigma y^2 - (\Sigma y)^2}{n\Sigma xy - \Sigma x\Sigma y} = \infty \qquad (16\text{-}3)$$

If there is no correlation between the two variables being studied, the product of the slopes given by Eq. 16-1 and 16-2 is zero, that is,

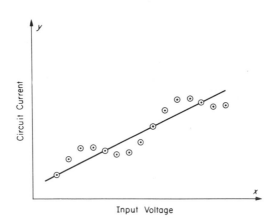

FIG. 16-1. Relation between y and x and regression line which would show poor correlation. The experimental points in the form shown would be obtained when the circuit contains resistors with two or more tunnel diodes in series.

$$\frac{n\Sigma xy - \Sigma x\Sigma y}{n\Sigma x^2 - (\Sigma x)^2} \times \frac{n\Sigma xy - \Sigma x\Sigma y}{n\Sigma y^2 - (\Sigma y)^2} = 0$$

Conversely, when there is a perfect correlation, i.e., all the points lie exactly on each of the two regression lines, the lines coincide; their slopes are therefore equal, namely,

$$\frac{n\Sigma xy - \Sigma x\Sigma y}{n\Sigma x^2 - (\Sigma x)^2} = \frac{n\Sigma y^2 - (\Sigma y)^2}{n\Sigma xy - \Sigma x\Sigma y}$$

or

$$\frac{n\Sigma xy - \Sigma x\Sigma y}{n\Sigma x^2 - (\Sigma x)^2} \times \frac{n\Sigma xy - \Sigma x\Sigma y}{n\Sigma y^2 - (\Sigma y)^2} = 1 \qquad (16\text{-}4)$$

Thus we find that the value of the product on the left-hand side of Eq. 16-4 gives a measure of correlation: when the value is zero, there is no correlation; when it is unity, the correlation is perfect. We call the square root of this product[1] the *correlation coefficient* and denote it by r:

$$r = \frac{n\Sigma xy - \Sigma x\Sigma y}{\sqrt{[n\Sigma x^2 - (\Sigma x)^2][n\Sigma y^2 - (\Sigma y)^2]}} \qquad (16\text{-}5)$$

In terms of the variables X, Y referred to $(\bar{x}, \bar{y})$, r can be written as

$$r = \frac{\Sigma XY}{\sqrt{\Sigma X^2 \Sigma Y^2}} \qquad (16\text{-}6)$$

The correlation coefficient r can also be defined as

$$r = \sqrt{\frac{\text{Explained variation}}{\text{Total variation}}} \qquad (16\text{-}7)$$

[1] Or the geometric mean of the two values.

We can note that r is symmetrical with respect to x and y so that the correlation coefficient of a line of regression of y on x is the same as that of regression of x on y. Correlation is, in fact, concerned only with the association between the variables and not with their dependence or independence.

The correlation coefficient r must lie in the range $0 \leq |r| \leq 1$ but in practice, because of random errors, $0 < |r| < 1$.

To interpret the meaning of r calculated by Eq. 16-5 or 16-6 we use Table A-11. This gives the values of r which can be expected at a given level of significance from observations drawn by chance when there is no correlation. If the absolute value of the calculated r exceeds the tabulated value, we conclude that correlation exists, and the level of significance represents the probability of our having drawn the wrong conclusion. We may note that r is related to t.

Table A-11 is entered with the appropriate number of degrees of freedom and the total number of variables. In the case of regression of the type given by Eq. 15-1, the total number of variables is 2 and the number of degrees of freedom is $n - 2$, where n is the total number of observations.

The sign of r tells us whether y increases with an increase in x (r is positive) or whether y decreases with an increase in x (r is negative). Figure 16-2 shows diagrammatically some of the possible correlations.

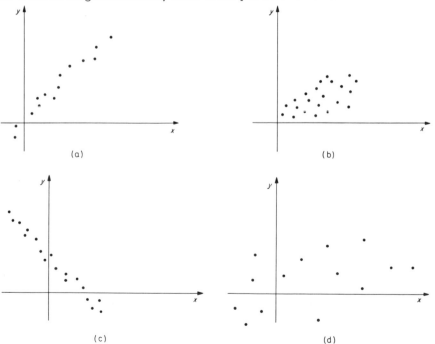

FIG. 16-2. Correlations: (a) high positive; (b) low positive; (c) high negative; (d) none (the variables are independent).

It can be shown that the square of the correlation coefficient is equal
to the ratio of the sum of squares of deviations accounted for by regression
to the total sum of squares of deviations about the mean. The correlation
coefficient is thus an estimate of association between the variables and is
valid only when the observations are randomly drawn.

The level of significance of correlation given by the correlation coefficient is the same as the level of significance of the slope of the regression
line given by the t test of Eq. 15-32 (see Appendix E).

Example. Find the correlation coefficient r for the first example in
Chapter 15 on the relation between normal stress and shear resistance
of a soil.

To calculate r given by Eq. 16-6, we require ΣXY, ΣX^2 and ΣY^2. In
tabular form:

X	Y	XY	X^2	Y^2
-5	-5.3	26.5	25	28.09
-3	-2.8	8.4	9	7.84
-1	-1.2	1.2	1	1.44
$+1$	$+1.0$	1.0	1	1.00
$+3$	$+3.4$	10.2	9	11.56
$+5$	$+4.9$	24.5	25	24.01
$\Sigma = 0$	0	71.8	70	73.94

Hence

$$r = \frac{71.8}{\sqrt{70 \times 73.94}} = 0.998$$

For two variables and $\nu = 6 - 2 = 4$, Table A-11 gives $r = 0.917$ at the
1 percent level of significance. The value at the 0.1 percent level is 0.974.
There is therefore an excellent correlation between the normal stress and
shear resistance of the soil tested.

CORRELATION AND CAUSATION

We have seen how the correlation coefficient is used to find the degree of
association that exists between two variables y and x. A high correlation coefficient proves the existence of a close mathematical relation between the
variables, but it is important to realize that this does not necessarily imply
causation. For example, if we find correlation between some measured
quantity, such as speed of reaction, and time (say, between 8 A.M. and
noon), it does not follow that the observed quantity is a function of time of
operation. It may well be that time is not the true *independent* variable but
enters the picture only insofar as it is associated with temperature which
naturally rises as the day progresses. It is thus the temperature that is
the causative variable.

Per contra, when a low correlation coefficient is obtained, the conclusion

that the independent variable does not influence the quantity being measured is not necessarily correct. It is possible that other factors exist, mask-
ing or nullifying the effect of the independent variable on the dependent
variable. In either case the determination of causation involves a scientific
study of the subject, possibly using additional experimental data, statistics
being merely one of the more powerful tools in arriving at the right answer.

SOLVED PROBLEM

16-1. Find the correlation coefficient for Solved Problem 15-4.
Solution:
The coefficient of correlation is given by

$$r = \frac{\Sigma XY}{\sqrt{\Sigma X^2 \Sigma Y^2}} = \frac{1,692.355}{\sqrt{1,702.385 \times 1,682.682}}$$

$$= 0.9999$$

This means that the correlation is virtually perfect.

PROBLEMS

16-1. Find the correlation coefficient of the regression of Prob. 15-5, and determine the significance of the regression.

16-2. Is the correlation between y and x significant?

x	56	58	60	70	72	75	77	77	82	87	92	104	125
y	51	60	69	54	70	65	49	60	63	61	64	84	75

16-3. A correlation coefficient based on a sample of size 16 was calculated to
be 0.38. Determine whether we can conclude that the corresponding population
correlation differs from zero at a significance level of (*a*) 5 percent, (*b*) 1 percent.
(Use $t = \dfrac{r\sqrt{n-2}}{\sqrt{1-r^2}}$ in Appendix E.)

16-4. Find by a trial method the minimum sample size necessary in order to
conclude that a correlation coefficient of 0.38 differs significantly from zero at the
1 percent level.

16-5. The compressive strength of concretes[2] with three different aggregate-
cement ratios was measured on four test specimens for each mix. Using the mean
strength of each mix, obtain the regression line of strength on aggregate-cement
ratio, and the correlation coefficient. Test the significance of the slope.

Spec. No. / Agg.-cem. ratio	Strength, psi		
	4	5	6
1	5,830	6,590	6,340
2	6,130	6,170	7,040
3	5,920	6,450	6,980
4	5,800	6,360	6,630

[2] P. J F. Wright, "Statistical Methods in Concrete Research," *Magazine of Concrete Re
search*, Vol. 5, No. 15 (March 1954) p. 147.

chapter 17

Multiple Linear Regression

In many practical cases a variable may depend on more than one independent variable. If the independent variables vary entirely randomly, we can use simple regression as in the case of one independent variable, although this leads to some loss in the precision of our estimate. However, if the independent variables tend to vary according to some pattern, simple regression leads to misleading results, and multiple regression has to be used. The difference between the two methods lies in the fact that multiple regression establishes the effect of one independent variable with the other independent variables kept constant, while simple regression does not control the other variables.

An example of a problem involving multiple regression is afforded by the influence of the temperatures of air and of the coolant on the efficiency of an engine. Because of the influence of weather, the two temperatures are likely to be low or high at the same time, and a single correlation cannot eliminate the effect of one variable when the effect of the other is measured; it is the multiple correlation that achieves this.

REGRESSION EQUATION

Let us consider the general case of a linear relation between the mean value of the dependent variable y and independent variables $x_1, x_2, \ldots, x_k$; this can be expressed as

$$y = b_0 + b_1 x_1 + b_2 x_2 + \cdots + b_k x_k \qquad (17\text{-}1)$$

where b_0 is a constant and $b_1, b_2, \ldots, b_k$ are partial regression coefficients. Equation 17-1 represents a plane in $(k + 1)$ dimensions.

As shown in Appendix F, the plane passes through the centroid of all the observed values, i.e., Eq. 17-1 is satisfied by $(\bar{y}, \bar{x}_1, \bar{x}_2, \ldots, \bar{x}_k)$ where $\bar{y}, \bar{x}_1, \ldots, \bar{x}_k$ are means of all the values of $y, x_1, \ldots, x_k$ respectively. Hence

$$\bar{y} = b_0 + b_1 \bar{x}_1 + b_2 \bar{x}_2 + \cdots + b_k \bar{x}_k$$

or

$$b_0 = \bar{y} - b_1 \bar{x}_1 - b_2 \bar{x}_2 - \cdots - b_k \bar{x}_k$$

Substituting in Eq. 17-1, we obtain

$$y - \bar{y} = b_1 (x_1 - \bar{x}_1) + b_2 (x_2 - \bar{x}_2) + \cdots + b_k (x_k - \bar{x}_k) \qquad (17\text{-}2)$$

The coefficients are determined using the method of least squares; for simplicity we shall consider the case of two independent variables only, that is,

$$y = b_0 + b_1 x_1 + b_2 x_2$$

with n sets of observations. In each case, the residual is given as

$$\epsilon = y - (b_0 + b_1 x_1 + b_2 x_2) \tag{17-3}$$

and the sum of squares of residuals in the n sets is

$$\Sigma \epsilon^2 = \Sigma [y - (b_0 + b_1 x_1 + b_2 x_2)]^2 \tag{17-4}$$

Using the principle of least squares, we mimimize $\Sigma \epsilon^2$, that is, we satisfy the condition that the partial derivatives of $\Sigma \epsilon^2$ with respect to b_0, b_1, and b_2 are all zero:

$$\frac{\partial(\Sigma \epsilon^2)}{\partial b_0} = -2\Sigma[y - (b_0 + b_1 x_1 + b_2 x_2)] = 0$$

$$\frac{\partial(\Sigma \epsilon^2)}{\partial b_1} = -2\Sigma x_1 [y - (b_0 + b_1 x_1 + b_2 x_2)] = 0$$

$$\frac{\partial(\Sigma \epsilon^2)}{\partial b_2} = -2\Sigma x_2 [y - (b_0 + b_1 x_1 + b_2 x_2)] = 0$$

Hence the normal equations can be written:

$$\left. \begin{aligned} \Sigma y &= n b_0 + b_1 \Sigma x_1 + b_2 \Sigma x_2 \\ \Sigma x_1 y &= b_0 \Sigma x_1 + b_1 \Sigma x_1^2 + b_2 \Sigma x_1 x_2 \\ \Sigma x_2 y &= b_0 \Sigma x_2 + b_1 \Sigma x_1 x_2 + b_2 \Sigma x_2^2 \end{aligned} \right\} \tag{17-5}$$

The solution of this system of three simultaneous equations gives the values of b_0, b_1, and b_2.

SHORTER COMPUTATION

We can simplify the process of finding the equation to the regression plane by choosing the centroid as origin. Let

$$Y = y - \bar{y}$$
$$X_1 = x_1 - \bar{x}_1$$
$$\cdot \qquad \cdot \qquad \cdot$$
$$\cdot \qquad \cdot \qquad \cdot$$
$$\cdot \qquad \cdot \qquad \cdot$$
$$X_k = x_k - \bar{x}_k$$

Thus, Eq. 17-2 becomes

$$Y = b_1 X_1 + b_2 X_2 + \cdots + b_k X_k$$

and the residual

$$\epsilon - Y - (b_1 X_1 + b_2 X_2 + \cdots + b_k X_k)$$

Considering two independent variables X_1 and X_2 only and taking partial derivatives of $\Sigma\epsilon^2$ with respect to b_1 and b_2, we obtain

$$\Sigma X_1 Y = b_1 \Sigma X_1^2 + b_2 \Sigma X_1 X_2$$
$$\Sigma X_2 Y = b_1 \Sigma X_1 X_2 + b_2 \Sigma X_2^2$$

(17-6)

The solution of the system of these two equations gives the values of the regression coefficients, and hence the equation to the regression plane.

Example. From an experimental study on the stabilization of a highly plastic clay, molding water content for optimum density was found to be linearly dependent on the percentages of lime and pozzolan mixed with the clay. The following results were obtained:

Water content in percent y	Percent of lime x_1	Percent of pozzolan x_2
27.5	2.0	18.0
28.0	3.5	16.5
28.8	4.5	10.5
29.1	2.5	2.5
30.0	8.5	9.0
31.0	10.5	4.5
32.0	13.5	1.5

Fit an equation of the form $y = b_0 + b_1 x_1 + b_2 x_2$ to the above data.

The equation can be readily obtained by means of the table on page 211. Using Eqs. 17-6,

$$118.21170 b_1 - 110.54078 b_2 = 40.99563$$
$$-110.54078 b_1 + 258.23270 b_2 = -53.20647$$

Solving for b_1 and b_2 by elimination, we get

$$b_1 = 0.257004, \quad b_2 = -0.096026$$

Now

$$\bar{y} = b_0 + b_1 \bar{x}_1 + b_2 \bar{x}_2$$

Substituting for b_1, b_2, $\bar{y}$, $\bar{x}_1$, and $\bar{x}_2$, we obtain

$$b_0 = 28.691$$

Thus the required equation is

$$y = 28.691 + 0.257 x_1 - 0.0960 x_2$$

USE OF MATRICES

As we have seen, multiple linear regression leads to a set of simultaneous equations, which have to be solved. Such simultaneous equations can be represented in the following compact matrix form:

$$AX = B$$

y	x_1	x_2	$Y = y - \bar{y}$	$X_1 = x_1 - \bar{x}_1$	$X_2 = x_2 - \bar{x}_2$	YX_1	YX_2	X_1^2	X_2^2	$X_1 X_2$
27.5	2.0	18.0	−1.985	−4.428	+9.072	8.78958	−18.00792	19.60718	82.30118	−40.17081
28.0	3.5	16.5	−1.486	−2.929	+7.572	4.35239	−11.25199	8.57904	57.33518	−22.17838
28.8	4.5	10.5	−0.686	−1.929	+1.571	1.32329	−1.07771	3.72104	2.46804	−3.03046
29.1	2.5	2.5	−0.386	−3.928	−6.429	1.51621	+2.48159	15.42918	41.33204	+25.25311
30.0	8.5	9.0	+0.514	+2.071	+0.071	1.06449	+0.03649	4.28904	0.00504	+0.14704
31.0	10.5	4.5	+1.514	+4.071	−4.429	6.16349	−6.70551	16.57304	19.61604	−18.03046
32.0	13.5	1.5	+2.515	+7.072	−7.428	17.78608	−18.68142	50.01318	55.17518	−52.53082
$\Sigma = 206.4$	45.0	62.5	0	0	0	40.99563	−53.20647	118.21170	258.23270	−110.54078

$$\bar{y} = \frac{\Sigma y}{n} = \frac{206.4}{7} = 29.486$$

$$\bar{x}_1 = \frac{\Sigma x_1}{n} = \frac{45.0}{7} = 6.429$$

$$\bar{x}_2 = \frac{\Sigma x_2}{n} = \frac{62.5}{7} = 8.929$$

where A and B are matrices obtained from the experimental data, and X is the unknown vector (the regression coefficients to be determined).

In the case where only two coefficients b_1 and b_2 are involved,

$$A = \begin{bmatrix} \Sigma X_1^2 & \Sigma X_1 X_2 \\ \Sigma X_1 X_2 & \Sigma X_2^2 \end{bmatrix} \qquad X = \begin{bmatrix} b_1 \\ b_2 \end{bmatrix} \qquad B = \begin{bmatrix} \Sigma X_1 Y \\ \Sigma X_2 Y \end{bmatrix} \qquad (17\text{-}7)$$

Writing the matrix equation in full, we have

$$b_1 \Sigma X_1^2 + b_2 \Sigma X_1 X_2 = \Sigma X_1 Y$$
$$b_1 \Sigma X_1 X_2 + b_2 \Sigma X_2^2 = \Sigma X_2 Y \qquad (17\text{-}6)$$

The matrices A and B are written in a similar manner for more than two unknowns.

In many instances the inverse of matrix A, denoted by A^{-1}, is required. The inverse of a matrix is defined by the relation:

$$A^{-1}A = \text{unit matrix}$$

Writing this in full, and if

$$A^{-1} = \begin{bmatrix} e_{11} & e_{12} \\ e_{21} & e_{22} \end{bmatrix} \qquad (17\text{-}8)$$

then

$$\begin{bmatrix} e_{11} & e_{12} \\ e_{21} & e_{22} \end{bmatrix} \begin{bmatrix} \Sigma X_1^2 & \Sigma X_1 X_2 \\ \Sigma X_1 X_2 & \Sigma X_2^2 \end{bmatrix} = \begin{bmatrix} 1 & 0 \\ 0 & 1 \end{bmatrix} \qquad (17\text{-}9)$$

The simultaneous equations are:

$$\left. \begin{array}{l} e_{11} \Sigma X_1^2 + e_{12} \Sigma X_1 X_2 = 1 \\ e_{11} \Sigma X_1 X_2 + e_{12} \Sigma X_2^2 = 0 \\ e_{21} \Sigma X_1^2 + e_{22} \Sigma X_1 X_2 = 0 \\ e_{21} \Sigma X_1 X_2 + e_{22} \Sigma X_2^2 = 1 \end{array} \right\} \qquad (17\text{-}10)$$

The solution of Eqs. 17-10 gives

$$\left. \begin{array}{l} e_{11} = \dfrac{\Sigma X_2^2}{\Sigma X_1^2 \Sigma X_2^2 - (\Sigma X_1 X_2)^2} \\[3mm] e_{22} = \dfrac{\Sigma X_1^2}{\Sigma X_1^2 \Sigma X_2^2 - (\Sigma X_1 X_2)^2} \\[3mm] e_{12} = e_{21} = \dfrac{-\Sigma X_1 X_2}{\Sigma X_1^2 \Sigma X_2^2 - (\Sigma X_1 X_2)^2} \end{array} \right\} \qquad (17\text{-}11)$$

provided that the determinant of $A \neq 0$, i.e., the denominator in Eq. 17-11 is different from zero. Otherwise, values for e_{11}, e_{22}, e_{12}, and e_{21} will be infinite.

There are two main uses of finding A^{-1} (Eq. 17-8). The first is when we want to check whether there is an association between the independent variables which have been used previously and a new dependent variable, e.g., between the water-cement ratio of concrete, the specific gravity of aggregate, and the density of the resulting concrete. If there is an association, then the matrix A is unchanged and so is A^{-1}. Thus, the unknown vector X can be easily found in the following manner:

Multiply both sides of $AX = B$ by A^{-1}. Thus

$$A^{-1}AX = A^{-1}B$$

But $A^{-1}A =$ unit matrix. Therefore

$$X = A^{-1}B$$

In full:

$$\begin{bmatrix} b_1 \\ b_2 \end{bmatrix} = \begin{bmatrix} e_{11} & e_{12} \\ e_{21} & e_{22} \end{bmatrix} \begin{bmatrix} \Sigma X_1 Y \\ \Sigma X_2 Y \end{bmatrix} \tag{17-12}$$

or

$$\left. \begin{aligned} b_1 &= e_{11}\Sigma X_1 Y + e_{12}\Sigma X_2 Y \\ b_2 &= e_{21}\Sigma X_1 Y + e_{22}\Sigma X_2 Y \end{aligned} \right\} \tag{17-13}$$

The second main use of the inverse matrix A^{-1} is in calculating the standard error of the partial regression coefficients, and hence the confidence intervals for such coefficients.

CONFIDENCE LIMITS OF A PARTIAL REGRESSION COEFFICIENT

To obtain the standard deviation of each partial regression coefficient we need the residual variance of the dependent variable y, denoted by s_y^2. We can write

$$s_y^2 = \frac{\Sigma \epsilon_i^2}{n - k - 1} \tag{17-14}$$

where $\epsilon_i =$ deviation of observed value of y from the value given by the regression plane, that is,

$$\epsilon_i = y - \hat{y}$$

where

$\hat{y} =$ estimate of y from the regression plane

$n =$ number of observations of y

$k =$ number of independent variables on which y depends

For two independent variables, x_1 and x_2, the residual variance becomes, after shifting the origin to the centroid ($\bar{y}, \bar{x}_1, \bar{x}_2$),

$$s_y^2 = \frac{\Sigma \epsilon_i^2}{n - k - 1} = \frac{\Sigma(Y - \hat{Y})^2}{n - 2 - 1} = \frac{\Sigma[Y - (b_1 X_1 + b_2 X_2)]^2}{n - 3}$$

$\hat{Y}$ being the estimated value given by the regression equation. Expanding the term in the brackets,

$$s_y^2 = \frac{\Sigma Y^2 - 2b_1 \Sigma Y X_1 - 2b_2 \Sigma Y X_2 + b_1^2 \Sigma X_1^2 + b_2^2 \Sigma X_2^2 + 2b_1 b_2 \Sigma X_1 X_2}{n - 3}$$

Multiplying the first of Eqs. 17-6 by b_1 and the second by b_2, and substituting the values of $b_1^2 \Sigma X_1^2$ and $b_2^2 \Sigma X_2^2$ in the above expression, we obtain

$$s_y^2 = \frac{\Sigma Y^2 - b_1 \Sigma Y X_1 - b_2 \Sigma Y X_2}{n - 3} \tag{17-15}$$

The standard deviation of a partial regression coefficient is estimated from the sample as

$$s_{b_j} = s_y \sqrt{e_{jj}} \tag{17-16}$$

where in the general case $j = 1, 2, \ldots, k$ and e_{jj} is the corresponding diagonal element of A^{-1}. Thus for the two regression coefficients b_1 and b_2 we have

$$s_{b_1} = s_y \sqrt{e_{11}}$$

and

$$s_{b_2} = s_y \sqrt{e_{22}} \tag{17-17}$$

We can now test the significance of the regression coefficients. This is important since we may have assumed independent variables which do not significantly influence y. The significance of b_1 is tested by

$$t = \frac{b_1}{s_{b_1}} \tag{17-18}$$

Similar tests are applied to the other coefficients. The number of degrees of freedom is $n - 3$, as 3 constraints were used in fixing the plane, i.e., in determining the values of $\bar{y}$, b_1, and b_2.

If a regression coefficient is found not to be statistically significant, we have to revise our equation. The independent variable which does not significantly influence the dependent variable is deleted, and new regression coefficients are computed.

If b_1 is significant, its confidence interval is given by $b_1 \pm t s_{b_1}$.

If we want to establish whether a regression coefficient b_j differs significantly from a value (e.g., a theoretical value) b_j^0, we apply the t test:

$$t = \frac{|b_j - b_j^0|}{s_b} \tag{17-19}$$

The null hypothesis is rejected at the stipulated level of significance if t exceeds the critical value given in Table A-8, with $\nu = n - k - 1$ degrees of freedom.

SIGNIFICANCE OF MULTIPLE REGRESSION AS A WHOLE

Sometimes the assumed regression equation may prove to be statistically not significant. Whether this is so is determined by a comparison of the variance contributed by the regression and the error variance s_y^2, using the F test.

For 3 coefficients, b_0, b_1, and b_2 ($k = 2$) the sum of squares of deviations in y accounted for by regression is:

$$\Sigma c^2 = b_1 \Sigma YX_1 + b_2 \Sigma YX_2$$

We compute therefore F as

$$F = \frac{(\Sigma c^2)/k}{s_y^2} \tag{17-20}$$

with the number of degrees of freedom $v_1 = k = 2$ for the numerator, and $v_2 = n - k - 1 = n - 3$ for the denominator.

If the computed F is greater than the value tabulated in Table A-10 for the given level of significance, then the hypothesis that all the true partial regression coefficients are equal to zero is rejected.

MULTIPLE-CORRELATION COEFFICIENT

The square of the population multiple-correlation coefficient is defined as the fraction of the total variance of y which is contributed by its regression upon the variables x_1, x_2, ... This coefficient may be estimated from the square of the sample multiple-correlation coefficient:

$$r^2 = \frac{\Sigma c^2}{\Sigma Y^2} \tag{17-21}$$

where r is the multiple-correlation coefficient. As in the case of simple linear regression, a value of zero gives no correlation between y and the variables x_1, x_2, ..., whereas a value of 1 means that all the sample points lie exactly on the regression plane (in the case of three independent variables).

To test the significance of r, we use Table A-11, with the total number of variables of ($k + 1$), and the number of degrees of freedom equal to $v = n - k - 1$. We reject the null hypothesis that the population multiple correlation coefficient is zero if $|r|$ exceeds the tabulated value at the specified level of significance. When the hypothesis is rejected, we say that the regression of y on the variables x_1, x_2, ... accounts for a significant amount of variation in y.

The degree of association between any two variables can be checked in a manner similar to that described in Chapter 16. Thus

$$r_{yx_1} = \frac{\Sigma X_1 Y}{\sqrt{\Sigma X_1^2 \Sigma Y^2}}, \qquad r_{yx_2} = \frac{\Sigma X_2 Y}{\sqrt{\Sigma X_2^2 \Sigma Y^2}}$$

$$r_{x_1 x_2} = \frac{\Sigma X_1 X_2}{\sqrt{\Sigma X_1^2 \Sigma X_2^2}}, \qquad \text{etc.} \tag{17-22}$$

SOLVED PROBLEM

17-1. An experiment was conducted at the University of Saskatchewan to determine the relation between the thermal conductivity of sandy textured soils and their moisture content and dry density. The following data were collected in the field by means of a thermal conductivity probe and an Uhland core sampler: (ρ denotes the dry density of soil in lb/ft^3)

Sample number	Thermal conductivity, (Btu in.)/(°F hr ft²) K	Moisture content, by volume in.³/ft, M	$e^{0.028\rho}$
1	7.9	1.80	10.80
2	6.7	0.84	14.20
3	9.4	0.87	17.90
4	5.2	1.31	10.80
5	4.7	1.41	8.30
6	11.6	3.54	11.13
7	6.8	2.92	6.48
8	7.9	2.68	6.00
9	5.0	1.17	12.10
10	9.7	4.76	6.87
11	12.8	3.63	11.20
12	13.4	1.77	12.80
13	7.7	2.79	9.65
14	11.5	2.78	12.80

(a) Fit an equation of the form:

$$K = a_0 + a_1 M + a_2 e^{0.028\rho}$$

(b) Use the F test to check whether or not this form of an equation is statistically significant;

(c) Use the t test to check the significance of the partial regression coefficients at the 5 percent level;

(d) Calculate the multiple-correlation coefficient r, and test its significance.

Solution:

(a) The computation is shown in the table on page 217.

Equations 17-6 become (a being used instead of b):

$$18.113a_1 - 28.253a_2 = 21.924$$

$$-28.253a_1 + 136.651a_2 = 30.209$$

Solving for a_1 and a_2 by elimination, we get

$$a_1 = 2.2955; \quad a_2 = 0.6957$$

Now

$$\bar{y} = a_0 + a_1 \bar{x}_1 + a_2 \bar{x}_2$$

or

$$8.593 = a_0 + 2.2955 \times 2.305 + 0.6957 \times 10.788$$

Hence

$$a_0 = -4.203$$

Sample number	$y \equiv \bar{K}$	$x_1 \equiv M$	$x_2 \equiv e^{0.028D}$	$Y = y - \bar{y}$	$X_1 = x_1 - \bar{x}_1$	$X_2 = x_2 - \bar{x}_2$	YX_1	YX_2	X_1^2	X_2^2	X_1X_2	Y^2
1	7.9	1.80	10.80	−0.693	−0.505	+0.012	+0.350	−0.008	0.255	0.0001	−0.006	0.480
2	6.7	0.84	14.20	−1.893	−1.465	+3.412	+2.773	−6.459	2.146	11.642	−4.999	3.583
3	9.4	0.87	17.90	+0.807	−1.435	+7.113	−1.158	+5.740	2.059	50.595	−10.207	0.651
4	5.2	1.31	10.80	−3.393	−0.995	+0.012	+3.376	−0.041	0.990	0.0001	−0.012	11.512
5	4.7	1.41	8.30	−3.893	−0.895	−2.488	+3.484	+9.686	0.801	6.190	+2.227	15.155
6	11.6	3.54	11.13	+3.007	+1.235	+0.342	+3.714	+1.028	1.525	0.117	+0.422	9.042
7	6.8	2.92	6.48	−1.793	+0.615	−4.308	−1.103	+7.724	0.378	18.559	−2.649	3.215
8	7.9	2.68	6.00	−0.693	+0.375	−4.787	−0.260	+3.317	0.141	22.915	−1.795	0.480
9	5.0	1.17	12.10	−3.593	−1.135	+1.312	+4.078	−4.714	1.288	1.721	−1.489	12.910
10	9.7	4.76	6.87	+1.107	+2.455	−3.918	+2.718	−4.337	6.027	15.351	−9.619	1.225
11	12.8	3.63	11.20	+4.208	+1.325	+0.412	+5.576	+1.734	1.756	0.170	+0.546	17.707
12	13.4	1.77	12.80	+4.808	−0.535	+2.012	−2.572	+9.674	0.286	4.048	−1.076	23.117
13	7.7	2.79	9.65	−0.893	+0.485	−1.138	−0.433	+1.016	0.235	1.295	−0.552	0.797
14	11.5	2.78	12.80	+2.907	+0.475	+2.012	+1.381	+5.849	0.226	4.048	+0.956	8.451
$\Sigma =$	120.30	32.27	151.03	0	0	0	21.924	30.209	18.113	136.651	−28.253	108.325

$$\bar{y} = \frac{\Sigma y}{n} = \frac{120.30}{14} = 8.593$$

$$\bar{x}_1 = \frac{\Sigma x_1}{n} = \frac{32.27}{14} = 2.305$$

$$\bar{x}_2 = \frac{\Sigma x_2}{n} = \frac{151.03}{14} = 10.788$$

Therefore we can write

$$y = -4.203 + 2.296x_1 + 0.696x_2$$

or

$$K = -4.203 + 2.296M + 0.696e^{0.028\rho}$$

(b) Compute

$$\Sigma c^2 = a_1 \Sigma YX_1 + a_2 \Sigma YX_2$$
$$= 2.2955 \times 21.924 + 0.6957 \times 30.209$$
$$= 71.3429$$

From Eq. 17-15,

$$s_y^2 = \frac{108.325 - 71.3429}{14 - 3} = 3.362$$

Hence

$$s_y = 1.834 \text{ (Btu in.)}/(\degree\text{F hr ft}^2)$$

From Eq. 17-20,

$$F = \frac{\Sigma c^2/k}{s_y^2} = \frac{71.3429}{3.362 \times 2} = 10.610$$

For $\nu_1 = 2$, $\nu_2 = n - 3 = 14 - 3 = 11$, Table A-10 gives $F = 7.20$ at the 1 percent level of significance. Since the calculated $F = 10.610$ is greater than 7.20, we reject the hypothesis that the regression is not significant. The thermal conductivity depends therefore on moisture content and dry density.

(c) Now

$$\Sigma X_1^2 \Sigma X_2^2 - (\Sigma X_1 X_2)^2 = 18.113 \times 136.651 - (-28.253)^2 = 1{,}676.927$$

Using Eqs. 17-11,

$$e_{11} = \frac{\Sigma X_2^2}{1{,}676.927} = \frac{136.651}{1{,}676.927} = 0.08149$$

$$e_{22} = \frac{\Sigma X_1^2}{1{,}676.927} = \frac{18.113}{1{,}676.927} = 0.01080$$

Then from Eqs. 17-17,

$$s_{a_1} = 1.834 \times \sqrt{0.08149} = 0.524$$
$$s_{a_2} = 1.834 \times \sqrt{0.01080} = 0.191$$

From Eq. 17-18, for a_1,

$$t_{a_1} = \frac{|a_1|}{s_{a_1}} = \frac{2.2955}{0.524} = 4.381$$

From Table A-8, for $\nu = n - k - 1 = 14 - 2 - 1 = 11$, $t = 3.106$ at the 1 percent level of significance and 4.437 at the 0.1 percent level. Since $t_{a_1} > 3.106$, the coefficient a_1 is significant at the 1 percent level and indeed at nearly the 0.1 percent level. Also, for a_2,

$$t_{a_2} = \frac{|a_2|}{0.191} = \frac{0.6957}{0.191} = 3.642$$

Again a_2 is significant at the 1 percent level since $t_{a_2} > 3.106$.

(d) From Eq. 17-21, the square of the multiple correlation coefficient is:

$$r^2 = \frac{\Sigma c^2}{\Sigma Y^2} = \frac{71.3429}{108.325} = 0.6586$$

Hence

$$r = 0.812$$

From Table A-11, with $k + 1 = 3$ variables and $\nu = n - k - 1 = 14 - 2 - 1 = 11$, $r = 0.753$ at the 1 percent level of significance. Since the calculated value is greater than the tabulated one, we conclude that the regression of y on the x variables accounts for a significant amount of variation in y.

PROBLEMS

17-1. It is believed that the extent of a certain reaction (y) depends on the temperature of the ingredient A (x_1), temperature of ingredient B (x_2), and rate of flow (x_3), the relation being of the form $y = a + b_1 x_1 + b_2 x_2 + b_3 x_3$.

The test results are as follows:

x_1	x_2	x_3	y
11	58	11	126
32	21	13	92
15	22	28	107
26	55	27	120
9	41	21	103
31	18	20	84
12	56	20	113
29	40	27	110
13	57	30	104
10	21	12	83
33	40	19	85
31	58	29	104

(a) Determine the constants of the hyperplane in four-dimensional space.

(b) Use the F test to check the significance of this form of regression equation.

(c) Use the t test to check the significance of the partial regression coefficients b_1, b_2, and b_3 at the 5 percent level.

(d) Compute the multiple correlation coefficient r, and test its significance.

(e) Find the linear correlation coefficients for y and x_1, x_2, and x_3, respectively.

17-2. Grains used to propel rockets are made by extrusion through a die under pressure. The grain diameter y is dependent not only on the die shape, but also on the powder temperature x_1, the die temperature x_2, and the rate of extrusion x_3.

Previous experiments have indicated that there is a relation of the form

$$y = a + b_1 x_1 + b_2 x_2 + b_3 x_3$$

An experiment was conducted on a particular type of grain with the following coded results:

x_1, °F	x_2, °F	x_3, in./min	y
21	41	12	81
35	29	15	92
31	30	24	105
20	35	21	101
25	31	19	97
37	47	13	93
30	45	16	85
34	31	25	87
29	34	22	102
22	37	9	94
27	28	8	86
33	39	14	84
30	33	17	109
28	38	23	110
23	36	18	103

(a) Find the partial regression coefficients a, b_1, b_2, and b_3.

(b) Compute the residual variance of the grain diameter y.

(c) Check on the significance of the regression as a whole by means of an F test.

(d) Use the t test to check the significance of the partial regression coefficients b_1, b_2, and b_3 at the 1 percent level of significance.

(e) Calculate the multiple correlation coefficient r, and test its significance.

chapter 18

Analysis of Variance

In Chapter 14 we showed that if a process of manufacture or a system of testing involves a number of independent factors each of which contributes to the scatter of results, and therefore to variance, then the variance for the whole system is equal to the sum of the component variances of the individual factors. It is important to remember that it is variance and not standard deviation that is additive.

METHOD OF ANALYSIS

This property of variance is the basis of a numerical technique, known as *analysis of variance*, which enables us to compute the variance of the component factors and to assess the relative importance of the various components. For example, if we take k samples of a product, each sample consisting of n items, the analysis of variance enables us to split the variance of all kn items into variance *between samples* (due to variation in the process, say, from day to day) and variance *within samples* (which represents the inherent variation, or the experimental error). Each variance is calculated as the sum of squares of deviations divided by the appropriate number of degrees of freedom, and the variances are compared by the F test. The procedure is best illustrated by an example.

Example. Four different air injection systems ($k = 4$) are used, and we want to test whether there is a significant difference between them. We choose $n = 5$ items of each system and measure the efficiency of the injection in each item. The results can be tabulated as shown in the table at the top of page 222. The table gives three estimates of variance. The first is the overall variance which is based on the total sum of squares of deviations for all $kn = 4 \times 5$ observations and represents thus the variance of all individuals considered as forming a single sample.

The right-hand column of the table gives this sum of squares as 1,273 and the number of degrees of freedom is $(4 \cdot \times 5) - 1 = 19$. Hence the mean square is $1,273/19 = 67.0$.

The second estimate of population variance is obtained from the sum of squares of deviations within the samples, and is the sum of values which are obtained in calculating the variance for each group separately, namely,

$$292 + 256 + 216 + 64 = 828$$

Sample (System)	A	B	C	D	All systems
Efficiency x	35	21	35	21	112
	24	31	27	17	99
	46	17	39	21	123
	30	37	20	23	110
	40	29	29	28	126
Σx.............	175	135	150	110	570
$\bar{x}$.................	35	27	30	22	28.5
Σx^2	6,417	3,901	4,716	2,484	17,518
$\dfrac{(\Sigma x)^2}{n}$............	6,125	3,645	4,500	2,420	16,245
Sum of squares of deviations[1] = $\Sigma x^2 - \dfrac{(\Sigma x)^2}{n}$....	292	256	216	64	1,273

The number of degrees of freedom is the sum of the numbers for each sample, that is, $4 \times (5 - 1) = 16$. Hence the mean square is $828/16 = 51.75$.

The third and last estimate is obtained from the sample mean. Their deviations from the mean of means, $\bar{x} = 28.5$, are $35 - 28.5$, $27 - 28.5$, $30 - 28.5$, and $22 - 28.5$; that is, 6.5, -1.5, 1.5, -6.5. The sum of squares of deviations is thus $6.5^2 + 1.5^2 + 1.5^2 + 6.5^2 = 89$. The number of degrees of freedom is one less than the number of samples, that is, 3. Thus the mean square is $89/3 = 29.67$. This is an estimate of variance of the mean $s_{\bar{x}}^2$ of $n = 5$ items. This variance is related to the sample variance s^2 by the equation:

$$s_{\bar{x}} = \frac{s}{\sqrt{n}} \tag{18-1}$$

so that $s^2 = 29.67 \times 5 = 148.35$. The estimate is based on 3 degrees of freedom, so that the sum of squares is $148.35 \times 3 = 445.05$.

These results can be summarized as follows:

Source of variance	Sum of squares	Degrees of freedom	Mean square
Within samples (systems)	828	16	51.75
Between samples (systems).......	445	3	148.35
Total	1,273	19	67.0

The row of totals shows that both the total sum of squares and the total number of degrees of freedom have been separated into two parts corresponding to the factors in the variation of the data.

[1] Since $\Sigma (x - \bar{x})^2 = \Sigma x^2 - \dfrac{(\Sigma x)^2}{n}$ (see Chapter 4).

The last column gives the *mean squares*, which are ratios of the sum of squares (column 2) to the appropriate number of degrees of freedom (column 3).

USUAL METHOD OF COMPUTATION

The method just outlined explains the analysis of variance but is longer than necessary for routine use. A shorter way of computing the mean squares is to omit the calculations for the individual observations, so that only the values of Σx need be found in the table of the preceding example. We proceed as follows:

(*a*) Find the sum of all observations:
$$\Sigma x = 175 + 135 + 150 + 110 = 570$$

(*b*) Find the term:[2]
$$\frac{(\Sigma x)^2}{kn} = \frac{570^2}{4 \times 5} = 16,245$$

(*c*) Find the sum of squares:
$$\Sigma x^2 = 35^2 + 24^2 + \cdots + 21^2 + 31^2 + \cdots + 23^2 + 28^2 = 17,518$$

(*d*) Hence, obtain the total sum of squares of deviations:
$$\Sigma x^2 - \frac{(\Sigma x)^2}{kn} = 17,518 - 16,245 = 1,273$$

(*e*) Compute the sum of squares for sample means:
$$\frac{\Sigma(\Sigma x)^2}{n} - \frac{(\Sigma x)^2}{kn} = \frac{175^2 + 135^2 + 150^2 + 110^2}{5} - 16,245 = 445$$

We can arrange these results in a tabular form, the numbers of degrees of freedom being as before. The values for "within samples" are obtained by subtraction, and the mean squares are calculated by dividing the appropriate sum of squares by the number of degrees of freedom.

Source of variance	Sum of squares	Degrees of freedom	Mean square
Between samples.....................	445	3	148.35
Within samples	828	16	51.75
Total	1,273	19	—

Such a computation is quicker, but it does not offer a check on arithmetic.

We may note that it is usual to arrange the table for the analysis of variance in such a way that the "Totals" appear in the bottom line, i.e., the subtraction is made "upwards."

[2] Known as "correction due to the mean."

TEST ON HOMOGENEITY OF VARIANCES

Having obtained the two values of mean squares, we test their homogeneity by means of the F test. Both these values of mean squares are estimates of the variance of the population, so that if the F test indicates no significant difference, we would conclude that the different air injection systems do not introduce a variation in excess of the variation between individual tests for the same injection system. This is so in our case, since

$$F = \frac{148.35}{51.75} = 2.86$$

with 3 degrees of freedom for the numerator and 16 degrees of freedom for the denominator. Table A-10 gives $F = 3.24$ at the 5 percent level of significance. We conclude, therefore, that the different injection systems do not differ in their efficiency.

We should note that the test we apply is one-sided[3] as we want to answer the question: Is the variance between samples significantly greater than the variance within samples? It cannot be the other way round, as the scatter in any arrangement cannot be less than the random variation between individuals.

It is, of course, possible in a particular case for the variance within samples to be greater than the variance between samples, but the difference cannot be significant.

SIMPLIFYING THE COMPUTATIONS

In the analysis of variance we are primarily concerned with comparing variances, so that reducing the data in a constant proportion does not affect our conclusions. We can, therefore, simplify the data and achieve a considerable saving in computation by subtraction of a constant number or a division by a constant number, or both. If the actual values of variance are required, the division has to be taken into account. The use of this simplification, known as coding, is illustrated in one of the examples in Chapter 3.

MULTIFACTOR ANALYSIS

The analysis of variance can be extended to cases where a number of factors affect the observations. A simple case with three components is where we have, say, k different cements, each of which is tested once by n operators. We want to analyze the variance into the components: "between operators," "between cements," and "residual." The variance between operators is that which would be obtained if there were no varia-

---

[3] The F test is a one-sided test.

tion between the individual cements and no inherent variation in the method of test. Similarly, the variance between cements is that which would be obtained if there were no variation between the operators and no inherent variation in the method of test. The residual includes the error variance (which is similar to the variance within samples in the preceding example) and also the effect of interaction between the variables. The latter is the influence of the variation in one variable on another, for example, if the effect of different operators varies with the type of cement. (We can imagine that operator A tends to read "high" when values are high but reads "low" when values are low). If we want to estimate the error variance free from interactions, it would be necessary to repeat the tests—an operation known as *replication*. This is considered in Chapter 20.

It should be realized that the present chapter is no more than an introduction to the analysis of variance—one of the most powerful methods of statistical analysis.[4]

SOLVED PROBLEMS

18-1. The influence of angle of dip of strata in a certain area on the form of the drainage basins was investigated. A ridge was divided into segments named "low dip," "medium-low dip," etc., as shown below. In each segment, the length of stream channels on the ridge flanks was taken from the dip slope. The data on the lengths of streams in miles are summarized as follows:

Low dip	Medium-low dip	Medium dip	Steep dip
$\bar{x} = 0.261$	$\bar{x} = 0.296$	$\bar{x} = 0.312$	$\bar{x} = 0.135$
$s = 0.21$	$s = 0.17$	$s = 0.19$	$s = 0.08$
$n = 44$	$n = 44$	$n = 44$	$n = 44$

Does the steepness of the dip influence the length of the stream, i.e., do the means of all samples belong to the same population?

Solution:

We set up a null hypothesis of no significant difference between the four means. Calculate

$$F = \frac{\text{variance from sample means}}{\text{average variance within the samples}}$$

Now

$$\bar{\bar{x}} = \frac{0.261 + 0.296 + 0.312 + 0.135}{4} = 0.251$$

Thus

$$s_{\bar{x}}^2 = \frac{(0.261 - 0.251)^2 + (0.296 - 0.251)^2 + (0.312 - 0.251)^2 + (0.135 - 0.251)^2}{4 - 1}$$

$$= 0.00643$$

[4] It may be noted that the t test is the simplest case of the analysis of variance.

But

$$s^2 = ns_{\bar{x}}^2 = 44 \times 0.00643$$
$$= 0.2831$$

Estimate of variance from the individual measurements within the samples

$$= \frac{n_1 s_1^2 + n_2 s_2^2 + n_3 s_3^2 + n_4 s_4^2}{n_1 + n_2 + n_3 + n_4 - 4}$$

$$= \frac{44[(0.21)^2 + (0.17)^2 + (0.19)^2 + (0.08)^2]}{4 \times 44 - 4}$$

$$= 0.0295$$

Therefore

$$F = \frac{0.2831}{0.0295} = 9.5816$$

for $\nu_1 = 3$ and $\nu_2 = 4 \times 44 - 4 = 172$, Table A-10 indicates that the probability for such a value of F occurring by chance is less than 0.1 percent. Therefore, the difference in means is very significant, and it is concluded that the steepness of the dip influences the length of the stream.

18-2. An experiment was carried out to measure the strain sensitivity of Stresscoat for different curing temperatures, which were applied with no sensible error. We wish to determine whether the observed differences in the mean values of the strain sensitivity for the different temperatures have been influenced by random sampling errors. The following results were obtained.

	Curing temperature, °F				
	80	92	105	118	132
Strain sensitivity ($\times 10^{-5}$)	83	75	56	50	49
	70	62	59	52	35
	78	70	48	38	48
	71	81	54	42	47
	73	71	61	53	41
	81	79	58	41	38

Number of columns, $k = 5$
Sample size in each column $n = 6$
Total number of observations $kn = 30$

	Curing temperature, °F					Totals for all temperatures
	80	92	105	118	132	
Σx	456	438	336	276	258	1,764
$\bar{x}$	76	73	56	46	43	$\bar{\bar{x}} = 58.8$
Σx^2	34,804	32,212	18,922	12,902	11,264	110,104
$\dfrac{(\Sigma x)^2}{n}$	34,656	31,974	18,816	12,696	11,094	103,723.2
$\Sigma x^2 - \dfrac{(\Sigma x)^2}{n}$ ..	148	238	106	206	170	6,380.8

The mean square is

$$\frac{6,380.8}{kn-1} = \frac{6,380.8}{29} = 220.03$$

The total for the sum of squares of the samples is

$$148 + 238 + 106 + 206 + 170 = 868$$

with the number of degrees of freedom $\nu = k(n-1) = 5(6-1) = 25$. Therefore

$$\text{Mean square} = \frac{868}{25} = 34.72$$

The mean square deviation of sample means from the mean of means is

$$s_{\bar{x}}^2 = \frac{(76-58.8)^2 + (73-58.8)^2 + (56-58.8)^2 + (46-58.8)^2 + (43-58.8)^2}{5-1}$$

$$= \frac{918.80}{4} = 229.7$$

Hence

$$s^2 = s_{\bar{x}}^2 \times n = 229.7 \times 6 = 1,378.2$$

Summarizing, we have

Source of variance	Sum of squares	Degrees of freedom	Mean square
Within samples	868	25	34.72
Between samples...................	5,512.8	4	1,378.2
Total	6,380.8	29	220.03

The variance ratio is

$$F = \frac{1,378.2}{34.72} = 39.69$$

For the degrees of freedom $\nu_1 = 4$, $\nu_2 = 25$, Table A-10 gives at the 1 percent level of significance $F = 4.18$. Since the calculated $F \gg 4.18$, it can be confidently concluded that the curing temperature influences the coating strain sensitivity, i.e., the observed difference in the means is not due to random errors.

Using the simplified and more usual method of computation,

1. The sum of all observations:

$$\Sigma x = 456 + 438 + 336 + 276 + 258$$
$$= 1,764$$

2. The correction for the mean:

$$\frac{(\Sigma x)^2}{kn} = \frac{(1,764)^2}{30} = 103,723.2$$

3. The total sum of squares:

$$\Sigma x^2 - \frac{(\Sigma x)^2}{kn} = 83^2 + 70^2 + \cdots + 38^2 - 103,723.2 = 6,380.8$$

4. The sum of squares for sample means:

$$\frac{\Sigma(\Sigma x)^2}{n} - \frac{(\Sigma x)^2}{kn} = \frac{456^2 + 438^2 + 336^2 + 276^2 + 258^2}{6} - 103,723.2$$

$$= 5,512.8$$

Tabulating:

Source of variance	Sum of squares	Degrees of freedom	Mean square
Between samples	5,512.8	4	1,378.2
Within samples....................	868.0	25	34.72
Total	6,380.8	29	—

Then continue as before.

18-3. The 24-hr water absorption (in percent of dry weight) of samples of concrete taken from five different types of precast concrete curbs made with different aggregates is shown in the table below.[5]

Curb type	A	B	C	D	E	All
Absorption x, percent	6.7 5.8 5.8 5.5	5.1 4.7 5.1 5.2	4.4 4.9 4.6 4.5	6.7 7.2 6.8 6.3	6.5 5.8 4.7 5.9	
Σx	23.8	20.1	18.4	27.0	22.9	112.2

It is required to determine whether there is a significant difference in the water absorption values of the curbs of different types.

Solution:

(*a*) The sum of all observations,

$$\Sigma x = 112.2$$

(*b*) Correction due to the mean,

$$C = \frac{(\Sigma x)^2}{kn} = \frac{(112.2)^2}{20} = 629.44$$

where k = number of types of curbs
n = sample size

(*c*) Total sum of squares = $\Sigma x^2 - C$

$$= 6.7^2 + 5.8^2 + \cdots + 5.9^2 - C$$

$$= 643.80 - 629.44$$

$$= 14.36$$

[5] P. J. F. Wright, "Statistical Methods in Concrete Research," *Magazine of Concrete Research*, Vol. 5, No. 15 (March 1954).

(d) Sum of squares for sample means $= \dfrac{\Sigma(\Sigma x)^2}{n} - C$

$$= \frac{23.8^2 + 20.1^2 + \cdots + 22.9^2}{4} - C$$

$$= 640.60 - 629.44$$

$$= 11.16$$

In tabular form:

Source of variance	Sum of squares	Degrees of freedom	Mean square
Between samples..................	11.16	4	2.79
Within samples	3.20	15	0.213
Total	14.36	19	—

$$\text{Variance ratio, } F = \frac{2.79}{0.213} = 13.1$$

For $\nu_1 = 4$ and $\nu_2 = 15$, Table A-10 gives $F = 4.89$ at the 1 percent level of significance, and we conclude therefore that the different types of curbs differ significantly in their absorption values.

18-4.   Creep, after a given period of time, was determined on mortar specimens made with 11 cements. It is suggested that creep is a function of the chemical composition of cement in the form:

$$y = a_1 x_1 + a_2 x_2 + a_3 x_3 + a_4 x_4 + a_5 x_5$$

where y = creep, and $x_1, \ldots, x_5$ are the compounds[6] of which the cement consists, expressed as a percentage of weight. (Because of the physical nature of the problem, it is assumed that the constant $a_o = 0$.) Thus, the coefficients $a_1, \ldots,$ a_5 represent the contribution to creep of one percent of the appropriate compound. This type of relationship implies that the same amount of any compound has the same effect, regardless of the total quantity of this or any other compound present. This also means that there is no interaction between the various compounds—an assumption not in disagreement with our general knowledge of the properties of cement.

On the basis of the values y and x given in the table at the top of page 230, we want to determine the coefficients in the equation postulated above, and to establish their significance.

Solution:

The matrix for the least square analysis is set out on page 230, the variables being entered in the expected order of importance (x_1, x_5, x_2, x_3, and x_4); this order does not, of course, affect the values of the regression coefficients.

[6] The actual compounds are:

$x_1 = 3\text{CaO} \cdot \text{SiO}_2$
$x_2 = 2\text{CaO} \cdot \text{SiO}_2$
$x_3 = 3\text{CaO} \cdot \text{Al}_2\text{O}_3$
$x_4 = 4\text{CaO} \cdot \text{Al}_2\text{O}_3 \cdot \text{Fe}_2\text{O}_3$
$x_5 = \text{Na}_2\text{O} \text{ (equivalent)}$

Cement number	x_1	x_2	x_3	x_4	x_5	y	Σx
1	42.2	25.3	15.6	6.9	0.75	52	90.75
2	23.1	40.0	15.3	9.1	1.13	50	88.63
3	37.2	29.6	14.9	7.1	0.80	35	89.60
4	37.3	31.2	3.5	16.6	0.65	37	89.25
5	36.6	25.4	14.6	11.1	0.78	49	88.48
6	32.6	36.0	13.8	6.0	0.66	45	89.06
7	35.0	36.5	12.5	5.4	0.56	32	89.96
8	50.1	26.5	10.7	1.1	0.24	47	88.64
9	64.5	10.0	12.1	7.5	0.23	32	94.33
10	41.0	39.0	3.7	10.0	0.34	48	94.04
11	29.0	52.0	5.3	9.3	0.23	42	95.83

For the sum of squares of residuals to be a minimum, the partial differential coefficients of the sum with respect to the coefficients $a_1, \ldots, a_5$ must all be zero. Hence,

$$\Sigma y x_1 = a_1 \Sigma x_1^2 + a_2 \Sigma x_1 x_2 + a_3 \Sigma x_1 x_3 + a_4 \Sigma x_1 x_4 + a_5 \Sigma x_1 x_5$$

$$.$$
$$.$$
$$.$$

$$\Sigma y x_5 = a_1 \Sigma x_5 x_1 + a_2 \Sigma x_5 x_2 + a_3 \Sigma x_5 x_3 + a_4 \Sigma x_5 x_4 + a_5 \Sigma x_5^2$$

This can be written in matrix form as:

$$
\begin{bmatrix}
\Sigma x_1^2 & \Sigma x_1 x_5 & \Sigma x_1 x_2 & \Sigma x_1 x_3 & \Sigma x_1 x_4 \\
\Sigma x_5 x_1 & \Sigma x_5^2 & \Sigma x_5 x_2 & \Sigma x_5 x_3 & \Sigma x_5 x_4 \\
\Sigma x_2 x_1 & \Sigma x_2 x_5 & \Sigma x_2^2 & \Sigma x_2 x_3 & \Sigma x_2 x_4 \\
\Sigma x_3 x_1 & \Sigma x_3 x_5 & \Sigma x_3 x_2 & \Sigma x_3^2 & \Sigma x_3 x_4 \\
\Sigma x_4 x_1 & \Sigma x_4 x_5 & \Sigma x_4 x_2 & \Sigma x_4 x_3 & \Sigma x_4^2
\end{bmatrix}
\begin{bmatrix}
a_1 \\ a_5 \\ a_2 \\ a_3 \\ a_4
\end{bmatrix}
=
\begin{bmatrix}
\Sigma x_1 y \\ \Sigma x_5 y \\ \Sigma x_2 y \\ \Sigma x_3 y \\ \Sigma x_4 y
\end{bmatrix}
$$

or $AX = Y$ where A is the known matrix on the left, X is the unknown vector, and Y is the known vector on the right. The numerical form of matrix A is shown below:

x_1	x_5	x_2	x_3	x_4	y
17,909.16	228.891	12,716.93	4,740.24	3,394.11	18,016.6
228.891	4.5385	206.027	78.508	55.098	278.01
12,716.93	206.027	12,390.0	3,705.26	2,939.44	15,160.1
4,740.24	78.508	3,705.26	1,574.24	911.93	5,253.9
3,394.11	55.098	2,939.44	911.93	888.71	3,825.5

The least square analysis yields:

$$a_1 = 0.1507206 \qquad a_4 = -0.578853$$

$$a_2 = 0.2161381 \qquad a_5 = 15.54991$$

$$a_3 = -0.346855$$

Thus the expected creep of mortar for the given conditions and range of composition of cements is:

$$y = 0.15x_1 + 0.22x_2 - 0.35x_3 - 0.58x_4 + 15.5x_5$$

The statistical significance of the coefficients of the preceding equation can now be tested by the analysis of variance.

For each coefficient in turn, we find the sum of squares accounted for by that coefficient. Thus if $\hat{y}$ is the value of y predicted by

$$\hat{y} = a_1 x_1$$

and since

$$\bar{y} = a_1 \bar{x}$$

we have

$$\hat{y} - \bar{y} = a_1(x_1 - \bar{x})$$

The total sum of squares is $\Sigma(y - \bar{y})^2$. This consists of $\Sigma(\hat{y} - \bar{y})^2$ accounted for by regression and a residual of $\Sigma(y - \hat{y})^2$, that is,

$$\Sigma(y - \bar{y})^2 = \Sigma(\hat{y} - \bar{y})^2 + \Sigma(y - \hat{y})^2$$

(since $\Sigma(\hat{y} - \bar{y}) = 0$).

Thus, the sum of squares accounted for by x_1 is

$$\Sigma(\hat{y} - \bar{y})^2 = \frac{\left[\Sigma xy - \dfrac{\Sigma x \Sigma y}{n}\right]^2}{\Sigma(x - \bar{x})^2}$$

The residual sum of squares is

$$\Sigma(y - \hat{y})^2 = \Sigma(y - \bar{y})^2 - \Sigma(\hat{y} - \bar{y})^2$$

The F test applied to the ratio of the mean square accounted for by the regression coefficient to the mean square of the residual gives the significance of the regression coefficient.

Source of variance	Sum of squares	Degrees of freedom	Mean square	Level of significance, in percent
Total (sum of squares of y values)	205.49000	11	—	
Regression on x_1	181.24688	1	181.24	0.1
Residual after fitting x_1	24.24312	10	2.424	
Reduction on fitting x_5	14.13201	1	14 13	1
Residual after fitting x_1, x_5	10.11111	9	1.123	
Reduction on fitting x_2	5.32681	1	5.327	5
Residual after fitting x_1, x_5, x_2	4.78430	8	0.598	not significant
Reduction on fitting x_3, x_4	0.12691	2	0.063	
Residual	4.65739	6	0.776	

It can be seen that the variables x_1, x_2, x_5 are significant at least at the 5 percent level; and once these coefficients have been fitted, the variables x_3 and x_4 do not contribute significantly to the regression.

The regression equation may, therefore, be modified to:

$$y = a_1 x_1 + a_2 x_2 + a_5 x_5$$

The new regression coefficients then become:

$$a_1 = 0.4473671$$
$$a_2 = 0.4934702$$
$$a_5 = 16.2925$$

hence

$$y = 0.45x_1 + 0.49x_2 + 16.3x_5$$

The 95 percent confidence limits for these coefficients were found to be ±0.2634, ±0.1740, and ±38.13, respectively. These show that creep cannot be reliably predicted on the basis of the data available. It seems probable, however, that the compounds x_1 and x_2 have a similar influence on creep, and that the influence of the compound x_5 is not negligible, even though its percentage content is comparatively low.

From the table of original data, it can be seen that the sum of the values of x_1, x_2, x_3, x_4, x_5 is approximately constant, and that the values of $(x_1 + x_2)$ and $(x_3 + x_4)$ are complementary; the order of magnitude of the values of x_5 is small compared with the other variables. Hence, a high value of $(x_1 + x_2)$ means a low value of $(x_3 + x_4)$, and vice versa, and there is a linear relationship between these two quantities. Thus, creep may be a function of either quantity, the other one being looked upon as a complementary filling.

This is confirmed by the analysis of variance in the following table in which regression on x_3 and x_4 was fitted first. The regression coefficients of x_3 and x_4 were found to be significant, and those of x_1 and x_2 to be not significant.

Source of variance	Sum of squares	Degrees of freedom	Mean square	Level of significance, in percent
Total............................	205.49000	11	—	
Regression on x_3, x_4...............	192.31079	2	96.15	0.1
Residual after fitting x_3, x_4	13.17921	9	1.46	
Reduction on fitting x_1, x_2, x_5	8.52182	3	2.84	10
Residual	4.65739	6	0.77	

The practical meaning of this situation is that the influences of the silicates (x_1 and x_2) and the aluminates (x_3 and x_4) on creep seem to be opposed to one another, but the regression analysis cannot tell which compound causes creep and which is inert, thereby apparently decreasing the magnitude of creep. A better insight into this mechanism must be obtained from further studies.

PROBLEMS

18-1. The resistance of wire from six sources was tested by taking five samples from each coil (source). Is there a significant difference between the resistances of the wires from the six sources?

Source	Resistance of sample				
	1	2	3	4	5
A	7.9	7.3	7.2	7.5	7.7
B	9.0	8.8	8.8	8.6	8.6
C	9.0	8.3	8.7	8.5	8.7
D	9.6	9.5	9.4	9.4	9.4
E	5.5	5.8	5.7	5.5	5.8
F	8.0	8.4	8.2	8.4	7.6

18-2. A student was checking the precision of five planimeters of different makes. He conducted his experiment by measuring with each planimeter a definite area four times. The coded results are shown below.

Planimeter				
1	2	3	4	5
6.6	5.6	7.5	7.1	5.2
6.0	6.2	5.2	7.0	6.3
6.5	7.1	5.4	6.5	6.8
7.6	5.3	6.8	7.4	7.1

Prepare the analysis of variance table and check whether the planimeters are homogeneous at the 5 percent level of significance.

18-3. A company manufacturing rubber seals for expansion joints suspected that the tensile strength of their product varied with different machines. The results are given below.

Machine	Strength, psi			
A	4,900	5,300	5,200	5,100
B	5,700	5,300	5,600	5,200
C	5,200	4,800	5,100	5,000
D	4,500	5,000	5,300	5,100

Do the machines have any effect on the tensile strength of the rubber seals? Use a 1 percent level of significance.

18-4. A procedure for measuring run-off was used to determine whether or not the type of terrain has an effect on the measured run-off. The experiment was carried out four times for each type of area with the following (coded) results:

Area A	Area B	Area C
40	43	35
32	47	42
38	40	36
42	41	34

Prepare the analysis of variance table. Test for area effects at the 5 percent level of significance.

18-5.   For the data of Prob. 13-11 use the analysis of variance to test whether there is a significant difference among the means of group A, B, and C.

chapter 19

Tolerance and Control Charts

This chapter gives a brief review of some of the graphical methods of presentation of data used mainly in production. While no fundamental principles of statistics are involved, the use of charts frequently enables us rapidly to assess the behavior of a system and to take appropriate action without delay.

In general terms, the product being controlled may be judged by *attributes* or by *variables*. The former refer to a property which either is or is not possessed, e.g., a defect; thus the products are divided into two categories only. The variables refer to quantities and measurements, and it is with this type of product that we shall deal first.

SPECIFICATION AND TOLERANCE LIMITS

In design specification limits on dimensions are usually set in the form of a nominal value and a plus or minus tolerance, for example, 1.000 ± 0.004 in. (The plus and minus deviations need not be equal.) Such limits ensure that the items manufactured are serviceable and can be assembled together with other parts. These are the *specification limits*. In the actual manufacture of the items a natural variation in dimensions occurs due to chance errors; from the distribution of these errors the proportion of items whose dimensions fall within *natural tolerance limits* can be calculated. An understanding of the difference between the two types of limits is of considerable importance.

A process of manufacture is said to be *stable* or *in control* if variations between individuals are due to chance only. Under such circumstances the data obtained by sampling are consistent with the hypothesis that the observations are random values from a population.

The variability of the process can be described by the population standard deviation σ. Table A-4 shows that, when the variate is normally distributed, all but 0.27 percent of observations will lie within a total range of 6σ. It follows that, if the specification limits are greater than 6σ, the process will produce items with a very small proportion of defectives (Fig. 19-1a). If, on the other hand, the specification limits are narrower than 6σ then a sensible proportion of defectives will inevitably be manufactured

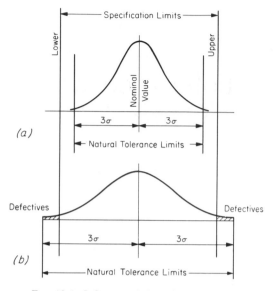

FIG. 19-1. Influence of the relation between
specification and natural tolerance limits on
the proportion of defectives.

(Fig. 19-1*b*). Should such a proportion of defectives be not acceptable the
only remedy lies in modifying the process, e.g., by using a more precise
machine. Before attempting this it may be wise to see whether the specification limits are not unduly restrictive and cannot be widened without
ill effects.

We may also note that if the natural tolerance limits are considerably
narrower than the specification limits the process of manufacture is "too
good" and, therefore, probably unnecessarily costly. In general terms, we
should aim at tolerance limits approximately coinciding with the specification limits.

STABILITY OF A PROCESS

The situation discussed in the preceding section exists when both the
mean and the standard deviation remain sensibly constant; we refer to
such a situation as *stable*. Conversely, the process is said to be *unstable* or
not in control when changes either in the mean or in variability take place.

In a general case, the method of manufacture is adjusted until the
process becomes stable. To establish this condition we take samples,
preferably all of equal size $n \not< 4$. Not less than about 25 samples are
required.

The population mean is estimated by the mean of the sample means $\bar{\bar{x}}$,
and the population standard deviation may be estimated from the variance

within samples, the average sample standard deviation, or the average sample range $\bar{R}$. The use of the last mentioned estimate is most common.

WARNING AND ACTION LIMITS

Having established the parameters of the process, we can describe limits which, if exceeded, will tell us that the process is out of control or is in danger of being so.

Two pairs of control limits are used. The first pair represents warning or *inner* limits. These are usually[1] set so that there is a 2.5 percent probability of a sample mean having a value below the lower limit, and a 2.5 percent probability of its having a value above the upper limit. The warning limits are thus drawn at a distance from the estimated population mean equal to 1.96 × standard deviation of the mean, that is, $\pm 1.96 \sigma_{\bar{x}}$.

Action or *outer* limits are usually[2] set so that there is a probability of 0.1 percent of the mean falling above the upper limit, and a probability of 0.1 percent of its falling below the lower limit. The distance of the limits from $\bar{x}$ is then $\pm 3.09 \sigma_{\bar{x}}$.

The values of $1.96 \sigma_{\bar{x}}$ and $3.09 \sigma_{\bar{x}}$ are obtained from Table A-4 for the normal distribution. We are justified in using this table even if the underlying population is not normally distributed as we are dealing with sample means. Thus once again the central limit theorem (see Chapter 10) has proved of great use.

MEAN CHART

We have defined a process in control as one whose mean and standard deviation do not significantly change. Each of these quantities can be plotted on an appropriate chart on which both the mean value and the warning and action limits are drawn.

Let us first deal with the mean chart. The population mean is estimated from the means of samples, as explained in Chapter 6, and is given by:

$$\bar{x} = \frac{\bar{x}_1 + \bar{x}_2 + \cdots + \bar{x}_k}{k} \tag{19-1}$$

where $\bar{x}_1, \bar{x}_2, \ldots$ are sample means and k is the number of samples.

To establish the warning and action limits for the mean we require an estimate of the standard deviation of the mean. Not distinguishing between estimates and true values, we can write the standard deviation of the mean as

$$\sigma_{\bar{x}} \simeq \frac{s}{\sqrt{n}} \tag{19-2}$$

[1] Other values may be used, depending on the process.
[2] A deviation from the mean of $\pm 3 \sigma_{\bar{x}}$ is also used.

where s = estimate of the population standard deviation and n = sample size. The value s can be estimated from the mean range R, using Eq. 4-11, whence

$$s = \bar{R}d \qquad (19\text{-}3)$$

The values of d are given in Table A-1. Hence the warning limits for the mean (MWL) are given by:

$$\bar{\bar{x}} \pm 1.96\,\sigma_{\bar{x}} = \bar{\bar{x}} \pm \frac{1.96s}{\sqrt{n}}$$

Thus

$$\text{MWL} = \bar{\bar{x}} \pm \frac{1.96\bar{R}d}{\sqrt{n}} \qquad (19\text{-}4)$$

It is convenient to let

$$A_w = \frac{1.96d}{\sqrt{n}} \qquad (19\text{-}5)$$

The values of A_w are given in Table A-12. Hence, the warning limits for the mean become

$$\text{MWL} = \bar{\bar{x}} \pm A_w\bar{R} \qquad (19\text{-}6)$$

By a similar argument the action limits for the mean (MAL) are:

$$\bar{\bar{x}} \pm 3.09\,\sigma_{\bar{x}} = \bar{\bar{x}} \pm \frac{3.09s}{\sqrt{n}}$$

$$\text{MAL} = \bar{\bar{x}} \pm \frac{3.09\bar{R}d}{\sqrt{n}} \qquad (19\text{-}7)$$

Let

$$A_A = \frac{3.09d}{\sqrt{n}} \qquad (19\text{-}8)$$

The action limits for the mean then become:

$$\text{MAL} = \bar{\bar{x}} \pm A_A\bar{R} \qquad (19\text{-}9)$$

The values of A_A are given in Table A-12.

If, during the operation, points fall outside the limits, we conclude (with the appropriate probability of being wrong) that the variability between samples is significantly greater than the variability within a sample. The chart gives thus the same result as the analysis of variance for between and within samples.

Example. Set up the control limits for the mean chart for the production of steel shafts. The mean of means is $\bar{\bar{x}} = 12.000$ in. and the mean range has been found to be $\bar{R} = 0.0093$ in. The samples are of size $n = 5$. From Table A-12 for $n = 5$,

$$A_w = 0.377$$

$$A_A = 0.594$$

Hence

$$\substack{\text{upper} \\ \text{lower}}\text{MWL} = \bar{\bar{x}} \pm A_w\bar{R} = 12.000 \pm 0.377 \times 0.0093$$

$$= \left.\begin{array}{l} 12.00351 \text{ in.} \\ 11.99649 \text{ in.} \end{array}\right\}$$

Now

$$\substack{\text{upper} \\ \text{lower}}\text{MAL} = \bar{\bar{x}} \pm A_A\bar{R} = 12.000 \pm 0.594 \times 0.0093$$

$$= \left.\begin{array}{l} 12.00552 \text{ in.} \\ 11.99448 \text{ in.} \end{array}\right\}$$

RANGE CHART

As we have said earlier, the mean chart is not sufficient to determine whether the process is stable. The mean of a sample may lie within the limits and yet individual observations may fall outside these limits. If this happened it would mean that the standard deviation is changing. For this reason we have to keep a record of the variability of observations within each sample, and this is best done by plotting the range of each sample on a control chart, known as a range chart.[3] In doing this we take advantage of the relation between range and standard deviation, given by Eq. 19-3.

In the range chart we mark warning and action limits in a manner similar to the limits on the mean chart. We may remember, however, that neither the range nor the standard deviation are normally distributed but have probability distributions related to the χ^2 distribution. The limits in the range chart are not symmetrically disposed about the mean range, $\bar{R}$.

We write the range warning limits (RWL):

$$\substack{\text{upper} \\ \text{lower}}\text{RWL} = \left.\begin{array}{l} D_{WU} \times \bar{R} \\ D_{Wl} \times \bar{R} \end{array}\right\} \tag{19-10}$$

and the range action limits (RAL):

$$\substack{\text{upper} \\ \text{lower}}\text{RAL} = \left.\begin{array}{l} D_{AU} \times \bar{R} \\ D_{AL} \times \bar{R} \end{array}\right\} \tag{19-11}$$

where the values of the factors D are given in Table A-13.

The coefficients for the range chart are based on normal distribution; however, even if the distribution is not normal, the control limits, especially the action limits, are reliable for most purposes.

We may note that the control limits for range widen as the sample size increases, while the mean chart becomes narrower with an increase in sample size.

Example. Find the range control limits for the data of the preceding example.

[3] The range chart thus tests the same hypothesis as Bartlett's test (see Chapter 14).

From Table A-13 for $n = 5$,

$$D_{WU} = 1.81$$
$$D_{WL} = 0.37$$
$$D_{AU} = 2.36$$
$$D_{AL} = 0.16$$

Hence

$$\substack{\text{upper} \\ \text{lower}} \text{RWL} = \frac{1.81}{0.37} \times 0.0093 = \left.\begin{array}{l} 0.016833 \text{ in.} \\ 0.003441 \text{ in.} \end{array}\right\}$$

and

$$\substack{\text{upper} \\ \text{lower}} \text{RAL} = \frac{2.36}{0.16} \times 0.0093 = \left.\begin{array}{l} 0.021948 \text{ in.} \\ 0.001488 \text{ in.} \end{array}\right\}$$

SCHEME OF OPERATION

We can now summarize the steps to be followed in the construction of mean and range charts to be used for the purpose of obtaining a continual check on the stability of a process.

(a) Determine the mean value $\bar{x}$ of the quantity which we are measuring; this is the mean value which the process could be expected to yield if it were functioning perfectly. The symbol $\bar{x}$ indicates the mean of means of a large number of random samples during a stable period.

(b) Determine the standard deviation σ of the measured quantity during this stable period. If this is not convenient, find the sample ranges during the same period, calculate the mean range $\bar{R}$, and estimate the standard deviation, using coefficient d of Table A-1.

(c) Find the values of A_w and A_A from Table A-12 for the sample sizes used, and hence establish the warning and action limits $\bar{x} \pm A_w\bar{R}$ and $\bar{x} \pm A_A\bar{R}$ respectively. Plot these limits on a chart which also shows $\bar{x}$. If any future observation falls outside the warning limits, further samples should be carefully watched, and if the trend persists, an investigation of the process should follow. An observation outside the action limits indicates that the process has gone out of control, and remedial action is immediately necessary.

(d) Find the upper and lower warning and action limits for range, using the D coefficients of Table A-13. Plot the mean range and the control limits. If any future sample range is found to be outside the action limits, the process is likely to have moved away from a stable position, and steps must be taken to find the cause and remedy the situation.

(e) If in establishing the control limits we find an occasional value outside the action limits, the value is disregarded and a new mean and new control limits are calculated. There is little theoretical justification for this except that, if the process is truly in control, a point outside the limits can be considered as not belonging to the population of items in control. Such a point is then considered to be an outlier and is rejected (cf. Chapter 11).

In general terms, if a process which was in control becomes unstable, we blame this on "assignable causes of variation," which we seek to remove. Such a cause may be identified as a specific part of the production process, but the possibility of poor sampling should not be ignored. Finally, it may be that the production process has changed (e.g., due to wear of some parts) and new control charts have to be set up.

Example. A manufacturer of a certain type of resistors decided to set up control charts for his product. Twenty-five samples of size $n = 4$ were taken. The means and range of each sample are shown below. Compute the limits for the mean and range charts for the process and check whether the process is in control. If so, estimate the standard deviation for the process. If the specification limits are 120 ± 8 ohms, is the process able to meet the specification?

Sample	Resistance in ohms		Sample	Resistance in ohms	
	Mean $\bar{x}$	Range R		Mean $\bar{x}$	Range R
1	122	10	15	120	13
2	126	6	16	125	12
3	118	5	17	118	5
4	121	8	18	119	8
5	126	11	19	124	4
6	125	5	20	121	3
7	119	4	21	125	7
8	121	3	22	121	5
9	124	11	23	120	4
10	125	14	24	121	4
11	123	10	25	119	6
12	124	9			
13	122	7		$\Sigma\bar{x} = 3,050$	$\Sigma R = 185$
14	121	11			

Hence

$$\bar{\bar{x}} = \frac{\Sigma\bar{x}}{n} = \frac{3,050}{25} = 122 \text{ ohms}$$

$$\bar{R} = \frac{\Sigma R}{n} = \frac{185}{25} = 7.4 \text{ ohms}$$

The trial control limits are computed with the aid of Tables A-12 and A-13 as follows:

For Mean Chart

$${}_{\text{lower}}^{\text{upper}}\text{Warning limits} = \bar{\bar{x}} \pm A_w \bar{R}$$

$$= 122.00 \pm 0.476 \times 7.4$$

$$= \left.\begin{array}{c} 125.52 \\ 118.48 \end{array}\right\} \text{ohms}$$

$${}_{\text{lower}}^{\text{upper}}\text{Action limits} = \bar{\bar{x}} \pm A_A \bar{R}$$

$$= 122.00 \pm 0.750 \times 7.4$$

$$= \left.\begin{array}{c} 127.55 \\ 116.45 \end{array}\right\} \text{ohms}$$

For Range Chart

$${}_{\text{lower}}^{\text{upper}}\text{Warning limits} = \left.\begin{array}{l} D_{WU}\bar{R} = 1.93 \times 7.4 = 14.28 \\ D_{WL}\bar{R} = 0.29 \times 7.4 = 2.15 \end{array}\right\} \text{ohms}$$

$${}_{\text{lower}}^{\text{upper}}\text{Action limits} = \left.\begin{array}{l} D_{AU}\bar{R} = 2.58 \times 7.4 = 19.09 \\ D_{AL}\bar{R} = 0.10 \times 7.4 = 0.74 \end{array}\right\} \text{ohms}$$

These limits, as well as the appropriate mean values, are shown in Figs. 19-2 and 19-3. The plots of the mean and the range for each sample show that all points fall inside the action limits. Four of the sample means fall outside the warning limits, but the corresponding ranges are inside the warning limits for the range; this indicates that the situation is not serious but has to be watched. We can therefore assume for the time being that the process can be brought into control at this level.

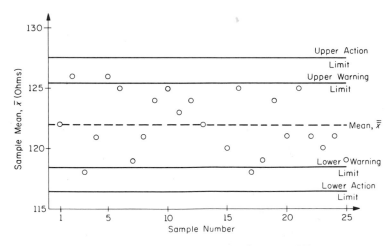

Fig. 19-2. Mean chart for the example on page 241.

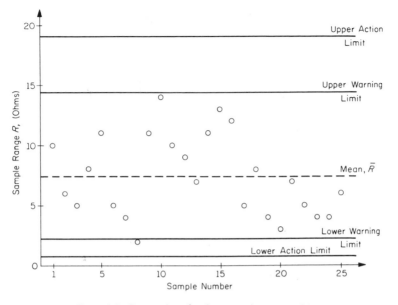

Fig. 19-3. Range chart for the example on page 241.

To obtain an estimate of the population standard deviation σ, we use Table A-1 for $n = 4$, $d = 0.4857$. Thus

$$s = \bar{R}d = 7.4 \times 0.4857 = 3.594 \text{ ohms}$$

The natural tolerance limits are

$$\bar{\bar{x}} \pm 3\sigma = 122 \pm 3 \times 3.594 = \left.\begin{array}{l} 111.22 \\ 132.78 \end{array}\right\} \text{ ohms}$$

The specification limits are 120 ± 8 ohms, that is, 112 to 128 ohms. The process does not, therefore, meet the specification.

CHARTS USING ATTRIBUTES

In dealing with attributes we are concerned with the binomial and Poisson distributions. The former is applicable when we are dealing with *defective* items, the latter when we count the number of *defects* per item.

If $\bar{p}$ is the mean proportion of defective items, then the mean number of defectives in a sample of size n is $n\bar{p}$. We may recall from Chapter 7 that the standard deviation of the number of defectives is $\sqrt{n\bar{p}q} = \sqrt{n\bar{p}(1 - \bar{p})}$. Hence we can write the action limits for the mean *number* of defectives as

$$\text{MAL} = n\bar{p} \pm 3.09 \sqrt{n\bar{p}(1 - \bar{p})} \qquad (19\text{-}12)$$

Instead of operating in terms of the number of defectives, we can express the control limits in terms of the *mean proportion* of defectives $\bar{p}$. The standard deviation of the mean proportion of defectives is

$$\frac{\sqrt{n\bar{p}q}}{n} = \sqrt{\frac{\bar{p}(1 - \bar{p})}{n}}$$

The action limits for the mean proportion of defectives are then

$$\text{Proportion AL} = \bar{p} \pm 3.09 \sqrt{\frac{\bar{p}(1 - \bar{p})}{n}} \qquad (19\text{-}13)$$

If a negative limit is obtained in Eq. 19-12 and 19-13, it is replaced by zero, as a negative proportion or number of defectives is not possible.

When dealing with an expected number of *defects* in a material np, the Poisson distribution is applicable. From Eq. 8-6 the standard deviation is $\sqrt{np}$. Thus in this case the action limits for the number of defects are

$$\text{Number AL} = np \pm 3.09\sqrt{np} \qquad (19\text{-}14)$$

Example. Thirty successive samples, each consisting of 50 machine bolts, were checked by a "go—no-go" gage. The results are shown below.

Find the mean proportion of defectives and calculate the upper and lower action limits for such a mean proportion. Are any of the plotted points outside these limits? If so, adjust the mean proportion of defectives and the corresponding limits for future production.

Sample	Number defective	Proportion defective p	Sample	Number defective	Proportion defective p
1	2	0.04	17	0	0
2	1	0.02	18	0	0
3	5	0.10	19	1	0.02
4	1	0.02	20	3	0.06
5	2	0.04	21	2	0.04
6	1	0.02	22	1	0.02
7	3	0.06	23	1	0.02
8	0	0	24	2	0.04
9	1	0.02	25	0	0
10	2	0.04	26	0	0
11	1	0.02	27	1	0.02
12	0	0	28	1	0.02
13	0	0	29	2	0.04
14	3	0.06	30	2	0.04
15	2	0.04			
16	2	0.04			$\Sigma p = 0.84$

The mean proportion of defectives is

$$\bar{p} = \frac{0.84}{30} = 0.028$$

The action limits are given by Eq. 19-13:

$$\text{Proportion AL} = \bar{p} \pm 3.09 \sqrt{\frac{\bar{p}(1 - \bar{p})}{n}}$$

$$\text{Proportion AL} = 0.028 \pm 3.09 \sqrt{\frac{0.028 \times 0.972}{50}}$$

$$= (-0.044, 0.1001)$$

We substitute zero for the lower limit, and write the limits as $(0, 0.1001)$.

Figure 19-4 shows the control limits and a plot of the proportion defective in each sample. It can be seen that all the points fall inside the limits, and we can therefore use these limits as control limits for future production. Had some points fallen outside, they could have been eliminated, and a new $\bar{p}$ and new limits should have been calculated from the remaining samples.

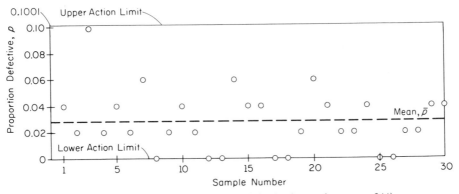

Fɪɢ. 19-4. Control chart for proportion defective (example on page 244).

Example. In producing aluminum sheets for a new type of aircraft it was required to set up control charts for the number of defects per sheet of a certain size. Twenty-five sample sheets were drawn and the number of defects per sheet was recorded. The results follow. On the basis of these results set up control limits for the number of defects for future production.

Sample	Number of defects per sheet	Sample	Number of defects per sheet
1	1	14	1
2	0	15	2
3	2	16	0
4	1	17	0
5	0	18	8
6	0	19	2
7	2	20	0
8	2	21	0
9	0	22	1
10	1	23	0
11	1	24	1
12	2	25	1
13	0		$\Sigma = 28$

The expected number of defects per sheet is

$$np = \frac{28}{25} = 1.12$$

From Eq. 19-14 the action limits for the number of defects are

$$np \pm 3.09 \sqrt{np} = 1.12 \pm 3.09 \times 1.059$$
$$= (-2.15, \ 4.39)$$

Substituting zero for the negative value, we write the limits as (0, 4.39). A plot of the control limits and of the number of defects in each sample (Fig. 19-5) shows that the 18th sheet falls outside the control limits. In this

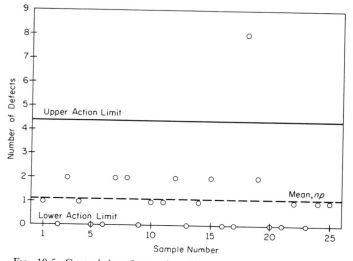

Fig. 19-5. Control chart for number of defects (example on page 245).

case it is best to base future work on a mean of defects np which does not include this particular sheet. We will now recalculate np and the control limits, ignoring the 18th sheet.

$$\Sigma \text{ number of defects } = 20$$

$$np = \frac{20}{24} = 0.833$$

Control limits are:

$$0.833 \pm 3.09 \sqrt{0.833}$$
$$= (-1.98, \ 3.65)$$

Thus the revised control limits are (0, 3.65).

It can be seen by inspection that none of the samples has a number of defects outside these new limits. Thus the new np and control limits can be used in future control work on the number of defects in the production of the aluminum sheets. We may add that these limits do not guarantee that a fixed percentage of the population will lie between them, as the probability of the number of defects falling between these limits depends on the mean expected number of defects np. For large n, np is approximately normally distributed, and hence we can assume that "almost" all the values will fall between the control limits.

ADVANTAGES OF QUALITY CONTROL

The notes on control charts given here are limited to basic principles, and a detailed study of the topic must be sought in one of the numerous books on quality control.

Quality control is used in all manufacturing processes, from pharmaceutics to concrete products. Its special feature is that it replaces a negative form of inspection—i.e., discarding of defective items—by a more positive form. The process is watched continually and systematically so that a departure from a stable condition is diagnosed early; appropriate action can then be taken; and the fault can be rectified before an excessive number of defectives has been manufactured. We must remember that quality control accepts the fact that some fraction of the items produced will be defective but makes it possible to ensure that the specified fraction is not exceeded.

SOLVED PROBLEMS

19-1. The mean range of shear strength of a certain kind of spot weld was determined from many tests on samples of six welds to be $\bar{R} = 35$ psi. Set up control limits for successive samples of size $n = 6$.

Solution:

From Table A-13, the factors for warning limits are $D_{WU} = 1.72$, $D_{WL} = 0.42$. For action limits the factors are: $D_{AU} = 2.22$, $D_{AL} = 0.21$. Hence

$$\text{upper}_{\text{lower}}\text{Warning limits} = \left. \begin{array}{l} D_{WU}\bar{R} = 1.72 \times 35 = 60.2 \text{ psi} \\ D_{WL}\bar{R} = 0.42 \times 35 = 14.7 \text{ psi} \end{array} \right\}$$

$$\text{upper}_{\text{lower}}\text{Action limits} = \left. \begin{array}{l} D_{AU}\bar{R} = 2.22 \times 35 = 77.7 \text{ psi} \\ D_{AL}\bar{R} = 0.21 \times 35 = 7.4 \text{ psi} \end{array} \right\}$$

19-2. Samples of six rings are taken at regular intervals from an assembly line for engine pistons. The inside diameters of the rings are measured, and the sample mean $\bar{x}$ and the sample range R are determined. For the first 30 samples, the sums of the means and of the ranges were as follows:

$$\Sigma\bar{x} = 135.81 \text{ in.}, \qquad \Sigma R = 0.063 \text{ in.}$$

(a) What are the control action limits for the mean and range charts?

(b) What are the 3σ natural tolerance limits for the ring diameter assuming that $\bar{\bar{x}}$ and $\bar{R}$ can be used to estimate the mean and standard deviation of the population?

(*c*) Is the process able to produce rings with inside diameters within the specification limits of 4.525 ± 0.005 in.?

(*d*) What proportion of rings will fall outside the specification limits if the process is in control with the calculated $\bar{x}$ and derived σ?

Solution:

(*a*) Compute

$$\bar{\bar{x}} = \frac{\Sigma \bar{x}}{n} = \frac{135.81}{30} = 4.527 \text{ in.}$$

$$\bar{R} = \frac{\Sigma R}{n} = \frac{0.063}{30} = 0.0021 \text{ in.}$$

From Table A-1, for $n = 6$, $d = 0.3945$. Hence

$$s = 0.0021 \times 0.3945 = 0.0008293$$

Mean Chart

$$\text{Action limits} = \bar{\bar{x}} \pm A_A \bar{R}$$

From Table A-12, for $n = 6$, $A_A = 0.498$
Hence

$$\text{Action limits} = 4.527 \pm 0.498 \times 0.0021$$
$$= 4.52805, \ 4.52595 \text{ in.}$$

Range Chart

$$^{\text{upper}}_{\text{lower}}\text{Action limit} = \frac{D_{AU} \bar{R}}{D_{AL} \bar{R}}$$

From Table A-13, for $n = 6$,

$$D_{AU} = 2.22, \quad D_{AL} = 0.21$$

Hence

$$\text{Upper action limit} = 2.22 \times 0.0021$$
$$= 0.00466 \text{ in.}$$
$$\text{Lower action limit} = 0.21 \times 0.0021$$
$$= 0.00044 \text{ in.}$$

(*b*) As instructed, we assume that $\sigma = s$. Hence,

$$\text{Natural tolerance limits} = \bar{\bar{x}} \pm 3\sigma$$
$$= 4.527 \pm 3 \times 0.0008293$$
$$= 4.524, \ 4.529 \text{ in.}$$

(*c*) The specification limits are 4.525 ± 0.005 = 4.520, 4.530 in. Since the natural tolerance limits fall within the specification, the process is able to meet the specification.

(d) We have:

$$\bar{\bar{x}} = 4.527 \text{ in.}, \qquad \sigma = 0.0008293 \text{ in.}$$

The specification limits are 4.520 and 4.530 in. Compute:

$$z_1 = \frac{4.530 - 4.527}{0.0008293} = 3.62$$

From Table A-4, the area under the normal probability curve for such a value of z is approximately 0.49984. Also

$$z_2 = \frac{4.527 - 4.520}{0.0008287} = 8.45$$

This deviation is so large that the corresponding area under the normal probability curve can be taken as 0.5000. The total area between the specification limits is

$$0.50000 + 0.49984 = 0.99984$$

Hence the percentage outside these limits is

$$1 - 0.99984 = 0.00016 \text{ or } 0.016 \text{ percent}$$

a very small percentage indeed!

19-3. A control chart for a new kind of plastics is to be initiated. Twenty-five samples of 100-yard plastic sheets from the assembly line were inspected for flaws during a period of time. The following results were obtained:

Sheet number	Number of flaws per sheet	Sheet number	Number of flaws per sheet
1	2	14	3
2	0	15	2
3	7	16	0
4	8	17	4
5	9	18	5
6	10	19	1
7	10	20	0
8	13	21	2
9	14	22	3
10	16	23	2
11	10	24	5
12	7	25	4
13	4		

Set up the necessary control chart.

Solution:

Compute the mean number of flaws

$$n p = \frac{\Sigma \text{ flaws}}{25}$$

$$= \frac{141}{25} = 5.64 \text{ flaws per sheet}$$

The control limits are:

$$np \pm 3.09\sqrt{np}$$
$$= 5.64 \pm 3.09\sqrt{5.64}$$
$$= -1.70, \ 12.98$$

Thus the control limits are (0, 12.98). These limits and the mean number of flaws per sheet, as well as the individual number of flaws per sheet, are shown in Fig. 19-6. It can be seen that the samples numbered 8, 9, and 10 fall outside the upper control limit. Removing the values for these samples and recalculating we get:

$$np = \frac{98}{22} = 4.45 \text{ flaws per sheet}$$

$$\text{New control limits} = 4.45 \pm 3.09\sqrt{4.45}$$
$$= -2.07, \ 10.97$$

i.e., the control limits are (0, 10.97). By inspection, it is seen that none of the remaining sheets has flaws outside these limits.

A close look at Fig. 19-6 will show what appears to be an approximately cyclic pattern of variation in the number of flaws in successive sheets. In such cases it is advisable to check the production process before continuing production since this trend is unlikely to be due to chance alone.

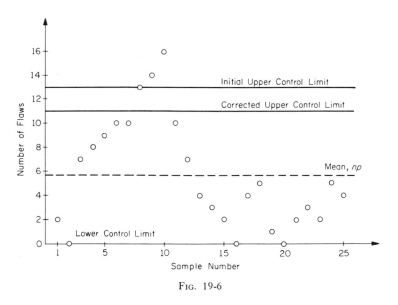

FIG. 19-6

PROBLEMS

19-1. From numerous tests it has been found that the mean strength and mean range of a certain timber are 3,510 and 390 psi, respectively. Using these values set up control limits for the mean chart when the sample size is 5.

19-2. Establish range and mean charts (containing warning and action limits) on the basis of the following data for samples of size $n = 3$:

Sample No.	Mean	Range	Sample No.	Mean	Range
1	11.97	0.5	13	17.87	8.7
2	14.87	6.3	14	14.97	0.1
3	15.35	7.5	15	14.60	9.8
4	15.72	6.6	16	14.12	7.7
5	11.12	4.9	17	13.21	7.5
6	11.06	6.7	18	12.86	1.2
7	11.97	9.9	19	12.38	9.8
8	12.27	6.9	20	16.99	6.5
9	12.85	0.1	21	18.35	7.6
10	13.23	8.3	22	18.52	4.0
11	16.12	5.1	23	14.13	8.4
12	16.61	3.2	24	14.60	9.8

19-3. Screws produced by an automatic machine are to be checked. A sample of 60 screws was checked by a go—no-go gage, and it was found that in 30 successive samples the following defective number of screws was obtained:

$$5, 4, 3, 1, 2, 0, 0, 0, 1, 2, 0, 1, 2, 1, 0, 1, 1,$$

$$0, 1, 0, 0, 1, 2, 0, 1, 0, 1, 0, 0, 1.$$

(*a*)   Is this process in control?

(*b*)   Taking the process in its present condition, will it produce screws of which 5 percent or less are defective?

19-4. Thirty 20-yard lengths of carpets were inspected, and the average number of defects per unit area was found to be 2.1. Compute the 2.5σ control limits. What are the probability limits corresponding to a probability of 0.3 percent of falling outside the upper control limits.

19-5. For the data on concrete strength given in Prob. 4-7:

(*a*)   Estimate the standard deviation from the mean range.

(*b*)   Construct control charts for the mean and range, and plot the means and the ranges on the respective charts.

(*c*)   Are any of the plotted points outside the action limits? If so, adjust the mean of means and the mean range and the corresponding limits for future production.

chapter 20

Introduction to the Design of Experiments

The statistical methods discussed in the preceding chapters are generally used in the interpretation of experimental results. In some cases the planning of the experiment, in the broad sense of the word, may be outside our control, but in others we may be able to decide the procedure and details of the tests. This should be done in the light of the statistical analysis which will be subsequently applied; more information can then be extracted from the given experimental effort than when the statistical aspects of the program are considered only *a posteriori*.

The design of experiments is thus of considerable importance. In general, we require some advance knowledge of the variability of results. Such information may be available from previous work or alternatively should be obtained from pilot tests.

In the present chapter we shall consider only two topics: the choice of size of the sample and the design of experiments involving several variables. No more than an introduction will be given in either case.

CHOICE OF SAMPLE SIZE

As we have seen in the earlier chapters, our decisions about populations or batches (such as their acceptability under specification) are usually based on tests on samples. A problem that often arises is how many observations should be made, so that the risk of making a wrong decision is acceptably small. Some risk is, of course, always present because of the random variation in results, but the risk becomes smaller as the number of observations increases. It is clear, however, that for reasons of economy of time and effort the testing should be kept to a minimum consistent with the maximum risk of a wrong decision which we are prepared to accept. In practice, there is thus a certain optimum testing effort. In this book we cannot evaluate the cost of testing or the economic results of making a wrong decision, and we shall therefore consider our decision-making on the basis of a specified risk of being wrong.[1]

The information required first of all is the distribution of the true mean value of the measured property of batches[2] of the material. Let us consider, for example, the strength of a plastic, and assume that in the past we received a sequence of batches of the plastic. From each batch k samples were taken and tested, and the mean of the k values was obtained. The means so obtained differ from one another for two reasons: They are estimates of different (batch) means, and they are also affected by the testing error (arising from sampling and measuring).

If $\bar{x}_i$ is the mean strength obtained from tests on batch i, then

$$\bar{x}_i = \mu_i + \epsilon_i$$

where μ_i is the true mean strength of batch i, and ϵ_i is the testing error. Hence,

$$\sigma_{\bar{x}}^2 = \sigma_\mu^2 + \frac{\sigma_T^2}{k}$$

where σ_μ^2 is the variance of μ, $\sigma_{\bar{x}}^2$ is the variance of the batch means available from the test results, and σ_T^2 is the variance of the testing error, assumed known.

In this manner σ_μ^2 can be readily estimated, and the distribution of the underlying strength of the plastic can be determined. Assume that this is as shown in Fig. 20-1a. Suppose further that the specification calls for a minimum strength of 3,000 psi. In practice, we obtain n test specimens of the plastic and find their strengths. If the mean strength is greater than 3,000 psi, we accept the batch of the plastic, and, if not, we reject it. The problem is: How large should n be?

To answer this, we have to consider the testing scheme which is characterized by the *power curve*. This shows the probability of a plastic from a batch of any given strength being accepted as satisfactory; hence, the power curve is related to the testing error. We shall recall from Chapter 13 that when we accept a value as being within a specified range while in fact it is not, we are committing a Type II error. Figure 20-1b shows the shape of the power curve.

The steepness of the power curve indicates the discriminating power of our testing scheme. The curve becomes steeper as the sample size increases and becomes vertical for $n = \infty$. In practice, we usually compro-

---

[1] Details of the method described in the following pages and its further development are presented clearly in *Statistical Methods in Research and Production*, ed. O. L. Davies (Edinburgh: Oliver and Boyd, Ltd., 1958).

[2] Since the tests refer usually to a batch of material, this term will be used in preference to a "finite population."

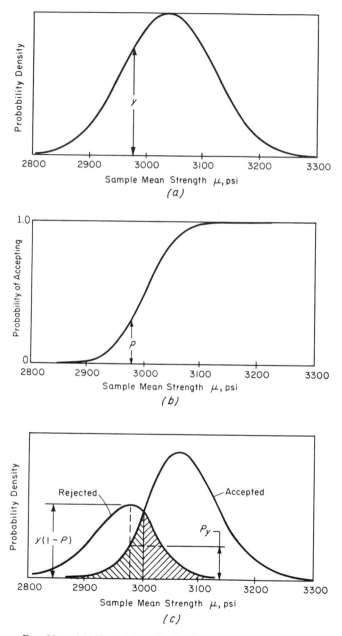

FIG. 20-1. (*a*) Underlying distribution.   (*b*) Power curve.
(*c*) Distribution of accepted and rejected batches.

mise between the advantage of increasing the discriminating power of our test and the increased cost of more extensive testing (which may be extremely high if the test is destructive).

The power curve can be used not only with a normal distribution but also a t distribution, and G. P. Sillitto computed the number of observations needed in a t test in order to control the probabilities of Type I and II errors.[3]

CONSTRUCTION OF THE POWER CURVE

As we have said, the ordinate of the power curve represents the probability P that a batch of any strength μ will be accepted. In our testing scheme, we perform n tests on samples from each batch and make our decision on the basis of whether the mean of our tests $\bar{x}$ is greater or smaller than 3,000 psi. The results from the n tests will differ among themselves because of the testing error, which can be considered as the resultant of the sampling and measurement errors. Such testing error can be estimated from the differences among the n determinations.

The underlying distribution of the strength of the plastic is normal, and this in practice must be the case since we are concerned with the distribution of means $\bar{x}$ (see central limit theorem, Chapter 10). Assuming that the distribution of testing errors is also normal, we can now obtain the probability P that, for any given value of mean batch strength μ, the sample mean $\bar{x}$ will exceed 3,000 and the batch will be accepted.

For n observations in a sample, the standard deviation of the sample mean is $\sigma_T/\sqrt{n}$. Thus we calculate

$$z = \frac{3,000 - \mu}{\sigma_T/\sqrt{n}}$$

and using Table A-4 find the probability P of z having at most this value. [This is $0.5 + F(z)$.]

A plot of P against μ gives the power curve (Fig. 20-1b). This curve is descriptive of the testing scheme and depends only on σ_T^2 and n.

It is important to note that the power curve is determined by two points only; this will be illustrated in an example later in this chapter.

DISTRIBUTION OF STRENGTH OF ACCEPTED AND REJECTED BATCHES

Because the discrimination of the power curve is not perfect, it is to be expected that some of the accepted batches will actually have a strength below 3,000 psi, and, conversely, some of the rejected batches will in fact have a strength above 3,000 psi.

[3] See W. Volk, *Applied Statistics for Engineers* (New York: McGraw-Hill Book Co., Inc., 1958).

To determine the relative frequency with which batches of a strength μ are offered *and* accepted, we multiply the ordinate y of Fig. 20-1a by the ordinate P of Fig. 20-1b. The product yP then gives the distribution of strength of the accepted batches. This is plotted against μ in Fig. 20-1c.

Similarly, the distribution of strength of batches offered and rejected is given by the product $y(1 - P)$. A plot of this is also given in Fig. 20-1c.

The area under the "accepted" curve, as a fraction of the sum of the areas under the two curves, represents the proportion of all the batches which are accepted. The remainder represents the proportion of rejected batches.

The proportion of cases in which we accept a batch of plastic when in fact its strength is below 3,000 psi is represented by the area under the "accepted" curve to the left of the abscissa of 3,000, as a fraction of the total area under both curves. Similarly, the proportion of cases in which we reject a batch when in fact its strength exceeds 3,000 psi is represented by the area under the "rejected" curve to the right of the abscissa of 3,000, as a fraction of the total area under both curves.

The acceptable level of the percentage of "wrong decisions" depends on the consequences. Obviously the level would have to be considerably lower when we are dealing with human life than when we fail to discriminate, for example, between the qualities of two products offered at the same price.

The method outlined here can also be used when full information about the underlying distribution is not available, but this is outside the scope of the present book.[4]

Example. We require limestone containing at least 92 percent calcium carbonate. From past experience the percentage of the carbonate in different batches is known to be normally distributed with a mean of 91 percent and a variance of 5 percent. The variance due to the testing error (i.e., sampling and measurement errors) obtained from a single test on each batch ($k = 1$) is known to be $\sigma_T^2 = 1$ (percent)^2. (NOTE: To avoid confusion it is preferable not to work in percentages but in "units.")

Obtain power curves for samples (per batch of the rock) of size $n = 1$, 4, 25, and ∞. Then, for $n = 4$:

(*a*) Obtain the distribution of the content of calcium carbonate in accepted and rejected batches;

(*b*) Calculate the percentage of batches accepted;

(*c*) Calculate the fraction of the accepted batches which in fact have a calcium carbonate content below 92 percent.

[4] See *Statistical Methods in Research and Production*, ed. O. L. Davies (Edinburgh: Oliver and Boyd, Ltd., 1958).

Solution: We are given that the variance of the batch contents is 5 and that the variance due to testing is 1. Therefore, since k equals 1, the variance of the underlying distribution exclusive of testing error is $5 - 1 = 4$, or the standard deviation is 2.

Thus we can assume that the underlying distribution is normal with mean = 91 and $\sigma = 2$. This distribution is plotted in Fig. 20-2a. To con-

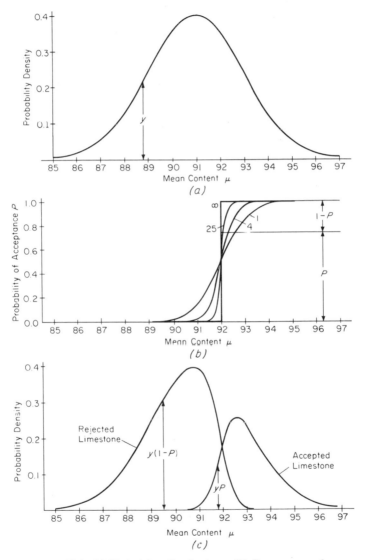

Fig. 20-2. (*a*) Underlying distribution. (*b*) Power curves for $n = 1, 4, 25$, and ∞. (*c*) Distribution of accepted and rejected batches of sample size $n = 4$.

struct the power curves for $n = 1, 4, 25,$ and ∞, we need to calculate P for

$$z = \frac{92 - \mu}{\sigma_T/\sqrt{n}}$$

Thus

for $n = 1$: $z = (92 - \mu)$
for $n = 4$: $z = (92 - \mu) \times 2$
for $n = 25$: $z = (92 - \mu) \times 5$
for $n = \infty$: $z = \infty$ for $\mu > 92$ and $\mu < 92$.

From Table A-4 we can find the probability P of z having at most the preceding values. [This is $0.5 - F(z)$ if $\mu < 92$, and it is $0.5 + F(z)$ for $\mu > 92$.] These values of P for various values of μ are shown in the following tables for the different values of n.

For $n = 1$:

μ	z	P
88.0	4.0	0.0000
88.4	3.6	0.0002
88.8	3.2	0.0007
89.2	2.8	0.0026
89.6	2.4	0.0082
90.0	2.0	0.0228
90.4	1.6	0.0548
90.8	1.2	0.1151
91.2	0.8	0.2119
91.6	0.4	0.3446
92.0	0.0	0.5000
92.4	−0.4	0.6554
92.8	−0.8	0.7881
93.2	−1.2	0.8849
93.6	−1.6	0.9452
94.0	−2.0	0.9772
94.4	−2.4	0.9918
94.8	−2.8	0.9974
95.2	−3.2	0.9993
95.6	−3.6	0.9998
96.0	−4.0	1.0000

For $n = 4$:

μ	z	P
90.0	4.0	0.0000
90.4	3.2	0.0007
90.8	2.4	0.0082
91.2	1.6	0.0548
91.6	0.8	0.2119
92.0	0.0	0.5000
92.4	−0.8	0.7881
92.8	−1.6	0.9452
93.2	−2.4	0.9918
93.6	−3.2	0.9993
94.0	−4.0	1.0000

For $n = 25$:

μ	z	P
91.0	5.0	0.0000
91.2	4.0	0.0000
91.4	3.0	0.0013
91.6	2.0	0.0228
91.8	1.0	0.1587
92.0	0.0	0.5000
92.2	−1.0	0.8413
92.4	−2.0	0.9772
92.6	−3.0	0.9987
92.8	−4.0	1.0000
93.0	−5.0	1.0000

For $n = \infty$:

$$z = \infty \quad \text{for any } \mu < 92 \quad \text{whence } P = 0.0000$$

$$z = -\infty \quad \text{for any } \mu > 92 \quad \text{whence } P = 1.0000$$

The plot of P versus μ gives the power curve. These curves are shown in Fig. 20-2b for $n = 1, 4, 25$, and ∞. The power curve for $n = \infty$ is sometimes called the *ideal* power curve.

(a) To obtain the distribution of the content of calcium carbonate in accepted and rejected batches, we have to find yP and $y(1 - P)$ for various values of μ, corresponding to $n = 4$. These values are given in the following table.

μ	y	P	yP	$y(1 - P)$
85.0	0.0044	0.0000	0.0000	0.0044
85.4	0.0079	0.0000	0.0000	0.0079
85.8	0.0136	0.0000	0.0000	0.0136
86.2	0.0224	0.0000	0.0000	0.0224
86.6	0.0355	0.0000	0.0000	0.0355
87.0	0.0540	0.0000	0.0000	0.0540
87.4	0.0790	0.0000	0.0000	0.0790
87.8	0.1109	0.0000	0.0000	0.1109
88.2	0.1497	0.0000	0.0000	0.1497
88.6	0.1942	0.0000	0.0000	0.1942
89.0	0.2420	0.0000	0.0000	0.2420
89.4	0.2897	0.0000	0.0000	0.2897
89.8	0.3332	0.0000	0.0000	0.3332
90.2	0.3683	0.0002	0.0001	0.3682
90.6	0.3910	0.0026	0.0010	0.3900
91.0	0.3989	0.0228	0.0091	0.3898
91.4	0.3910	0.1151	0.0450	0.3460
91.8	0.3683	0.3446	0.1269	0.2414
92.2	0.3332	0.6554	0.2184	0.1148
92.6	0.2897	0.8849	0.2564	0.0333
93.0	0.2420	0.9772	0.2365	0.0055
93.4	0.1942	0.9974	0.1937	0.0005
93.8	0.1497	0.9998	0.1497	0.0000
94.2	0.1109	1.0000	0.1109	0.0000
94.6	0.0790	1.0000	0.0790	0.0000

(continued)

μ	y	P	yP	$y(1 - P)$
95.0	0.0540	1.0000	0.0540	0.0000
95.4	0.0355	1.0000	0.0355	0.0000
95.8	0.0224	1.0000	0.0224	0.0000
96.2	0.0136	1.0000	0.0136	0.0000
96.6	0.0079	1.0000	0.0079	0.0000
97.0	0.0044	1.0000	0.0044	0.0000
97.4	0.0024	1.0000	0.0024	0.0000
97.8	0.0012	1.0000	0.0012	0.0000
98.2	0.0006	1.0000	0.0006	0.0000
$\Sigma =$	4.9947		1.5687	3.4260

The plots of yP and $y(1 - P)$ versus μ give the required distributions. These are shown in Fig. 20-2c.

(b)   The percentage of batches accepted is obtained from the ratio:

$$\frac{\Sigma(yP)}{\Sigma y} = \frac{1.5687}{4.9947} = 31.4 \text{ percent}$$

(c)   The fraction of the accepted batches which in fact have a calcium carbonate content below 92 percent is obtained by summing up the column yP from $\mu = 85.0$ to $\mu = 91.8$ (just below $\mu = 92$). This sum $= 0.1821$. Therefore the required fraction $= 0.1821/1.5687 = 11.6$ percent. This is equivalent to 3.64 percent of all the accepted and rejected batches. From Fig. 20-2c it can be observed that the mean content of calcium carbonate in rejected batches is 90.8 percent, and that in accepted batches equals 92.6 percent.

SIMPLIFIED CASE

In some cases a simpler approach to deciding on the size of the sample can be adopted. For example, this is the case in testing concrete where we may be concerned with the maximum error of the mean strength determined by tests on a sample.

The t tests of Chapter 13 can be written as

$$t = \frac{|\mu - \bar{x}|}{s_d}$$

where μ = population mean
  $\bar{x}$ = sample mean
  s_d = standard deviation of the sample mean

The value of t for the largest value of $|\mu - \bar{x}|$ corresponding to different levels of significance and numbers of degrees of freedom is given in Table A-8.

Now, $s_d = s/\sqrt{n}$, where s is the estimate of the population standard deviation from the sample, and n is sample size.

In tests on the compressive strength of concrete, the coefficient of variation within a sample is under many circumstances $V = 5$ percent.[5] Hence

$$s = \frac{V}{100} \mu = 0.05\mu$$

Expressing $| \mu - \bar{x} |$ as a percentage of the population mean, we put

$$E = \frac{\mu - \bar{x}}{\mu} \times 100$$

Then,

$$t = \frac{\mu E \sqrt{n}}{V \mu}$$

whence

$$E = \frac{Vt}{\sqrt{n}} \tag{20-1}$$

Working at the 10 percent level of significance,[5] and using a sample size $n = 3$, we have, from Table A-8, $t = 2.920$. Then,

$$E = \frac{0.05 \times 2.920}{\sqrt{3}} \times 100 = 8.5 \text{ percent}$$

Thus, for a sample of three specimens, the error of the mean will exceed 8.5 percent in 10 percent of the cases.

If V is based on a large number of tests, we reach in the limit t for an infinite number of degrees of freedom (cf. u of Chapter 13); at the 10 percent level of significance, we have $t = 1.645$. Then,

$$E = \frac{0.05 \times 1.645}{\sqrt{3}} \times 100 = 4.8 \text{ percent}$$

Thus, the mean of three specimens will indicate the *average* strength of concrete with an "error" of 4.8 percent of the mean, exceeded in 10 percent of the cases.

We can now consider the problem of determining the size of the sample n when the "error" in the estimated strength of concrete is not to exceed 5 percent in 90 percent of our tests. The coefficient of variation is assumed to be 5 percent. From Eq. 20-1

$$n = \left(\frac{Vt}{E}\right)^2 = \left(\frac{0.05 \times 1.645}{0.05}\right)^2 = 2.7 \tag{20-2}$$

The next higher integer is 3; that is, we require a sample of three specimens. This is indeed the number commonly used.

---

[5] W. A. Cordon, "Size and Number of Samples and Statistical Considerations in Sampling." ASTM, Special Technical Publication No. 169, 1955.

SAMPLING OF ATTRIBUTES

A sampling plan similar to that outlined in the earlier part of this chapter can be used with attributes, such as defective items. In fact, our case of distribution of strength can be considered as that of sampling of attributes, since each test can be classified as success (strength greater than 3,000 psi) or failure (strength smaller than 3,000 psi). In the general case, we expect a small number of failures, or defectives, and we can therefore use the Poisson distribution as a sufficiently good approximation. (This is justified when the proportion of defectives does not exceed 0.1.)

Suppose that to inspect a batch we draw a sample of 100, and accept the batch if the number of defectives does not exceed 2 but reject it if it does. Knowing the average number of defectives in the sample,[6] we can determine from the Poisson distribution (Fig. 8-1) the probability of our sample containing 0, 1, 2, 3 ... defectives. Conversely, from batches with different proportions of defectives (this being reflected in the average number of defectives in the samples), we can draw samples containing a specified number of defectives with a probability determined by the Poisson distribution. For example, if the batch being inspected contains 1.5 percent of defectives ($np = 1.5$), the probability of drawing a sample containing at least 3 defectives is 0.20 (from Fig. 8-1). Thus one sample out of five will contain 3 or more defectives. We might use a sample with at least 3 defectives as a basis for rejection of the batch. We know, however, that the percentage of defectives is 1.5 percent, so that we are wrong in our decision to reject in 20 percent of the cases.

Let us consider Fig. 8-1 further. We can observe that not more than 2 defectives in a sample would be obtained with a probability of 0.2 when the average number of defectives is as high as 4.3. We run thus a risk of 0.2 of accepting a batch containing 4.3 percent of defectives.

We can see thus that there is a definite probability of wrongly rejecting a batch and also of wrongly accepting a batch. These are, of course, the Type I and Type II errors, respectively. The former is simply the confidence level α, considered in Chapter 12. The latter, β, determines the power curve associated with any sampling plan.

Instead of specifying the sample size and the acceptable number of defectives in it, we can define the curve by two points, (p_1, α) and (p_2, β), where α is the probability of rejecting a batch in which the proportion of defectives is p_1, β is the probability of accepting a batch in which the proportion of defectives is p_2, and $p_2 > p_1$.

We can plot the power curve as shown in Fig. 20-1b, from which we read off the probabilities of accepting batches of different qualities.

The risk of a Type I error can be made as small as we wish by increas-

---

[6] This is directly related to the proportion of defectives in the material tested.

ing the acceptance interval, i.e., by increasing the acceptable number of defectives. We thus usually fix this risk, and to compare procedures we compare the Type II errors.

It is important to realize that the tacit assumption underlying the procedures outlined here is that a small number of defectives is admissible; otherwise, of course, a 100 percent inspection would be necessary, and there would be no question of sampling procedure.

We should further stress that the power curve alone provides no information about the quality of the material but only gives the probability of accepting a batch containing a specified proportion of defectives. To know the qualities of accepted and rejected material, we must know the underlying distribution of the material as manufactured (see Fig. 20-1a).

Finally, we should observe that information obtained from a sample of size n depends on the sample size only and is in no way related to the size of the batch from which the sample was drawn. Thus, provided the batches are homogeneous, it is more economical to test large batches than small ones.

Example. (a) Construct the power curve for a sampling plan such that the risk of rejecting a batch containing not more than the specified proportion of defectives p is 0.1, when the sample size $n = 50$, and we accept samples when the number of defectives per sample is $r \leq 2$.

(b) For approximately the same risk of wrong rejection, establish the decision rule when the sample size $n = 150$, and construct the power curve for this sampling plan.

Solution: (a) Fig. 8-1 shows that for the probability of 0.1 of rejecting a batch with the average number of defectives per sample np, the number r of observed defectives which is *exceeded* is as follows:

r	0	1	2	3	4	5
np	0.1	0.53	1.10	1.54	2.4	3.1

Thus, if we reject samples with $r > 2$, $np = 1.10$, whence the proportion of defectives in the batch is 0.022. Since the probability of accepting a batch is then 0.9, we have a point on the power curve (0.022, 0.9).

To find a second point, consider, for example, $p = 0.08$. Then $np = 4$, and for our decisions rule $r \leq 2$, Fig. 8-1 gives the probability of accepting a batch containing this proportion of defectives as 0.24. Thus the second point on the power curve is (0.08, 0.24).

Some of the other points are (from Fig. 8-1):

np	6	5	3	2	1	0
Proportion of defectives in batch p	0.12	0.1	0.06	0.04	0.02	0
Probability of accepting the batch	0.06	0.12	0.41	0.67	0.92	1.0

(b) When $n = 150$ and p is still 0.022, the average number of defects in a sample is $np = 150 \times 0.022 = 3.3$. However, bearing in mind that the actual number of defectives in a sample used as our decision rule must be an integer, we choose the nearest value of r, namely $r \leq 5$. For $np = 3.3$, this gives a probability of 0.12 of rejecting a batch containing not more than the specified proportion of defectives (i.e. a wrong rejection).

The power curve thus passes through the point (0.022, 0.88). From Fig. 8-1, the probability of accepting a batch containing a proportion of defectives $p = 0.06$ ($np = 9$) on the basis of our decision rule $r \leq 5$ is 0.12. Thus the second point on the power curve is (0.06, 0.12).

Some of the other points (from Fig. 8-1) are:

np	10	7.5	6	4.5	2.4	1.5	0
Proportion of defectives in batch p	0.067	0.05	0.04	0.03	0.016	0.01	0
Probability of accepting the batch	0.07	0.25	0.44	0.70	0.962	0.995	1.0

The two power curves are shown in Fig. 20-3. We can see that, while the risk of wrongly rejecting a batch is nearly the same with either sampling plan, the use of the larger sample ensures a better discrimination against acceptance of batches containing too great a proportion of defectives.

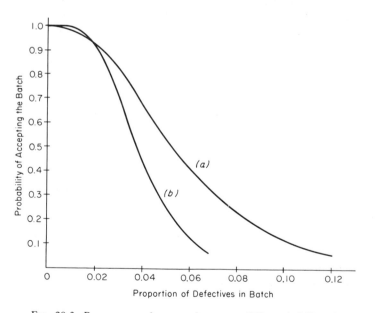

Fig. 20-3. Power curves for example on page 263; probability of wrongful rejection of 0.10. (a) Decision rule: accept batch when a sample of 50 contains not more than 2 defectives. (b) Decision rule: accept batch when a sample of 150 contains not more than 5 defectives.

RANDOMIZED BLOCKS

The first requirements of a properly designed experiment are that an unbiased estimate of error can be obtained and that the error be at a minimum. This can be achieved by the use of a randomized-block design.

Suppose that we wish to compare four methods of molding a plastic, and suppose further that the material arrives in batches large enough only to permit four tests per batch. From our knowledge of engineering materials, we expect the batches to vary from one another. In statistical terminology of design of experiments, a unit such as our batch would be called a *block*.

The term has its origin in agricultural experiments where it denoted a strip of land consisting of adjacent plots believed to be more similar to one another than plots chosen at random. This greater homogeneity of units within the block than of those chosen at random is the essential feature of a block.[7] However, the homogeneity must be related to the measurements of the dependent variable, and blocks should not be formed on the basis of irrelevant or unrelated variables. Thus blocks are normally formed on the basis of prior information about the units, but when dealing with random units, we can use blocks to control some sources of variation not associated with the units. For example, if we suspect a day-to-day variation in laboratory conditions, we may consider all the units tested the same day as a block. In the analysis of variance the day-to-day variation would be eliminated from the estimate of error.

Suppose further that we are going to use each method of molding, which we shall call *treatment*, four times, i.e., *replicate* four times. The question is: How should we arrange the tests?

It does not require any knowledge of statistics to realize that to assign each block to one treatment would be purposeless, for the observed differences might be those between blocks and not between treatments; we would have no information on the basis of which to decide which is the case. It is obvious then that the blocks have to be distributed between the treatments.

The distribution could be made at random, e.g., by assigning a letter *A*, *B*, *C*, or *D* to the four treatments, and writing *A* on four cards, *B* on another four cards, and so on, putting all 16 cards in a hat, and withdrawing four for each block. We would thus determine the treatment to which the four components of each block should be subjected. An actual drawing from a hat has produced the following:

Block	Treatment			
1	D	C	A	A
2	B	A	C	C
3	D	D	B	D
4	B	B	A	C

[7] If all subjects are homogeneous, nothing is gained by the use of blocks.

This procedure would enable us to estimate the differences between the treatments, but the error of the mean value for each treatment would include the differences between blocks. Specifically, treatment D would be applied only to blocks 1 and 3, and no treatment would be applied to specimens from all four blocks. It is obvious then that we should apply each treatment to each block, so that the mean value for each treatment is independent of the differences between the blocks. Our test program might thus be as follows:

Block	Treatment			
1	*A*	*B*	*C*	*D*
2	*A*	*B*	*C*	*D*
3	*A*	*B*	*C*	*D*
4	*A*	*B*	*C*	*D*

It is possible, however, that some uncontrolled variables are acting, and these could influence our results. For example, if only four treatments can be performed in a day, treatment *A* would be applied first, and, say, with a lower temperature of the machine, we might obtain a consistently "low" reading. Or, the last treatment might be done in a hurry, and the reading could be "high." To remove such a bias, we should randomize the treatments by determining the order for each block by drawing letters *A*, *B*, *C*, and *D* from a hat. As an example, the following results have been obtained:

Block	Treatment			
1	*D*	*C*	*A*	*B*
2	*A*	*D*	*B*	*C*
3	*A*	*B*	*C*	*D*
4	*C*	*B*	*A*	*D*

This then is the randomized block.

Since the units in each block are more homogeneous than units selected at random, the differences between blocks can be taken into account in the analysis of variance with the result that the estimate of experimental error will be smaller than if randomized selection had been used.

The analysis of variance of the results of a randomized block experiment is best illustrated by means of an example. We may note that the number of blocks for any treatment must be the same, so that all the observations in the testing program as designed are necessary. Should one be missing (through mishap, breakdown, etc.) it has to be replaced by an estimate. On the other hand, with a randomized-groups design, the analysis of variance can be applied for unequal numbers of experiments for each treatment.

Example. In order to establish the temperature of complete melting of cadmium and tin alloys with various percentages of cadmium, a large piece from each of five different alloys was obtained and was cut into four smaller pieces, each of which was tested for the complete melting state. Find the influence of the content of cadmium on the melting state of the alloys. What can be said about the homogeneity of each individual large piece of alloy? The data are given in the following table.

Solution: (*a*) Compute the row, column, and the grand totals as shown in the table.

Block t (% lead)	Melting point, °C				Totals
	Replications (pieces) r				
	1	2	3	4	
40	201	185	182	179	747
50	200	195	220	199	814
60	257	240	224	225	946
70	252	228	275	250	1,005
80	280	275	277	260	1,092
Totals	1,190	1,123	1,178	1,113	$G = 4,604$

(*b*) Obtain the correction factor:

$$C = \frac{G^2}{tr} = \frac{(4,604)^2}{5 \times 4} = 1,059,840.80$$

(*c*) Square every measurement and add:

$$(201)^2 + (185)^2 + \cdots + (277)^2 + (260)^2 = 1,082,234.00$$

(*d*) (Replications) Square the totals of each column, sum these squares, and divide by the number of measurements in each column:

$$\frac{(1,190)^2 + (1,123)^2 + (1,178)^2 + (1,113)^2}{5} = 1,060,736.40$$

(*e*) (Blocks) Square the totals of each row, sum these squares, and divide by the number of measurements in each row:

$$\frac{(747)^2 + (814)^2 + (946)^2 + (1,005)^2 + (1,092)^2}{4} = 1,079,502.50$$

The table for the analysis of variance is:

Source of variation	Sum of squares (s.s.)	Degrees of freedom ν	Mean square
Replications	(*d*) − C = 895.60	$r - 1 = 3$	298.53
Blocks	(*e*) − C = 19,661.70	$t - 1 = 4$	4,915.43
Error	1,835.90	$(r - 1)(t - 1) = 12$	152.99
Totals	(*c*) − C = 22,393.20	$rt - 1 = 19$	

Error sum of squares = total (s.s.) − replication (s.s.) − block (s.s.)

$$= 22{,}393.20 - 895.60 - 19{,}661.70$$

$$= 1{,}835.90$$

$$\text{Value of } F \text{ for blocks} = \frac{4{,}915.43}{152.99} = 32.13$$

Referring to Table A-10, for $\nu_1 = 4$ and $\nu_2 = 12$, $F = 5.41$ at the 1 percent level of significance. We conclude therefore that the block effect is significant at that level, i.e., the cadmium content affects the melting state of the alloy. The value of F for replications $= 298.53/152.99 = 1.95$ which is not significant at the 5 percent level ($\nu_1 = 3$ and $\nu_2 = 12$). We can therefore state that there is no evidence of each of the large pieces of alloy being nonhomogeneous.

LATIN SQUARES

Let us now consider the situation where we have, say, five treatments to be compared. We have 25 specimens but only 5 can be tested in any one day. We have no prior information about the specimen which would enable us to arrange them in blocks. We might suspect, however, that there may be some variation between observations made on different days, and to eliminate this effect, we would consider a group of 5 specimens tested on the same day as a block. We would therefore assign the specimens at random to each day, and of the day's block subject one to each treatment, *A*, *B*, *C*, *D*, and *E*. The procedure would be, for example, to number cards corresponding to the specimens as 1 to 25, and to make cards with letters *A* to *E*. We could then draw one number card and one letter card at a time, and this would determine which specimens are to be tested on the first day, and in what order. The letter card would then be replaced, and a further draw would determine the tests for the second day, etc.

The analysis of variance of these results would be the same as for the randomized blocks, and the day-to-day variation would be removed from the estimate of the experimental error.

It is possible, however, that the time of the day affects the results. To remove this error, we would arrange our testing program so that each treatment occurs not only once every day but also once at a particular time of the day. Denoting the five parts of a working day by numbers 1, 2, 3, 4, and 5, we would arrange the test program so that each treatment occurs once and only once in each row and each column, as shown, for example, in the table at the top of page 269.

Such an arrangement is known as a Latin square. Since it is a square, the number of observations (specimens) must be equal to the square of the number of treatments. Thus with a large number of treatments, the total testing effort is high, but a high reduction in errors is achieved as every row and every column is a complete replication. The experiment should be designed so that the differences among rows and columns represent major sources of variation.

Day	Part of the day				
	1	2	3	4	5
1	*A*	*B*	*C*	*D*	*E*
2	*E*	*A*	*B*	*C*	*D*
3	*D*	*E*	*A*	*B*	*C*
4	*C*	*D*	*E*	*A*	*B*
5	*B*	*C*	*D*	*E*	*A*

Example. It is desired to know whether the rate of flow of fuels through different types of nozzles is affected by temperature. An experiment was carried out by 6 operators, *A*, *B*, . . . , *F*, chosen at random, at 6 different temperatures on 6 different types of nozzles. The coded results are shown in the following table.

Solution: First, the totals for each row, column, operator, and the grand total *G* are computed as shown:

Temperature, °F	Volume of fuel through nozzle						Totals
	Nozzle type						
	1	2	3	4	5	6	
0	*A* 24	*D* 20	*E* 22	*C* 17	*F* 12	*B* 18	113
5	*E* 20	*A* 15	*C* 18	*F* 11	*B* 19	*D* 10	93
10	*D* 16	*C* 22	*B* 24	*E* 18	*A* 13	*F* 15	108
20	*C* 24	*E* 32	*F* 27	*B* 22	*D* 30	*A* 24	159
40	*B* 26	*F* 29	*D* 28	*A* 32	*E* 30	*C* 27	172
80	*F* 33	*B* 34	*A* 30	*D* 28	*C* 29	*E* 33	187
Totals	143	152	149	128	133	127	*G* = 832
Operator	*A*	*B*	*C*	*D*	*E*	*F*	Total
Totals for operators	138	143	137	132	155	127	832

Second, the correction factor *C* is calculated:

$$C = \frac{G^2}{r^2} = \frac{(832)^2}{(6)^2} = 19,228.44$$

Then, (*a*) The sum of the squares of all measurements is obtained:

$$(24)^2 + (20)^2 + (22)^2 + \cdots + (29)^2 + (33)^2 = 20,884$$

(*b*) The sum of squares of row totals is obtained, and then divided by the number of measurements in each row, that is, 6:

$$\frac{(113)^2 + (93)^2 + (108)^2 + (159)^2 + (172)^2 + (187)^2}{6} = 20,486.00$$

(c)   Similarly for the columns:

$$\frac{(143)^2 + (152)^2 + (149)^2 + (128)^2 + (133)^2 + (127)^2}{6} = 19,326.00$$

(d)   Similarly for the operators:

$$\frac{(138)^2 + (143)^2 + (137)^2 + (132)^2 + (155)^2 + (127)^2}{6} = 19,306.67$$

We can now form the table of the analysis of variance:

Source of variation	Sums of squares (s.s.)	Degrees of freedom ν	Mean square
Temperature (rows)	$(b) - C = 1{,}257.56$	$r - 1 = 5$	251.51
Nozzle type (columns)	$(c) - C = \ \ \ \ 97.56$	$r - 1 = 5$	19.51
Operators (treatments)	$(d) - C = \ \ \ \ 78.23$	$r - 1 = 5$	15.65
Residual error	222.21	$(r - 1)(r - 2) = 20$	11.11
Totals	$(a) - C = 1{,}655.56$	$r^2 - 1 = 35$	

The residual error of the sum of squares

= total (s.s.) − rows (s.s.) − columns (s.s.) − treatments (s.s.)

= 1,655.56 − 1,257.56 − 97.56 − 78.23

= 222.21

Each mean square is obtained by dividing the sums of squares by the corresponding degrees of freedom ν. The variance ratio F is then computed for the different effects:

Temperature:

$$F = \frac{\text{mean square of temperature variation}}{\text{mean square of residual error}} = \frac{251.51}{11.11} = 22.64$$

Nozzle type:

$$F = \frac{19.51}{11.11} = 1.76$$

Operator:

$$F = \frac{15.65}{11.11} = 1.41$$

From Table A-10, for $\nu_1 = 5$ and $\nu_2 = 20$, the F values are 4.10 at the 1 percent level of significance, 2.71 at the 5 percent level of significance, and 2.16 at the 10 percent level of significance.

We conclude that the temperature effect is significant at the 1 percent level of significance (in fact, it passes the 0.1 percent level[8]). However, both the nozzle type and the operators' effects do not reach the 10 percent

[8] See R. A. Fisher and F. Yates, *Statistical Tables for Biological and Medical Research* (Edinburgh: Oliver and Boyd, Ltd., 1963).

level of significance. (They fall between the 10 percent and the 20 percent level.[8]) Thus we can state that no definite effect on the volume of fuel due to different nozzles or operators is established.

Let us pursue further the effect of temperature on the volume of fuel. The mean volumes for the various temperatures are:

0°F	5°F	10°F	20°F	40°F	80°F
18.83	15.50	18.00	26.50	28.67	31.17

The estimated standard error of each of such means is $s_{\bar{x}} = \sqrt{s^2/n}$, where s^2 = residual error mean square = 11.11, and $n = r = 6$. Thus the estimated error of each mean, $s_{\bar{x}} = \sqrt{11.11/6} = 1.361$. For testing the difference between a pair of means, the standard error is

$$\sqrt{2}s_{\bar{x}} = \sqrt{2} \times 1.361 = 1.924$$

From Table A-8, the value of t at the 5 percent level of significance, for $\nu = 20$, is $t = 2.086$. Thus we have for the 95 percent confidence limits: $\pm(2.086)(1.924) = \pm 4.01$; that is, the difference between two means must be at least ± 4.01 in order to reach significance at this level.

$$\text{Mean volume} = \frac{832}{6 \times 6} = 23.11$$

and the 95 percent confidence interval = $23.11 \pm 4.01 = (27.12, 19.10)$.

By comparing the mean volumes for the various temperatures, we may be led to suspect that the temperature effects fall into 3 sets: (0°F, 5°F, 10°F), (20°F, 40°F), (80°F), but further study of the problem is outside the scope of this book.

BALANCED INCOMPLETE BLOCKS

The above procedure is simple but can be applied only if each block is large enough to include all the treatments. Suppose, however, that each batch is large enough only to make four specimens, but we want to compare five treatments.

The most efficient procedure is to use five batches of four, and to replicate each of the five treatments four times, the arrangement being that of a balanced incomplete block. This is illustrated below:

	Batch Number				
	1	2	3	4	5
Treatment	A	A	A	A	B
	B	B	B	C	C
	C	C	D	D	D
	D	E	E	E	E

We can note that:

(*a*)   Each treatment occurs once and only once in four of the batches;

(*b*)   Any specified pair of treatments occurs in three of the batches (e.g., *A* and *B* can be compared in batches 1, 2, and 3);

(*c*)   The two batches in which a direct comparison of treatments (e.g., *A* and *B* in batches 4 and 5) is not possible can provide a means of comparison for they each contain the remaining three treatments, *C*, *D*, and *E*. The average of these three can be considered as a "standard" against which the difference between *A* and *B* can be assessed.

Thus, although the blocks are incomplete, for none of them contains the full number of treatments, they are balanced because each treatment occurs to the same extent. The disadvantage of this method is that the number of replications necessary may be large, generally t treatments requiring $(\sqrt{t} + 1)$ replications.

MULTIPLE FACTOR EXPERIMENTS

The various blocks considered up to now are applicable only to experiments containing one independent variable, which we termed treatment. In many practical cases, we may have several independent variables. This problem is often approached by keeping all independent variables but one constant in each series of tests. While this may appear to be a reasonable approach, it is not always the best one, for the variables (referred to as factors) must necessarily be kept constant at an arbitrary value. The influence on some property of a variation in the factor *A* when the factor *B* is kept constant at value B_1 may be different from the influence when $B = B_2$. To detect this type of behavior, we may use the *factorial design* of experiments,[9] which has the additional advantage of giving the greatest amount of information about the given system of variables for the given amount of work. Specifically, information can be obtained about the *interaction* of the variables, i.e., the dependence of the effect of one factor on the value of another. This may be of considerable importance in many engineering applications. As a simple example, let us consider tests on the durability of concrete, in which we may vary the water/cement ratio, the type of aggregate, and the type of admixture. Suppose the following tests have been made:

Test number	Water/cement ratio	Type of aggregate	Type of admixture
1	0.4	normal weight	variable
2	variable	lightweight	*A*
3	0.7	variable	*B*

[9] An excellent treatment of this topic is given by K A Brownlee, *Industrial Experimentation* (London: H.M.S.O., 1960).

Test 1 may tell us which admixture is best from the standpoint of dura-bility, but this finding may not be true when we use lightweight instead of normal aggregate or a water/cement ratio of 0.7 instead of 0.4. The same may apply to the influence of aggregate when different admixtures or water/cement ratios are used. Of course, none of these variables may interact, admixture A being better than B whatever the other factors, and if we *know* this to be the case we need not worry about interaction. If, however, the assumption is unwarranted, ignoring the interaction may lead to completely erroneous conclusions.

In some cases we may choose deliberately to sacrifice the precision of the estimates of interactions, especially those of higher order, and reduce the size of the block, with an increase in the precision with which the average effects of the factors are estimated. This is the principle of *confounding*.

It is important to note that factorial experiments can be applied only when the dependent variable is a function of the sums of the functions of the independent variables, namely:

$$S = F_1(x) + F_2(y) + F_3(z) + \cdots \tag{20-3}$$

This limitation is not as restrictive as might appear at first since trans-formation can often reduce other forms to that of Eq. 20-3. For example,

$$S = x^b(\sin y)e^{fz}$$

can be transformed to

$$\log S = b \log x + \log \sin y + fz$$

CLASSICAL THREE-FACTOR EXPERIMENT

Let us consider the problem of the durability of concrete, and denote a measure of this dependent variable by x, and the three independent vari-ables by P, Q, and R. We assume that all the variables can be expressed quantitatively, e.g., the type of aggregate can be measured by its den-sity, etc.

Suppose that we have in hand data on the durability of concrete when P, Q, and R have values P_1, Q_1, and R_1, respectively. We now want to find the effect of changing the values to P_2, Q_2, and R_2; we are thus con-cerned with only two levels of each variable.

Let us denote the effect on x of changing P from P_1 to P_2 by $(P_1 - P_2)_x$. To determine this we observe, say, the value of x for P_1, Q_1, R_1 [denoted by $(P_1Q_1R_1)_x$] and the value of x for P_2, Q_1, R_1, that is, $(P_2Q_1R_1)_x$. We have thus

$$(P_1 - P_2)_x = (P_1Q_1R_1)_x - (P_2Q_1R_1)_x$$

This tells us nothing about $(P_1 - P_2)_x$ when $R = R_2$, and to deter-mine this we would have to find

$$(P_1 - P_2)_x = (P_1Q_1R_2)_x - (P_2Q_1R_2)_x$$

The procedure would be similar for $Q = Q_2$, and the appropriate combinations of the different values of Q and R.

The second important observation concerns the experimental error. If we make only one observation at P_1, Q_1, R_1 and one at P_2, Q_1, R_1, we cannot tell whether the difference between the observed values of x is real or is due to the errors of sampling, testing, etc. To make an estimate of the experimental error, at least two replications of each experiment are necessary. Thus, in order to determine $(P_1 - P_2)_x$, $(Q_1 - Q_2)_x$, and $(R_1 - R_2)_x$, each at *one* level of the other two factors, we have to make, for example, each of the following experiments twice: P_1, Q_1, R_1; P_2, Q_1, R_1; P_1, Q_2, R_1; and P_1, Q_1, R_2. This is a total of eight observations.

FACTORIAL THREE-FACTOR EXPERIMENT

Let us now consider the factorial design of the experiment. Here we need to perform experiments for all the possible combinations of the three factors, namely: P_1, Q_1, R_1; P_1, Q_2, R_1; P_1, Q_1, R_2; P_2, Q_1, R_1; P_2, Q_2, R_1; P_2, Q_1, R_2; P_2, Q_2, R_2; and P_1, Q_2, R_2. The number required is thus eight, which is the same as in the classical case.

Brownlee[10] represents the above combinations as coordinates of points on a system of axes P, Q, and R, with P_1, Q_1, R_1 as origin (Fig. 20-4).

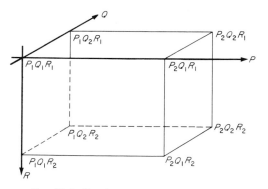

FIG. 20-4. Graphical representation of three-factor experiment.

Then $(P_1 - P_2)$, $(Q_1 - Q_2)$, and $(R_1 - R_2)$ are the edges of a rectangular parallelepiped. This enables us to visualize how to obtain an estimate of $(P_1 - P_2)_x$ for the various levels of the other two factors. Consider the plane containing the four points whose P coordinate is P_1. The average value of the dependent variable for these points characterizes P_1. Likewise, the average value for the plane containing the points for which $P = P_2$ characterizes P_2. The difference of the two averages is $(P_1 - P_2)_x$, that is, the effect on the dependent variable of changing the value of P from P_1 to P_2.

[10] *Ibid.*

Although the effects of the other two factors cancel out only approximately, the accuracy of our determination is twice as high as in the classical design since each value is a mean of four observations instead of the two in the classical case (for the same total number of experiments). The full number of observations enters every comparison, even though each treatment contains only a limited number of observations.

But the main advantage of factorial design lies in the fact that it enables us to estimate the interactions between the factors. For example, in order to estimate the interaction between Q and R, we average the values of the dependent variable for the pairs of points differing in P only. These are:

$$(Q_1 R_1)_x^P \qquad (Q_2 R_1)_x^P$$
$$(Q_1 R_2)_x^P \qquad (Q_2 R_2)_x^P$$

The top line gives $(Q_1 - Q_2)_x$ at $R = R_1$, and the bottom line gives $(Q_1 - Q_2)_x$ at $R = R_2$. Since each value is an average of two results, we can estimate the experimental error and hence determine whether $(Q_1 - Q_2)_x$ at $R = R_1$ is significantly different from $(Q_1 - Q_2)_x$ at $R = R_2$. If the difference is significant, there is interaction between Q and R. The same procedure can be used to determine the other interactions, and this gives us additional information on how each factor operates.

If the interactions are not significant, our results provide a better basis for generalized statements about the effects of each factor than if each factor had been tested with the others held at constant and arbitrary levels.

Example. An experiment was conducted to determine the pull-off force in pounds on glued parts of a piece of furniture. The completely randomized experiment was carried out by two operators at two temperatures and two humidities. There were $n = 10$ observations for each treatment, and the data were as follows:

Pull-off force, lb (coded)							
Temperature, cold (A_1)				Temperature, hot (A_2)			
Humitity 50% (B_1)		Humidity 90% (B_2)		Humidity 50% (B_1)		Humidity 90% (B_2)	
Operator C_1	Operator C_2	Operator C_1	Operator C_2	Operator C_1	Operator C_2	Operator C_1	Operator C_2
9	20	27	31	35	41	42	50
16	22	28	30	39	40	40	43
20	16	19	26	32	35	35	47
18	21	15	20	28	39	30	52
24	15	17	27	25	29	21	30
12	14	14	29	40	34	36	39
15	22	27	17	33	28	47	54
16	21	29	18	32	41	49	29
14	19	25	27	28	45	50	45
13	17	23	28	29	42	53	51
$\Sigma =$ 157	187	224	253	321	374	403	440

$G = 2,359$

Solution: Total up the columns as shown. Then

(a)   Calculate the correction factor

$$C = \frac{G^2}{8n} = \frac{(2,359)^2}{80} = 69,561.01$$

(b)   Sum the squares of all observations:

$$(9)^2 + (16)^2 + \cdots + (45)^2 + (51)^2 = 80,151.00$$

(c)   Sum the squares of the totals of each column, and divide this sum by the number of individual observations, that is, $n = 10$:

$$\frac{(157)^2 + (187)^2 + \cdots + (440)^2}{10} = 77,272.90$$

To test whether the treatment means differ significantly, we proceed as follows:

$$\text{Sum of squares for total} = (b) - C = 80,151.00 - 69,561.01$$
$$= 10,589.99$$

$$\text{Sum of squares for treatments} = (c) - C = 77,272.90 - 69,561.01$$
$$= 7,711.89$$

Thus in tabular form:

Source of variation	Sum of squares (s.s.)	ν	Mean square
Treatments.............	7,711.89	$t - 1 = 7$	1,101.7
Within treatments	2,878.10	$t(n - 1) = 72$	39.97
Total	10,589.99	79	

$$\text{Within treatments sum of squares} = \text{total (s.s.)} - \text{treatments (s.s.)}$$
$$= 2,878.10$$

Testing the treatments mean square for significance, we have

$$F = \frac{1,101.7}{39.97} = 27.6$$

which is much greater than the value of F for $\nu_1 = 7$ and $\nu_2 = 72$, from Table A-10 at the 1 percent level of significance. We therefore conclude that the treatment means differ very significantly.

PARTITIONING THE TREATMENTS SUM OF SQUARES

The treatments sum of squares, having 7 degrees of freedom, can be divided into 7 components, each with one degree of freedom, i.e.,

1. Sum of squares for A, the temperature effect
2. Sum of squares for B, the humidity effect

3. Sum of squares for C, the operator effect
4. Interaction between the temperature effect and humidity effect, $A \times B$
5. Interaction between the temperature effect and operator effect, $A \times C$
6. Interaction between the humidity effect and operator effect, $B \times C$
7. Interaction among the temperature, humidity, and operator effects, $A \times B \times C$

THE MAIN EFFECTS A, B, AND C

To compare A_1 with A_2, we have the sum of pull-off forces:
for $A_1 = 157 + 187 + 224 + 253 = 821$ lb
for $A_2 = 321 + 374 + 403 + 440 = 1{,}538$ lb
For each of these the sum is based upon $4 \times 10 = 40$ measurements. Thus

$$\text{Sum of squares for } A = \frac{(821)^2 + (1538)^2}{40} - C$$

$$= 75{,}987.13 - 69{,}561.01 = 6{,}426.12$$

Similarly, to compare B_1 with B_2, we have the sum of pull-off forces:
for $B_1 = 157 + 187 + 321 + 374 = 1{,}039$ lb
for $B_2 = 224 + 253 + 403 + 440 = 1{,}320$ lb

$$\text{Sum of squares for } B = \frac{(1{,}039)^2 + (1{,}320)^2}{40} - C$$

$$= 70{,}548.03 - 69{,}561.01 = 987.02$$

To compare C_1 with C_2, we take the sum of pull-off forces:
for $C_1 = 157 + 224 + 321 + 403 = 1{,}105$ lb
for $C_2 = 187 + 253 + 374 + 440 = 1{,}254$ lb

$$\text{Sum of squares for } C = \frac{(1{,}105)^2 + (1{,}254)^2}{40} - C$$

$$= 69{,}838.53 - 69{,}561.01 = 277.52$$

THE INTERACTIONS A × B, B × C, A × C, A × B × C

The interactions sum of squares may be obtained from the formula

$$A \times B \text{ interaction sum of squares} = \frac{[(a + d) - (b + c)]^2}{(4)(n_1)}$$

where the factors a, b, c, and d are sums corresponding to the arrangement shown in the following table:

	B_1	B_2
A_1	a	b
A_2	c	d

and n_1 is the number of observations contributing to each of the above sums; that is, $2 \times 10 = 20$ observations in our case. Similarly, the tables for interactions $A \times C$ and $B \times C$ are as follows:

	C_1	C_2
A_1	a	b
A_2	c	d

	C_1	C_2
B_1	a	b
B_2	c	d

Thus the sum for

$$A_1 B_1 = a = 157 + 187 = 344$$
$$A_1 B_2 = b = 224 + 253 = 477$$
$$A_2 B_1 = c = 321 + 374 = 695$$
$$A_2 B_2 = d = 403 + 440 = 843$$

Similarly, the sum for

$$A_1 C_1 = a = 157 + 224 = 381$$
$$A_1 C_2 = b = 187 + 253 = 440$$
$$A_2 C_1 = c = 321 + 403 = 724$$
$$A_2 C_2 = d = 374 + 440 = 814$$

Finally, the sum for

$$B_1 C_1 = a = 157 + 321 = 478$$
$$B_1 C_2 = b = 187 + 374 = 561$$
$$B_2 C_1 = c = 224 + 403 = 627$$
$$B_2 C_2 = d = 253 + 440 = 693$$

In tabular form:

	B_1	B_2	$\Sigma =$
A_1	344	477	821
A_2	695	843	1,538
$\Sigma =$	1,039	1,320	2,359

	C_1	C_2	$\Sigma =$
A_1	381	440	821
A_2	724	814	1,538
$\Sigma =$	1,105	1,254	2,359

	C_1	C_2	$\Sigma =$
B_1	478	561	1,039
B_2	627	693	1,320
$\Sigma =$	1,105	1,254	2,359

Substituting the numerical values of a, b, c, and d in the formula, we obtain for:

$$A \times B \text{ interaction sum of squares} = \frac{[(344 + 843) - (477 + 695)]^2}{(4)(20)}$$
$$= 2.81$$

$$A \times C \text{ interaction sum of squares} = \frac{[(381 + 814) - (440 + 724)]^2}{(4)(20)}$$
$$= 12.01$$

$$B \times C \text{ interaction sum of squares } = \frac{[(478 + 693) - (561 + 627)]^2}{(4)(20)}$$

$$= 3.61$$

The number of degrees of freedom associated with any interaction sum of squares equals the product of the degrees of freedom associated with the factors for which the interaction is being calculated; that is, the number of degrees of freedom for $A \times B$ interaction sum of squares is the number of degrees of freedom for factor A times the number of degrees of freedom for factor B, viz. $1 \times 1 = 1$. Thus the number of degrees of freedom for each of $A \times B$, $A \times C$, $B \times C$, $A \times B \times C$ interaction sums of squares is 1.

Since the treatments sum of squares is known, then

$$\begin{aligned} A \times B \times C \text{ interaction} \atop \text{sum of squares} &= \text{treatment sum of squares} \\ &\quad - (\text{sum of the sums of squares for} \\ &\qquad A, B, C, A \times B, A \times C, \text{ and } B \times C) \\ &= 7{,}711.89 - (6{,}426.12 + 987.02 \\ &\qquad + 277.52 + 2.81 + 12.01 + 3.61) \\ &= 2.80 \end{aligned}$$

The summary of the complete analysis of variance is given in the following table:

	Source of variation	Sum of squares	ν	Mean square	F
A	Temperature	6,426.12	1	6,426.12	160.77
B	Humidity	987.02	1	987.02	24.69
C	Operator	277.52	1	277.52	6.94
$A \times B$	Temperature × humidity	2.81	1	2.81	
$A \times C$	Temperature × operator	12.01	1	12.01	
$B \times C$	Humidity × operator	3.61	1	3.61	
$A \times B \times C$	Temperature × humidity × operator	2.80	1	2.80	
Error	Within treatments	2,878.10	72	39.97	
Totals		10,589.99	79		

The values of F were obtained by dividing each of the mean squares by the error mean square, 39.97. Since the four interaction mean squares were less than the error mean square, the F values for these were not calculated, and we can say that the four interactions are not significant.

From Table A-10, we find that for $\nu_1 = 1$ and $\nu_2 = 72$, $F = 7.00$ approximately, at the 1 percent level of significance. Thus the main effects, A and B, are highly significant. The effect of C is almost significant at the 1 percent level. It is definitely significant at the 5 percent level, where $F = 3.98$ approximately.

MEANING OF THE MAIN AND INTERACTION EFFECTS

The main effect of A represents a comparison between the means of force for cold temperature A_1 and for the hot temperature A_2, averaged over the two levels of B and the two levels of C. The mean for A_1 is obtained from the original data and is equal to $821/40 = 20.525$ lb. The mean for $A_2 = 1,538/40 = 38.45$ lb. Since the A mean square is significant, we can conclude that these two means differ significantly; i.e., glued parts of a furniture piece become stronger with increase in temperature within the range of the experiment. Similarly, for the humidity effect B, the mean force for $B_1 = 1,039/40 = 25.975$ lb, and the mean force for $B_2 = 1,320/40 = 33.00$ lb. Since the analysis of variance showed the mean square for B to be significant, we can state that the means of forces for B_1 and B_2 differ significantly; i.e., the glued parts of the furniture become stronger with increase in humidity, in the range of the experiment. The same procedure can be followed in comparing the means of force, $1,105/40$ and $1,254/40$, for the two operators C_1 and C_2, respectively. The difference in means is significant at the 5 percent level, but not quite significant at the 1 percent level.

The meaning of the interaction effects being nonsignificant is that the difference between the means due to a main effect for one level is not significantly different from the difference between the means due to the same effect at a higher level. For example, the statement that $A \times C$ interaction mean square is not significant is interpreted to say that the difference between means of force due to A_1 and A_2 for the first level of C is not significantly different from the differences between the means of force due to A_1 and A_2 for the second level of C. With a nonsignificant $A \times C$ interaction, we can state that the A effect, the difference between the effect of A_1 and A_2 on the force, is independent of C; that is, we have approximately the same difference between the effect of A_1 and A_2 on the force regardless of the levels of C. Similar explanations can be made of the nonsignificance of $A \times B$, $B \times C$, and $A \times B \times C$.

GRAPHICAL INTERPRETATION

We can also examine interaction effects, say $A \times B$, by taking factor B for the x-axis and plotting the means of force for each level of A; that is, corresponding to B_1,

$$\text{Mean for } A_1 = \frac{344}{20} = 17.2 \text{ lb}$$

$$\text{Mean for } A_2 = \frac{695}{20} = 34.75 \text{ lb}$$

and corresponding to B_2:

$$\text{Mean for } A_1 = \frac{477}{20} = 23.85 \text{ lb}$$

$$\text{Mean for } A_2 = \frac{843}{20} = 42.15 \text{ lb}$$

These values are shown plotted in Fig. 20-5a. If the lines for A_1 and A_2 were exactly parallel, the $A \times B$ interaction would be zero. In fact, the lines are very nearly parallel (within the limits of random sampling), which shows that the $A \times B$ interaction is not significant. Similar graphical representation of the $A \times C$ and $B \times C$ interactions can be given.

For the nature of the $A \times B \times C$ interaction, we consider the $A \times B$ interaction separately for each level of C, as shown in the following table. This table shows the means of force due to A and B for each level of C, as obtained from the original data.

	C_1		C_2	
	B_1	B_2	B_1	B_2
A_1	15.7	22.4	18.7	25.3
A_2	32.1	40.3	37.4	44.0

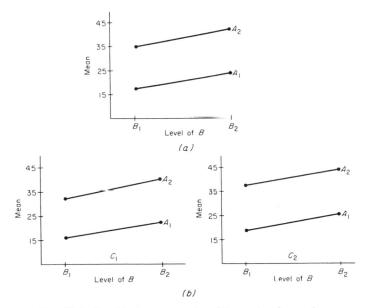

FIG. 20-5. Graphical representation of the results of example on page 275. (a) Means for levels of A at each level of B. (b) Means for levels of A at each level of B for C_1 and C_2, respectively.

The graphs for A_1 and A_2 versus B for levels C_1 and C_2, respectively, are shown in Fig. 20-5b. We notice that the forms of these graphs are similar, which confirms our finding of the nonsignificance of the $A \times B \times C$ interaction mean square. In other words, this nonsignificance means that the $A \times C$ interactions for the separate levels of B are of the same form; that the $A \times B$ interactions for the separate levels of C are of the same form; and that the $B \times C$ interactions for the separate levels of A are of the same form.

RANDOM NUMBERS

On several occasions we have achieved randomization by drawing numbered cards "from a hat." With a large number of items involved this becomes tedious, and it may be more convenient to use a table of random numbers, such as Table A-14.

There exist numerous methods of using the table. For example, in order to arrange the numbers 1 to 13 in a random order, we can select any row, column, or diagonal in the table, and record the numbers 1 to 13 as they occur.

It may be quicker to read all the numbers in order, and to divide each by 13, recording the remainder. Any remainder which has already been obtained is rejected. Since the remainders will be between 0 and 12 inclusive, we consider 0 as 13. We should note that since the highest possible two-digit multiple of 13 is 91, the remainders 1, 2,...8, have a higher chance of occurring than others. To remove this bias, we ignore the numbers 92, 93, ..., 99.

As an alternative, we can use the divisor 20 instead of 13, rejecting any number which gives 0, 14, 15, 16, 17, 18, 19. Thus, using the fifth column of Table A-14, we record: 7, 14̷, 6, 9, 0̷, 9̷, 2, 9̷, 15̷, 7, 0̷, 19̷, 2̷, 0̷, 0̷, 15̷, 4, 17̷, 14̷, 10, 1, 0̷, 11, 19̷, 4̷, 16̷, 3, 8, 0̷, 5, 19̷, 12, 13, that is, 7, 6, 9, 2, 4, 10, 1, 11, 3, 8, 5, 12, 13.

SOLVED PROBLEM

20-1. The breaking strength of a fabric has been determined from numerous tests to be 250 lb, with a standard deviation due to testing of 18 lb. Recently a new manufacturing process X was introduced which seems to increase the strength of the fabric.

(*a*) Find the criterion for rejecting the old manufacturing process A at a 1 percent level of significance when 36 specimens of the fabric are tested.

(*b*) Using the criterion found in (*a*), and assuming that the standard deviation remains due to testing at 18 lb, find the probability of accepting process A when process X has, in fact, improved on the mean strength to the value of 265 lb.

(*c*) Construct a power curve for the test of the hypothesis and interpret the graph.

Solution:

(a) From Table A-4 for a one-tailed test, at a 1 percent level of significance (see Fig. 20-6*a*), the value of z corresponding to $F(z) = 0.49$ is $z = 2.33$. But,

$$z = \frac{\bar{x} - 250}{\sigma_T/\sqrt{n}} = \frac{\bar{x} - 250}{18/\sqrt{36}} = \frac{\bar{x} - 250}{3}$$

$$= 2.33$$

Hence,

$$\bar{x} = 250 + 3 \times 2.33$$

$$= 257 \text{ lb}$$

Therefore, the criterion is: Reject the hypothesis that process X is the same as process A, if the mean breaking strength of 36 fabric specimens > 257 lb. Otherwise accept the hypothesis.

(b) Fig. 20-6*b* shows the two normal distributions corresponding to means of 250 lb and 265 lb. The probability of accepting process A when the new

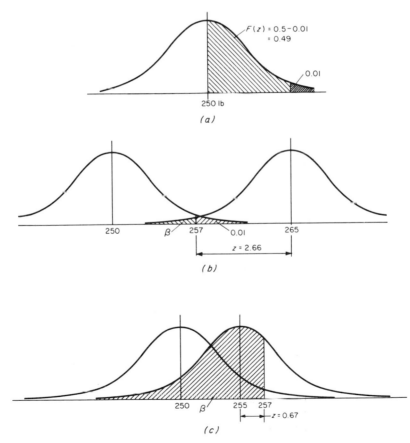

FIG. 20-6

mean breaking strength is actually 265 lb (Type II error) is represented by the region marked β. To calculate the probability of committing a Type II error, we proceed as follows: Deviation of 265 from 257 in terms of $\sigma_{\bar{x}}$ is

$$\frac{265 - 257}{\sigma_T/\sqrt{n}} = \frac{8}{18/6} = 2.66$$

Thus, using Table A-4, β = area under the right-hand normal curve to left of $z = 2.66$, that is, $0.5 - 0.4961 = 0.0039$ (small indeed).

(*c*)   In order to draw the power curve, we have to find β for various breaking strengths of the fabric manufactured by the new process X. Thus, if the breaking strength by the new process X is, say 255 lb, then its deviation from 257 lb in terms of $\sigma_{\bar{x}}$ is

$$\frac{257 - 255}{18/\sqrt{36}} = 0.67$$

Using Table A-4, β = shaded area in Fig. 20-6*c*, that is, $0.5 +$ the area under the right-hand normal curve between $z = 0$ and $z = 0.67$. Thus

$$\beta = 0.5 + 0.2486 = 0.7486$$

Following the above procedure, we can compile the following table for β corresponding to the mean breaking strength μ.

μ	240	245	250	255	260	265	270
β	1.0000	1.0000	0.9901	0.7486	0.1587	0.0039	0.0000

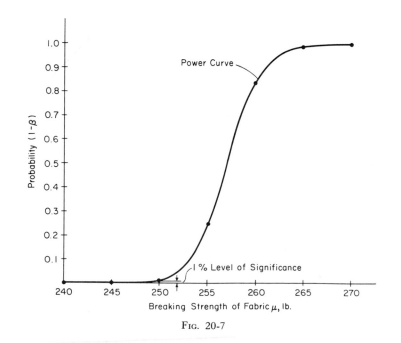

Fig. 20-7

Plotting μ versus $(1 - \beta)$ yields the power curve shown in Fig. 20-7. This curve indicates the power of the test to reject false hypothesis. We notice from this curve that the probability of rejecting process A if the new breaking strength is less than 250 lb is practically nil. On the other hand, we see that the curve rises sharply, so that it is with almost a certainty that we reject the hypothesis of maintaining process A when the mean breaking strength is greater than 265 lb. Note the point of inflection on the power curve at $\mu = 257$ lb and $(1 - \beta) = 0.5$.

PROBLEMS

20-1. From previous data it was found that a certain chemical process produced a mean yield of 10 units with a standard deviation $\sigma_T = 0.3$. It is believed that by a newly developed process the mean yield can be increased.

 (a) If it is agreed to run 36 tests, design a decision rule for rejecting the old process at the 1 percent level of significance.

 (b) Following this decision rule, what is the probability of accepting the old process, when in fact the new process has increased the yield to 10.8? Assume the same standard deviation as before.

 (c) Construct the power curve for the process with $\sigma_T = 0.3$.

 (d) What sample size is necessary if the power of the test is to be 98 percent?

20-2. A project requires the use of components whose density has a coded value of at least 100. It is known from past experience that the standard deviation due to testing is 11. It is decided that the probability of accepting components with a density of 94 is to be 0.1, and the probability of rejecting those with a density of 112 is to be 0.1. Find a sample size n in order to avoid having either risk exceed the desired value. Hence draw a power curve for these decision rules.

20-3. The average production figures for four shifts measured during four years are as shown below. Establish the production trends within the working day and over the years.

Year	Shift			
	12 mdnt–6 a.m.	6 a.m.–12 noon	12 noon–6 p.m.	6 p.m.–12 mdnt
1	9.8	12.1	15.8	11.7
2	9.5	11.8	15.5	11.7
3	11.8	15.5	17.2	13.6
4	13.9	15.4	17.2	14.6

20-4. In order to decide on the choice of a clay for the manufacture of artificial aggregate, samples were obtained from three sources and were treated by two processes. The coded results of the performance of the clay are as follows:

Process	Source			Process	Source		
	I	II	III		I	II	III
A	9	11	16	B	13	11	16
	12	13	15		15	13	17
	13	13	17		17	14	15
	16	15	16		12	13	18
	15	16	16		15	16	18

Test whether the performance depends on the source of clay or the process by which it was treated. The 5 percent level of significance is suggested as a basis for making decisions.

20-5. To check the variation of gage blocks and of the sensitive devices measuring them, the manufacturer chose at random five gage blocks and five micrometers and asked five quality control engineers, A, B, C, D, and E to carry out the experiment. The $\frac{1}{2}$-inch gage blocks were used with the following coded results:

Gage blocks	Micrometer				
	1	2	3	4	5
1	B 95	E 101	D 109	C 99	A 95
2	C 97	A 104	B 104	E 98	D 105
3	D 98	B 99	C 105	A 95	E 99
4	E 101	C 98	A 99	D 102	B 97
5	A 100	D 102	E 97	B 103	C 101

Assume there is no interaction present.

(*a*) Estimate the component of the variance due to micrometers.

(*b*) Estimate the component of the variance due to gage blocks.

(*c*) Estimate the component of the variance due to engineers.

(*d*) Test for micrometer and gage block effects at the 1 percent level of significance.

(*e*) Test for engineer effects at the 5 percent level of significance.

Appendices

Bessel's Correction

Consider a sample of size n drawn from a population with a mean μ and standard deviation σ.

Let x_i be an observation in the sample. Then

$$x_i - \mu = (x_i - \bar{x}) + (\bar{x} - \mu)$$
$$= (x_i - \bar{x}) - \epsilon$$

where $\epsilon = \mu - \bar{x}$ is the "error" or deviation of the sample mean, $\bar{x}$. Squaring, we obtain

$$(x_i - \mu)^2 = (x_i - \bar{x})^2 + \epsilon^2 - 2\epsilon(x_i - \bar{x})$$

For all the observations in the sample, we sum for i from 1 to n, and obtain

$$\Sigma(x_i - \mu)^2 = \Sigma(x_i - \bar{x})^2 + n\epsilon^2 - 2\epsilon\Sigma(x_i - \bar{x})$$

But

$$\Sigma(x_i - \bar{x}) = 0 \quad \text{by definition of } \bar{x}$$

Therefore

$$\Sigma(x_i - \mu)^2 = \Sigma(x_i - \bar{x})^2 + n\epsilon^2$$

If we repeat this calculation for a large number of samples, the mean value of the left-hand side of the above equation will (by definition of σ^2) tend to $n\sigma^2$. Similarly, the mean value of $n\epsilon^2 = n(\mu - \bar{x})^2$ will tend to n times the variance of $\bar{x}$, since ϵ represents the deviation of the sample mean from the population mean. Thus

$$n\epsilon^2 \longrightarrow n\left(\frac{\sigma^2}{n}\right)$$

whence

$$n\sigma^2 \longrightarrow \Sigma(x_i - \bar{x})^2 + \sigma^2$$

or

$$\Sigma(x_i - \bar{x})^2 \longrightarrow (n - 1)\sigma^2$$

Thus

$$\frac{\Sigma(x_i - \bar{x})^2}{n - 1} \longrightarrow \sigma^2$$

In other words, for a large number of random samples, the mean value of $\dfrac{\Sigma(x_i - \bar{x})^2}{n - 1}$ tends to σ^2, that is, it is an unbiased estimate of the variance of the population. The estimate is denoted by s^2. Thus

$$s^2 = \frac{\Sigma(x_i - \bar{x})^2}{n - 1}$$ [4-3]

Since the variance of the sample (taken as a finite population with a mean $\bar{x}$) σ^2 is given by

$$\sigma^2 = \frac{\Sigma(x_i - \bar{x})^2}{n}$$

Bessel's correction is

$$\frac{s^2}{\sigma^2} = \frac{n}{n - 1}$$

Mean and Standard Deviation of a Binomial Distribution

Consider the expansion

$$(q + p)^n = q^n + \frac{n}{1!} q^{n-1}p + \frac{n(n-1)}{2!} q^{n-2}p^2 + \cdots$$

$$+ \frac{n(n-1) \cdots (n-r+1)}{r!} q^{n-r}p^r + \cdots + p^n$$

where r varies from $r = 0$ to $r = n$. We can tabulate the following values:

r	Probability f	fr	fr^2	$fr^2 - fr$
0	q^n	0	0	0
1	$nq^{n-1}p$	$nq^{n-1}p$	$nq^{n-1}p$	0
2	$\dfrac{n(n-1)}{2!} q^{n-2}p^2$	$n(n-1)q^{n-2}p^2$	$2n(n-1)q^{n-2}p^2$	$n(n-1)q^{n-2}p^2$
.	.	.	.	.
.	.	.	.	.
.	.	.	.	.
$n-1$	$\dfrac{n!}{(n-1)!} qp^{n-1}$ $= nqp^{n-1}$	$n(n-1)qp^{n-1}$	$n(n-1)^2 qp^{n-1}$	$n(n-1)(n-2)qp^{n-1}$
n	p^n	np^n	$n^2 p^n$	$(n-1)np^n$
	$\Sigma f = (q+p)^n$ $= 1$	$\Sigma fr = np(q+p)^{n-1}$ $= np(1)^{n-1}$ $= np$		$\Sigma(fr^2 - fr) = n(n-1)p^2$ $\times (q+p)^{n-2}$ $= n(n-1)p^2$

Hence

$$\text{Mean} = \mu = \frac{\Sigma fr}{\Sigma f} = \frac{np}{1} = np \qquad [7\text{-}4]$$

Now

$$\Sigma(fr^2 - fr) = \Sigma fr^2 - \Sigma fr = n(n-1)p^2$$

Appendix B

Hence

$$\Sigma fr^2 = n(n-1)p^2 + \Sigma fr$$
$$= n(n-1)p^2 + np$$
$$= (np)^2 + np(1-p)$$
$$= \mu^2 + npq$$

From Eq. 4-4:

$$\sigma^2 = \frac{\Sigma fr^2}{\Sigma f} - \mu^2$$
$$= \frac{\mu^2 + npq}{1} - \mu^2$$
$$= npq$$

Hence

$$\sigma = \sqrt{npq} \qquad\qquad [7\text{-}5]$$

Mean and Standard Deviation of Terms of Expansion of $(\frac{1}{2} + \frac{1}{2})^{2n}$

Let the abscissae for which the expansion gives the ordinates vary in steps of Δx. We can then tabulate the values as shown on page 294. Hence

$$\text{Mean} = \mu = \frac{\Sigma f_i x_i}{\Sigma f_i} = 2np\,\Delta x$$

Since $p = \frac{1}{2}$,

$$\mu = n\Delta x \qquad [9\text{-}6]$$

Now

$$\Sigma[f_i x_i^2 - f_i x_i(\Delta x)] = \Sigma f_i x_i^2 - (\Delta x)\Sigma f_i x_i$$

Hence

$$\Sigma f_i x_i^2 = (\Delta x)\Sigma f_i x_i + (2n - 1)(2n)(\Delta x)^2 p^2 (q + p)^{2n-2}$$

$$= 2np(\Delta x)^2 + (2n - 1)(2n)(\Delta x)^2 p^2$$

Since $p = q = \frac{1}{2}$,

$$\Sigma f_i x_i^2 = n(\Delta x)^2 - \frac{n}{2}(\Delta x)^2 + n^2(\Delta x)^2$$

$$= \mu^2 + \frac{n}{2}(\Delta x)^2$$

From Eq. 4-4,

$$\sigma^2 = \frac{\Sigma f_i x_i^2}{\Sigma f_i} - \mu^2$$

$$= \mu^2 + \frac{n}{2}(\Delta x)^2 - \mu^2$$

or

$$\sigma^2 = \frac{n}{2}(\Delta x)^2 \qquad [9\text{-}7]$$

x_i	Probability f_i	$f_i x_i$	$f_i x_i^2$	$f_i x_i^2 - f_i x_i(\Delta x)$
0	q^{2n}	0	0	0
Δx	$2nq^{2n-1}p$	$2n\Delta x q^{2n-1}p$	$2n(\Delta x)^2 q^{2n-1}p$	0
$2\Delta x$	$\dfrac{2n(2n-1)}{2!}q^{2n-2}p^2$	$2n\Delta x(2n-1)q^{2n-2}p^2$	$4n(\Delta x)^2(2n-1)q^{2n-2}p^2$	$2n(\Delta x)^2(2n-1)q^{2n-2}p^2$
$\cdot$	$\cdot$	$\cdot$	$\cdot$	$\cdot$
$\cdot$	$\cdot$	$\cdot$	$\cdot$	$\cdot$
$(2n-1)\Delta x$	$2nqp^{2n-1}$	$(2n-1)\Delta x(2n)qp^{2n-1}$	$(2n-1)^2(\Delta x)^2(2n)qp^{2n-1}$	$(2n-2)(2n)(\Delta x)^2(2n-1)qp^{2n-1}$
$2n\Delta x$	p^{2n}	$2n\Delta x p^{2n}$	$4n^2(\Delta x)^2 p^{2n}$	$2n(\Delta x)^2(2n-1)p^{2n}$
	$\Sigma f_i = (q+p)^{2n} = 1$	$\begin{aligned}\Sigma f_i x_i &= 2np\Delta x(q+p)^{2n-1} \\ &= 2np\Delta x\end{aligned}$		$\begin{aligned}&\Sigma[f_i x_i^2 - f_i x_i(\Delta x)] \\ &= (2n-1)(2n)(\Delta x)^2 p^2(q+p)^{2n-2}\end{aligned}$

Evaluation of

$$\int_{-\infty}^{+\infty} e^{-\dfrac{X^2}{2\sigma^2}}\, dX$$

To evaluate the integral

$$I = \int_{-\infty}^{+\infty} e^{-\frac{X^2}{2\sigma^2}}\, dX$$

let

$$I_1 = \int_{-a}^{+a} e^{-\frac{X^2}{2\sigma^2}}\, dX$$

Using an arbitrary variable y, we can also write:

$$I_1 = \int_{-a}^{+a} e^{-\frac{y^2}{2\sigma^2}}\, dy$$

Hence

$$I_1^2 = \int_{-a}^{+a} \int_{-a}^{+a} e^{-\frac{(X^2+y^2)}{2\sigma^2}}\, dX dy$$

As a physical interpretation of this integral, we can imagine it to represent the volume under a surface of height $e^{-\frac{(X^2+y^2)}{2\sigma^2}}$ on a square base of side a (Fig. D-1).

Let the square be $ABCD$ as shown in the figure. If we inscribe and circumscribe the square $ABCD$ by two circles, then the integral I_1^2 will be intermediate in value between the integrals I_3 and I_4, corresponding respectively to the volumes with the two circles as a base. Using polar coordinates,

$$I_3 = \int_0^{+a} \int_0^{2\pi} e^{\frac{-r^2}{2\sigma^2}}\, r d\theta\, dr$$

and

$$I_4 = \int_0^{a\sqrt{2}} \int_0^{2\pi} e^{\frac{-r^2}{2\sigma^2}}\, r d\theta\, dr$$

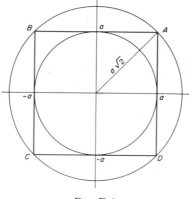

F<small>IG</small>. D-1

Hence

$$\int_0^{2\pi} d\theta \int_0^a r e^{\frac{-r^2}{2\sigma^2}} dr < I_1^2 < \int_0^{2\pi} d\theta \int_0^{a\sqrt{2}} r e^{\frac{-r^2}{2\sigma^2}} dr$$

However, as $a \to \infty$, the integrals on the right-hand side and left-hand side converge to

$$2\pi \int_0^\infty \sigma^2 \frac{r}{\sigma^2} e^{\frac{-r^2}{2\sigma^2}} dr = 2\pi\sigma^2 \left[-e^{\frac{-r^2}{2\sigma^2}} \right]_0^\infty$$

$$= 2\pi\sigma^2$$

Hence

$$I^2 = \lim_{a \to \infty} I_1^2 = 2\pi\sigma^2$$

or

$$\int_{-\infty}^{+\infty} e^{-\frac{X^2}{2\sigma^2}} dX = \sigma\sqrt{2\pi} \qquad\qquad [9\text{-}12]$$

Relation Between
t and r

Equation 15-32 gives the test for the significance of slope as

$$t = \frac{b}{s_b}$$

The correlation coefficient is given by Eq. 16-6 as

$$r = \frac{\Sigma X \hat{Y}}{\sqrt{\Sigma X^2 \Sigma Y^2}}$$

Now, from Eq. 15-18,

$$b = \frac{\Sigma XY}{\Sigma X^2}$$

and from Eq. 15-24,

$$s_b^2 = \frac{s_y^2}{\Sigma X^2}$$

Also, from Eq. 15-22,

$$s_y^2 = \frac{\Sigma \epsilon_i^2}{n - 2}$$
$$= \frac{\Sigma(Y - \hat{Y})^2}{n - 2}$$

Since

$$\hat{Y} = bX$$

we can expand:

$$\Sigma(Y - \hat{Y})^2 = \Sigma Y^2 - 2b\Sigma XY + b^2\Sigma X^2$$
$$= (\Sigma Y^2)\left[1 + \frac{b(b\Sigma X^2 - 2\Sigma XY)}{\Sigma Y^2}\right]$$
$$= (\Sigma Y^2)\left[1 + \frac{(\Sigma XY)(\Sigma XY - 2\Sigma XY)}{\Sigma X^2 \Sigma Y^2}\right]$$
$$= (\Sigma Y^2)\left[1 - \frac{(\Sigma XY)^2}{\Sigma X^2 \Sigma Y^2}\right]$$

Hence

$$s_b^2 = \frac{\Sigma Y^2}{(n-2)\Sigma X^2}\left[1 - \frac{(\Sigma XY)^2}{\Sigma X^2 \Sigma Y^2}\right]$$

and

$$t = \frac{\Sigma XY(n-2)^{1/2}(\Sigma X^2)^{1/2}}{(\Sigma X^2)\left\{\Sigma Y^2\left[1 - \frac{(\Sigma XY)^2}{\Sigma X^2 \Sigma Y^2}\right]\right\}^{1/2}}$$

$$= \frac{r\sqrt{n-2}}{\sqrt{1-r^2}}$$

Proof that the Regression Plane Contains the Centroidal Point

Let $(\bar{y}, \bar{x}_1, \bar{x}_2)$ be the centroid of all observations. Dividing the first of Eqs. 17-5 by n, we obtain

$$b_0 + b_1 \frac{\Sigma x_1}{n} + b_2 \frac{\Sigma x_2}{n} = \frac{\Sigma y}{n}$$

Hence the definition of centroid

$$b_0 + b_1 \bar{x}_1 + b_2 \bar{x}_2 = \bar{y}$$

which proves that $(\bar{y}, \bar{x}_1, \bar{x}_2)$ lies on the plane.

Tables

TABLE A-1
RANGE COEFFICIENT d

Number of observations n	Coefficient d	Number of observations n	Coefficient d
2	0.8862	14	0.2935
3	0.5908	15	0.2880
4	0.4857	16	0.2831
5	0.4299	17	0.2787
6	0.3945	18	0.2747
7	0.3698	19	0.2711
8	0.3512	20	0.2677
9	0.3367	24	0.2567
10	0.3249	50	0.2223
11	0.3152	100	0.1994
12	0.3069	1,000	0.1543
13	0.2998		

This table gives values of d in equation $s = \bar{R}d$ for the estimate of the standard deviations from mean range $\bar{R}$. This method of estimating s is valid only when the underlying variate is approximately normally distributed.

This table is reproduced by permission of the author and the publishers from a paper "On the Extreme Individuals and the Range of Samples Taken from a Normal Population," by L. H. C. Tippett, *Biometrika*, Vol. 17 (1925), pp. 364–387 and from Table 22 of *Biometrika Tables for Statisticians*, Vol. 1, (London: Cambridge University Press, 1954).

TABLE A-2
VALUES OF $e^{-\mu}$

μ	0.00	0.01	0.02	0.03	0.04	0.05	0.06	0.07	0.08	0.09
0.0	1.000	0.990	0.980	0.971	0.961	0.951	0.942	0.932	0.923	0.914

μ	0.0	0.1	0.2	0.3	0.4	0.5	0.6	0.7	0.8	0.9
0.0	1.000	0.905	0.819	0.741	0.670	0.607	0.549	0.497	0.449	0.407
1.0	0.368	0.333	0.301	0.273	0.247	0.223	0.202	0.183	0.165	0.150
2.0	0.135	0.122	0.111	0.100	0.091	0.082	0.074	0.067	0.061	0.055
3.0	0.050	0.045	0.041	0.037	0.034	0.030	0.028	0.025	0.023	0.020
4.0	0.018	0.016	0.015	0.014	0.013	0.011	0.010	0.0091	0.0082	0.0074
5.0	0.0067									

Intermediate values of $e^{-\mu}$ can be obtained by making use of the values in the upper part of the table. For example, the value of $e^{-1.11} = e^{-1.1} \times e^{-0.01} = 0.333 \times 0.990 = 0.330$.

TABLE A-3
ORDINATES OF THE NORMAL CURVE

$$y = \frac{1}{\sqrt{2\pi}} \, e^{\frac{-z^2}{2}}$$

z	.00	.01	.02	.03	.04	.05	.06	.07	.08	.09
.0	.3989	.3989	.3989	.3988	.3986	.3984	.3982	.3980	.3977	.3973
.1	.3970	.3965	.3961	.3956	.3951	.3945	.3939	.3932	.3925	.3918
.2	.3910	.3902	.3894	.3885	.3876	.3867	.3857	.3847	.3836	.3825
.3	.3814	.3802	.3790	.3778	.3765	.3752	.3739	.3725	.3712	.3697
.4	.3683	.3668	.3653	.3637	.3621	.3605	.3589	.3572	.3555	.3538
.5	.3521	.3503	.3485	.3467	.3448	.3429	.3410	.3391	.3372	.3352
.6	.3332	.3312	.3292	.3271	.3251	.3230	.3209	.3187	.3166	.3144
.7	.3123	.3101	.3079	.3056	.3034	.3011	.2989	.2966	.2943	.2920
.8	.2897	.2874	.2850	.2827	.2803	.2780	.2756	.2732	.2709	.2685
.9	.2661	.2637	.2613	.2589	.2565	.2541	.2516	.2492	.2468	.2444
1.0	.2420	.2396	.2371	.2347	.2323	.2299	.2275	.2251	.2227	.2203
1.1	.2179	.2155	.2131	.2107	.2083	.2059	.2036	.2012	.1989	.1965
1.2	.1942	.1919	.1895	.1872	.1849	.1826	.1804	.1781	.1758	.1736
1.3	.1714	.1691	.1669	.1647	.1626	.1604	.1582	.1561	.1539	.1518
1.4	.1497	.1476	.1456	.1435	.1415	.1394	.1374	.1354	.1334	.1315
1.5	.1295	.1276	.1257	.1238	.1219	.1200	.1182	.1163	.1145	.1127
1.6	.1109	.1092	.1074	.1057	.1040	.1023	.1006	.0989	.0973	.0957
1.7	.0940	.0925	.0909	.0893	.0878	.0863	.0848	.0833	.0818	.0804
1.8	.0790	.0775	.0761	.0748	.0734	.0721	.0707	.0694	.0681	.0669
1.9	.0656	.0644	.0632	.0620	.0608	.0596	.0584	.0573	.0562	.0551
2.0	.0540	.0529	.0519	.0508	.0498	.0488	.0478	.0468	.0459	.0449
2.1	.0440	.0431	.0422	.0413	.0404	.0396	.0387	.0379	.0371	.0363
2.2	.0355	.0347	.0339	.0332	.0325	.0317	.0310	.0303	.0297	.0290
2.3	.0283	.0277	.0270	.0264	.0258	.0252	.0246	.0241	.0235	.0229
2.4	.0224	.0219	.0213	.0208	.0203	.0198	.0194	.0189	.0184	.0180
2.5	.0175	.0171	.0167	.0163	.0158	.0154	.0151	.0147	.0143	.0139
2.6	.0136	.0132	.0129	.0126	.0122	.0119	.0116	.0113	.0110	.0107
2.7	.0104	.0101	.0099	.0096	.0093	.0091	.0088	.0086	.0084	.0081
2.8	.0079	.0077	.0075	.0073	.0071	.0069	.0067	.0065	.0063	.0061
2.9	.0060	.0058	.0056	.0055	.0053	.0051	.0050	.0048	.0047	.0046
3.0	.0044	.0043	.0042	.0041	.0039	.0038	.0037	.0036	.0035	.0034
3.1	.0033	.0032	.0031	.0030	.0029	.0028	.0027	.0026	.0025	.0025
3.2	.0024	.0023	.0022	.0022	.0021	.0020	.0020	.0019	.0018	.0018
3.3	.0017	.0017	.0016	.0016	.0015	.0015	.0014	.0014	.0013	.0013
3.4	.0012	.0012	.0012	.0011	.0011	.0010	.0010	.0010	.0009	.0009
3.5	.0009									
3.6	.0006									
3.7	.0004									
3.8	.0003									
3.9	.0002									

The above ordinates give the probability density for $z = (x - \mu)/\sigma$ deviations from the mean μ (that is, $z = 0$). To fit a normal frequency curve to observed data consisting of n observations, multiply the ordinate from the table for any value of z by n/σ. To fit a normal probability curve multiply the ordinate by $1/\sigma$.

The values for z up to 3.0 are taken from Table II of Fisher & Yates: *Statistical Tables for Biological, Agricultural, and Medical Research* published by Oliver & Boyd Ltd., Edinburgh, by permission of the authors and publishers. The values for the range $z = 3.1$ to $z = 3.9$ are reproduced by permission of the author and publishers from Table A-2 of *Methods of Statistical Analysis* by Cyril H. Goulden, 2nd ed. (New York: John Wiley & Sons, 1960).

TABLE A-4
AREAS UNDER THE NORMAL CURVE

$$F(z) = \int_0^z \frac{1}{\sqrt{2\pi}} e^{\frac{-z^2}{2}} dz$$

z	.00	.01	.02	.03	.04	.05	.06	.07	.08	.09
.0	.0000	.0040	.0080	.0120	.0159	.0199	.0239	.0279	.0319	.0359
.1	.0398	.0438	.0478	.0517	.0557	.0596	.0636	.0675	.0714	.0753
.2	.0793	.0832	.0871	.0910	.0948	.0987	.1026	.1064	.1103	.1141
.3	.1179	.1217	.1255	.1293	.1331	.1368	.1406	.1443	.1480	.1517
.4	.1554	.1591	.1628	.1664	.1700	.1736	.1772	.1808	.1844	.1879
.5	.1915	.1950	.1985	.2019	.2054	.2088	.2123	.2157	.2190	.2224
.6	.2257	.2291	.2324	.2357	.2389	.2422	.2454	.2486	.2518	.2549
.7	.2580	.2611	.2642	.2673	.2704	.2734	.2764	.2794	.2823	.2852
.8	.2881	.2910	.2939	.2967	.2995	.3023	.3051	.3078	.3106	.3133
.9	.3159	.3186	.3212	.3238	.3264	.3289	.3315	.3340	.3365	.3389
1.0	.3413	.3438	.3461	.3485	.3508	.3531	.3554	.3577	.3599	.3621
1.1	.3643	.3665	.3686	.3708	.3729	.3749	.3770	.3790	.3810	.3830
1.2	.3849	.3869	.3888	.3907	.3925	.3944	.3962	.3980	.3997	.4015
1.3	.4032	.4049	.4066	.4082	.4099	.4115	.4131	.4147	.4162	.4177
1.4	.4192	.4207	.4222	.4236	.4251	.4265	.4279	.4292	.4306	.4319
1.5	.4332	.4345	.4357	.4370	.4382	.4394	.4406	.4418	.4430	.4441
1.6	.4452	.4463	.4474	.4485	.4495	.4505	.4515	.4525	.4535	.4545
1.7	.4554	.4564	.4573	.4582	.4591	.4599	.4608	.4616	.4625	.4633
1.8	.4641	.4649	.4656	.4664	.4671	.4678	.4686	.4693	.4699	.4706
1.9	.4713	.4719	.4726	.4732	.4738	.4744	.4750	.4756	.4762	.4767
2.0	.4772	.4778	.4783	.4788	.4793	.4798	.4803	.4808	.4812	.4817
2.1	.4821	.4826	.4830	.4834	.4838	.4842	.4846	.4850	.4854	.4857
2.2	.4861	.4865	.4868	.4871	.4875	.4878	.4881	.4884	.4887	.4890
2.3	.4893	.4896	.4898	.4901	.4904	.4906	.4909	.4911	.4913	.4916
2.4	.4918	.4920	.4922	.4925	.4927	.4929	.4931	.4932	.4934	.4936
2.5	.4938	.4940	.4941	.4943	.4945	.4946	.4948	.4949	.4951	.4952
2.6	.4953	.4955	.4956	.4957	.4959	.4960	.4961	.4962	.4963	.4964
2.7	.4965	.4966	.4967	.4968	.4969	.4970	.4971	.4972	.4973	.4974
2.8	.4974	.4975	.4976	.4977	.4977	.4978	.4979	.4980	.4980	.4981
2.9	.4981	.4982	.4983	.4983	.4984	.4984	.4985	.4985	.4986	.4986
3.0	.4987	.4987	.4987	.4988	.4988	.4989	.4989	.4989	.4990	.4990
3.1	.4990	.4991	.4991	.4991	.4992	.4992	.4992	.4992	.4993	.4993
3.2	.4993	.4993	.4994	.4994	.4994	.4994	.4994	.4995	.4995	.4995
3.3	.4995	.4995	.4996	.4996	.4996	.4996	.4996	.4996	.4996	.4997
3.4	.4997	.4997	.4997	.4997	.4997	.4997	.4997	.4997	.4998	.4998
.	.									
.	.									
.	.									
4.0	.499968									
5.0	.4999997									

This table gives the probability of a random value of a normal variate falling *in* the range $z = 0$ to $z = z$ (in the *shaded area in figure*). The probability of the same variate having a deviation greater than z is given by 0.5 − probability from the table for the given z. The table refers to a single tail of the normal distribution; therefore the probability of a normal variate falling in the range $\pm z = 2 \times$ probability from the table for the given z. The probability of a variate falling outside the range $\pm z$ is $1 - 2 \times$ probability from the table for given z.

The values in this table were obtained by permission of authors and publishers from: C. E. Weatherburn, *Mathematical Statistics* (London: Cambridge University Press, 1957) (for $z = 0$ to $z = 3.1$); C. H. Richardson, *An Introduction to Statistical Analysis* (New York: Harcourt, Brace & World, Inc., 1944) (for $z = 3.2$ to $z = 3.4$); A. H. Bowker and G. J. Lieberman, *Engineering Statistics* (Englewood Cliffs, N. J.: Prentice-Hall, Inc., 1959) (for $z = 4.0$ and 5.0).

TABLE A-5

VALUES OF EXTREME DEVIATE $\dfrac{|x_m - \bar{x}|}{s_e}$ NOT REJECTED AS AN OUTLIER

ν \ n	5 percent level						
	3	4	5	6	7	8	9
10	2.02	2.29	2.49	2.63	2.75	2.85	2.93
11	1.99	2.26	2.44	2.58	2.70	2.79	2.87
12	1.97	2.22	2.40	2.54	2.65	2.75	2.83
13	1.95	2.20	2.38	2.51	2.62	2.71	2.79
14	1.93	2.18	2.35	2.48	2.59	2.68	2.76
15	1.92	2.16	2.33	2.46	2.56	2.65	2.73
16	1.90	2.14	2.31	2.44	2.54	2.63	2.70
17	1.89	2.13	2.30	2.42	2.52	2.61	2.68
18	1.88	2.12	2.28	2.41	2.51	2.59	2.66
19	1.87	2.11	2.27	2.39	2.49	2.58	2.65
20	1.87	2.10	2.26	2.38	2.48	2.56	2.63
24	1.84	2.07	2.23	2.35	2.44	2.52	2.59
30	1.82	2.04	2.20	2.31	2.40	2.48	2.55
40	1.80	2.02	2.17	2.28	2.37	2.44	2.51
60	1.78	1.99	2.14	2.25	2.33	2.41	2.47
120	1.76	1.97	2.11	2.21	2.30	2.37	2.43
∞	1.74	1.94	2.08	2.18	2.27	2.33	2.39

	1 percent level						
10	2.76	3.05	3.25	3.39	3.50	3.59	3.67
11	2.71	3.00	3.19	3.33	3.44	3.53	3.61
12	2.67	2.95	3.14	3.28	3.39	3.48	3.55
13	2.63	2.91	3.10	3.24	3.34	3.43	3.51
14	2.60	2.87	3.06	3.20	3.30	3.39	3.47
15	2.57	2.84	3.02	3.16	3.27	3.35	3.43
16	2.55	2.81	3.00	3.13	3.24	3.32	3.39
17	2.52	2.79	2.97	3.10	3.21	3.29	3.36
18	2.50	2.77	2.95	3.08	3.18	3.27	3.34
19	2.49	2.75	2.92	3.06	3.16	3.24	3.31
20	2.47	2.73	2.91	3.04	3.14	3.22	3.29
24	2.43	2.68	2.85	2.97	3.07	3.15	3.22
30	2.38	2.62	2.79	2.91	3.01	3.08	3.15
40	2.34	2.57	2.73	2.85	2.94	3.02	3.08
60	2.30	2.52	2.68	2.79	2.88	2.95	3.01
120	2.25	2.48	2.62	2.73	2.82	2.89	2.95
∞	2.22	2.43	2.57	2.68	2.76	2.83	2.88

(continued)

An outlier is rejected if its value exceeds the tabulated value at the requisite level of significance.

x_m = greatest or smallest value that can be expected in a sample of size n at the given level of significance.

s_e = estimate of standard deviation from a sample with ν degrees of freedom.

This table is adapted by permission of author and publishers from a paper "Tables of Percentage Points of the 'Studentized' Extreme Deviate from the Sample Mean" by K. R. Nair in *Biometrika*, Vol. 39 (1952), pp. 189–191.

A slight revision of the above values has been suggested by H. A. David in a paper "Revised Upper Percentage Points of the Extreme Studentized Deviate from the Sample Mean," *Biometrika*, Vol. 43 (1956), pp. 449–451.

TABLE A-5 (Continued)

ν \ n	0.1 percent level						
	3	4	5	6	7	8	9
10	3.54	3.84	4.04	4.17	4.28	4.35	4.40
11	3.49	3.80	3.99	4.12	4.23	4.30	4.36
12	3.45	3.75	3.94	4.07	4.19	4.26	4.31
13	3.41	3.71	3.90	4.03	4.14	4.22	4.28
14	3.38	3.67	3.86	4.00	4.10	4.18	4.24
15	3.35	3.64	3.83	3.96	4.06	4.15	4.21
16	3.32	3.51	3.80	3.93	4.03	4.12	4.18
17	3.29	3.58	3.77	3.90	4.00	4.09	4.15
18	3.27	3.55	3.74	3.88	3.98	4.06	4.12
19	3.25	3.53	3.72	3.85	3.95	4.03	4.10
20	3.23	3.51	3.70	3.83	3.93	4.01	4.08
24	3.16	3.44	3.62	3.75	3.85	3.93	4.00
30	3.08	3.36	3.53	3.66	3.76	3.84	3.90
40	3.01	3.27	3.44	3.57	3.66	3.74	3.81
60	2.93	3.19	3.35	3.47	3.56	3.64	3.70
120	2.85	3.10	3.26	3.37	3.46	3.53	3.59
∞	2.78	3.01	3.17	3.28	3.36	3.43	3.48

TABLE A-6
CHAUVENET'S CRITERION FOR REJECTION OF OUTLIERS

Sample size n	$\dfrac{\|x_m - \bar{x}\|}{s}$	Sample size n	$\dfrac{\|x_m - \bar{x}\|}{s}$
2	1.15	20	2.24
3	1.38	25	2.33
4	1.53	30	2.39
5	1.64	40	2.50
6	1.73	50	2.58
7	1.80	60	2.64
8	1.86	80	2.74
9	1.91	100	2.81
10	1.96	150	2.94
11	2.00	200	3.02
12	2.04	300	3.14
13	2.07	400	3.23
14	2.10	500	3.29
16	2.15	600	3.34
18	2.20	1,000	3.48

An outlier may be rejected if the actual value of $\dfrac{\|x_m - \bar{x}\|}{s}$ exceeds the tabulated value.

x_m = value of outlier
$\bar{x}$ = sample mean
s^2 = estimate of variance from sample
n = sample size

Tables

TABLE A-7
DISTRIBUTION OF χ^2

Probability of a deviation greater than χ^2

Degrees of freedom ν	0.99	0.95	0.90	0.80	0.70	0.50	0.30	0.20	0.10	0.05	0.01	0.001
1	.000157	.00393	.0158	.0642	.148	.455	1.074	1.642	2.706	3.841	6.635	10.827
2	.0201	.103	.211	.446	.713	1.386	2.408	3.219	4.605	5.991	9.210	13.815
3	.115	.352	.584	1.005	1.424	2.366	3.665	4.642	6.251	7.815	11.345	16.268
4	.297	.711	1.064	1.649	2.195	3.357	4.878	5.989	7.779	9.488	13.277	18.465
5	.554	1.145	1.610	2.343	3.000	4.351	6.064	7.289	9.236	11.070	15.086	20.517
6	.872	1.635	2.204	3.070	3.828	5.348	7.231	8.558	10.645	12.592	16.812	22.457
7	1.239	2.167	2.833	3.822	4.671	6.346	8.383	9.803	12.017	14.067	18.475	24.322
8	1.646	2.733	3.490	4.594	5.527	7.344	9.524	11.030	13.362	15.507	20.090	26.125
9	2.088	3.325	4.168	5.380	6.393	8.343	10.656	12.242	14.684	16.919	21.666	27.877
10	2.558	3.940	4.865	6.179	7.267	9.342	11.781	13.442	15.987	18.307	23.209	29.588
11	3.053	4.575	5.578	6.989	8.148	10.341	12.899	14.631	17.275	19.675	24.725	31.264
12	3.571	5.226	6.304	7.807	9.034	11.340	14.011	15.812	18.549	21.026	26.217	32.909
13	4.107	5.892	7.042	8.634	9.926	12.340	15.119	16.985	19.812	22.362	27.688	34.528
14	4.660	6.571	7.790	9.467	10.821	13.339	16.222	18.151	21.064	23.685	29.141	36.123
15	5.229	7.261	8.547	10.307	11.721	14.339	17.322	19.311	22.307	24.996	30.578	37.697
16	5.812	7.962	9.312	11.152	12.624	15.338	18.418	20.465	23.542	26.296	32.000	39.252
17	6.408	8.672	10.085	12.002	13.531	16.338	19.511	21.615	24.769	27.587	33.409	40.790
18	7.015	9.390	10.865	12.857	14.440	17.338	20.601	22.760	25.989	28.869	34.805	42.312
19	7.633	10.117	11.651	13.716	15.352	18.338	21.689	23.900	27.204	30.144	36.191	43.820
20	8.260	10.851	12.443	14.578	16.266	19.377	22.775	25.038	28.412	31.410	37.566	45.315
21	8.897	11.501	13.240	15.445	17.182	20.377	23.858	26.171	29.615	32.671	38.932	46.797
22	9.542	12.338	14.041	16.314	18.101	21.337	24.939	27.301	30.813	33.924	40.289	48.268
23	10.196	13.091	14.848	17.187	19.021	22.337	26.018	28.429	32.007	35.172	41.638	49.728
24	10.856	13.848	15.659	18.062	19.943	23.337	27.096	29.553	33.196	36.415	42.980	51.179
25	11.524	14.611	16.473	18.940	20.867	24.337	28.172	30.675	34.382	37.652	44.314	52.620
26	12.198	15.379	17.292	19.820	21.792	25.336	29.246	31.795	35.563	38.885	45.642	54.052
27	12.879	16.151	18.114	20.703	22.719	26.336	30.319	32.912	36.741	40.113	46.963	55.476
28	13.565	16.928	18.939	21.588	23.647	27.336	31.391	34.027	37.916	41.337	48.278	56.893
29	14.256	17.708	19.768	22.475	24.577	28.336	32.461	35.139	39.087	42.557	49.588	58.302
30	14.953	18.493	20.599	23.364	25.508	29.336	33.530	36.250	40.256	43.773	50.892	59.703

This table gives the probability α of a variate falling in the shaded area of the figure, i.e., outside the range 0 to χ^2 for a given number of degrees of freedom ν. For larger values of ν, the expression $\sqrt{2\chi^2} - \sqrt{2\nu - 1}$ may be used as a normal deviate with unit standard deviation, remembering that the probability for χ^2 corresponds to that of a single tail of the normal curve. For example, let $\chi^2 = 147.92$, $\nu = 113$; then $z = \sqrt{295.84} - \sqrt{225} = 2.2$, corresponding to an area $= 0.4861$ from Table A-4. Therefore the probability of a variate exceeding z is $0.5000 - 0.4861 = 0.0139$, which is highly significant.

This table is taken from Table IV of Fisher & Yates: *Statistical Tables for Biological, Agricultural, and Medical Research* published by Oliver & Boyd Ltd., Edinburgh, by permission of the authors and publishers.

TABLE A-8
DISTRIBUTION OF t

Degrees of freedom ν	Probability α			
	0.10	0.05	0.01	0.001
1	6.314	12.706	63.657	636.619
2	2.920	4.303	9.925	31.598
3	2.353	3.182	5.841	12.941
4	2.132	2.776	4.604	8.610
5	2.015	2.571	4.032	6.859
6	1.943	2.447	3.707	5.959
7	1.895	2.365	3.499	5.405
8	1.860	2.306	3.355	5.041
9	1.833	2.262	3.250	4.781
10	1.812	2.228	3.169	4.587
11	1.796	2.201	3.106	4.437
12	1.782	2.179	3.055	4.318
13	1.771	2.160	3.012	4.221
14	1.761	2.145	2.977	4.140
15	1.753	2.131	2.947	4.073
16	1.746	2.120	2.921	4.015
17	1.740	2.110	2.898	3.965
18	1.734	2.101	2.878	3.922
19	1.729	2.093	2.861	3.883
20	1.725	2.086	2.845	3.850
21	1.721	2.080	2.831	3.819
22	1.717	2.074	2.819	3.792
23	1.714	2.069	2.807	3.767
24	1.711	2.064	2.797	3.745
25	1.708	2.060	2.787	3.725
26	1.706	2.056	2.779	3.707
27	1.703	2.052	2.771	3.690
28	1.701	2.048	2.763	3.674
29	1.699	2.045	2.756	3.659
30	1.697	2.042	2.750	3.646
40	1.684	2.021	2.704	3.551
60	1.671	2.000	2.660	3.460
120	1.658	1.980	2.617	3.373
∞	1.645	1.960	2.576	3.291

This table gives the values of t corresponding to various values of the probability α (level of significance) of a random variable falling inside the shaded areas in the figure, for a given number of degrees of freedom ν available for the estimation of error. For a one-sided test the confidence limits are obtained for $\alpha/2$.

This table is taken from Table III of Fisher & Yates: *Statistical Tables for Biological, Agricultural, and Medical Research* published by Oliver & Boyd Ltd., Edinburgh, by permission of the authors and publishers.

TABLE A-9
SIGNIFICANCE OF A DIFFERENCE BETWEEN TWO MEANS
WITH DIFFERENT VARIANCES

	ν_1	θ						
		0°	15°	30°	45°	60°	75°	90°
5 percent level	6	2.447	2.440	2.435	2.435	2.435	2.440	2.447
	8	2.447	2.430	2.398	2.364	2.331	2.310	2.306
$\nu_2 = 6$	12	2.447	2.423	2.367	2.301	2.239	2.193	2.179
	24	2.447	2.418	2.342	2.247	2.156	2.088	2.064
	∞	2.447	2.413	2.322	2.201	2.082	1.993	1.960
	6	2.306	2.310	2.331	2.364	2.398	2.430	2.447
	8	2.306	2.300	2.294	2.292	2.294	2.300	2.306
$\nu_2 = 8$	12	2.306	2.292	2.262	2.229	2.201	2.183	2.179
	24	2.306	2.286	2.236	2.175	2.118	2.077	2.064
	∞	2.306	2.281	2.215	2.128	2.044	1.982	1.960
	6	2.179	2.193	2.239	2.301	2.367	2.423	2.447
	8	2.179	2.183	2.201	2.229	2.262	2.292	2.306
$\nu_2 = 12$	12	2.179	2.175	2.169	2.167	2.169	2.175	2.179
	24	2.179	2.168	2.142	2.112	2.085	2.069	2.064
	∞	2.179	2.163	2.120	2.064	2.011	1.973	1.960
	6	2.064	2.088	2.156	2.247	2.342	2.418	2.447
	8	2.064	2.077	2.118	2.175	2.236	2.286	2.306
$\nu_2 = 24$	12	2.064	2.069	2.085	2.112	2.142	2.168	2.179
	24	2.064	2.062	2.058	2.056	2.058	2.062	2.064
	∞	2.064	2.056	2.035	2.009	1.983	1.966	1.960
	6	1.960	1.993	2.082	2.201	2.322	2.413	2.447
	8	1.960	1.982	2.044	2.128	2.215	2.281	2.306
$\nu_2 = \infty$	12	1.960	1.973	2.011	2.064	2.120	2.163	2.179
	24	1.960	1.966	1.983	2.009	2.035	2.056	2.064
	∞	1.960	1.960	1.960	1.960	1.960	1.960	1.960

(continued)

TABLE A-9 (Continued)

	ν_1	θ						
		0°	15°	30°	45°	60°	75°	90°
1 percent level	6	3.707	3.654	3.557	3.514	3.557	3.654	3.707
	8	3.707	3.643	3.495	3.363	3.307	3.328	3.355
$\nu_2 = 6$	12	3.707	3.636	3.453	3.246	3.104	3.053	3.055
	24	3.707	3.631	3.424	3.158	2.938	2.822	2.797
	∞	3.707	3.626	3.402	3.093	2.804	2.627	2.576
	6	3.355	3.328	3.307	3.363	3.495	3.643	3.707
	8	3.355	3.316	3.239	3.206	3.239	3.316	3.355
$\nu_2 = 8$	12	3.355	3.307	3.192	3.083	3.032	3.039	3.055
	24	3.355	3.301	3.158	2.988	2.862	2.805	2.797
	∞	3.355	3.295	3.132	2.916	2.723	2.608	2.576
	6	3.055	3.053	3.104	3.246	3.453	3.636	3.707
	8	3.055	3.039	3.032	3.083	3.192	3.307	3.355
$\nu_2 = 12$	12	3.055	3.029	2.978	2.954	2.978	3.029	3.055
	24	3.055	3.020	2.938	2.853	2.803	2.793	2.797
	∞	3.055	3.014	2.909	2.775	2.661	2.595	2.576
	6	2.797	2.822	2.938	3.158	3.424	3.631	3.707
	8	2.797	2.805	2.862	2.988	3.158	3.301	3.355
$\nu_2 = 24$	12	2.797	2.793	2.803	2.853	2.938	3.020	3.055
	24	2.797	2.785	2.759	2.747	2.759	2.785	2.797
	∞	2.797	2.777	2.726	2.664	2.613	2.585	2.576
	6	2.576	2.627	2.804	3.093	3.402	3.626	3.707
	8	2.576	2.608	2.723	2.916	3.132	3.295	3.355
$\nu_2 = \infty$	12	2.576	2.595	2.661	2.775	2.909	3.014	3.055
	24	2.576	2.585	2.613	2.664	2.726	2.777	2.797
	∞	2.576	2.576	2.576	2.576	2.576	2.576	2.576

This table gives values of d for known values of ν_1, ν_2, and θ, where tan $\theta = s_1/s_2$, and ν_1 and ν_2 are the corresponding numbers of degrees of freedom. If the difference of means exceeds $d \sqrt{s_1^2 + s_2^2}$, then it is significant at the specified level.

This table is taken from Table VI of Fisher & Yates: *Statistical Tables for Biological, Agricultural, and Medical Research* published by Oliver & Boyd Ltd., Edinburgh, by permission of the authors and publishers.

TABLE A-10
DISTRIBUTION OF VARIANCE RATIO F
5 Percent Level of Significance

$P(F)$

F

$\nu_2 \backslash \nu_1$	1	2	3	4	5	6	7	8	9	10	12	15	20	24	30	40	60	120	∞
1	161.45	199.50	215.71	224.58	230.16	233.99	236.77	238.88	240.54	241.88	243.91	245.95	248.01	249.05	250.09	251.14	252.20	253.25	254.32
2	18.51	19.00	19.16	19.25	19.30	19.33	19.35	19.37	19.38	19.40	19.41	19.43	19.45	19.45	19.46	19.47	19.48	19.49	19.50
3	10.13	9.55	9.28	9.12	9.01	8.94	8.89	8.85	8.81	8.79	8.74	8.70	8.66	8.64	8.62	8.59	8.57	8.55	8.53
4	7.71	6.94	6.59	6.39	6.26	6.16	6.09	6.04	6.00	5.96	5.91	5.86	5.80	5.77	5.75	5.72	5.69	5.66	5.63
5	6.61	5.79	5.41	5.19	5.05	4.95	4.88	4.82	4.77	4.74	4.68	4.62	4.56	4.53	4.50	4.46	4.43	4.40	4.36
6	5.99	5.14	4.76	4.53	4.39	4.28	4.21	4.15	4.10	4.06	4.00	3.94	3.87	3.84	3.81	3.77	3.74	3.70	3.67
7	5.59	4.74	4.35	4.12	3.97	3.87	3.79	3.73	3.68	3.64	3.57	3.51	3.44	3.41	3.38	3.34	3.30	3.27	3.23
8	5.32	4.46	4.07	3.84	3.69	3.58	3.50	3.44	3.39	3.35	3.28	3.22	3.15	3.12	3.08	3.04	3.01	2.97	2.93
9	5.12	4.26	3.86	3.63	3.48	3.37	3.29	3.23	3.18	3.14	3.07	3.01	2.94	2.90	2.86	2.83	2.79	2.75	2.71
10	4.96	4.10	3.71	3.48	3.33	3.22	3.14	3.07	3.02	2.98	2.91	2.84	2.77	2.74	2.70	2.66	2.62	2.58	2.54
11	4.84	3.98	3.59	3.36	3.20	3.09	3.01	2.95	2.90	2.85	2.79	2.72	2.65	2.61	2.57	2.53	2.49	2.45	2.40
12	4.75	3.89	3.49	3.26	3.11	3.00	2.91	2.85	2.80	2.75	2.69	2.62	2.54	2.51	2.47	2.43	2.38	2.34	2.30
13	4.67	3.81	3.41	3.18	3.03	2.92	2.83	2.77	2.71	2.67	2.60	2.53	2.46	2.42	2.38	2.34	2.30	2.25	2.21
14	4.60	3.74	3.34	3.11	2.96	2.85	2.76	2.70	2.65	2.60	2.53	2.46	2.39	2.35	2.31	2.27	2.22	2.18	2.13
15	4.54	3.68	3.29	3.06	2.90	2.79	2.71	2.64	2.59	2.54	2.48	2.40	2.33	2.29	2.25	2.20	2.16	2.11	2.07
16	4.49	3.63	3.24	3.01	2.85	2.74	2.66	2.59	2.54	2.49	2.42	2.35	2.28	2.24	2.19	2.15	2.11	2.06	2.01
17	4.45	3.59	3.20	2.96	2.81	2.70	2.61	2.55	2.49	2.45	2.38	2.31	2.23	2.19	2.15	2.10	2.06	2.01	1.96
18	4.41	3.55	3.16	2.93	2.77	2.66	2.58	2.51	2.46	2.41	2.34	2.27	2.19	2.15	2.11	2.06	2.02	1.97	1.92
19	4.38	3.52	3.13	2.90	2.74	2.63	2.54	2.48	2.42	2.38	2.31	2.23	2.16	2.11	2.07	2.03	1.98	1.93	1.88
20	4.35	3.49	3.10	2.87	2.71	2.60	2.51	2.45	2.39	2.35	2.28	2.20	2.12	2.08	2.04	1.99	1.95	1.90	1.84
21	4.32	3.47	3.07	2.84	2.68	2.57	2.49	2.42	2.37	2.32	2.25	2.18	2.10	2.05	2.01	1.96	1.92	1.87	1.81
22	4.30	3.44	3.05	2.82	2.66	2.55	2.46	2.40	2.34	2.30	2.23	2.15	2.07	2.03	1.98	1.94	1.89	1.84	1.78
23	4.28	3.42	3.03	2.80	2.64	2.53	2.44	2.37	2.32	2.27	2.20	2.13	2.05	2.00	1.96	1.91	1.86	1.81	1.76
24	4.26	3.40	3.01	2.78	2.62	2.51	2.42	2.36	2.30	2.25	2.18	2.11	2.03	1.98	1.94	1.89	1.84	1.79	1.73
25	4.24	3.39	2.99	2.76	2.60	2.49	2.40	2.34	2.28	2.24	2.16	2.09	2.01	1.96	1.92	1.87	1.82	1.77	1.71
26	4.23	3.37	2.98	2.74	2.59	2.47	2.39	2.32	2.27	2.22	2.15	2.07	1.99	1.95	1.90	1.85	1.80	1.75	1.69
27	4.21	3.35	2.96	2.73	2.57	2.46	2.37	2.31	2.25	2.20	2.13	2.06	1.97	1.93	1.88	1.84	1.79	1.73	1.67
28	4.20	3.34	2.95	2.71	2.56	2.45	2.36	2.29	2.24	2.19	2.12	2.04	1.96	1.91	1.87	1.82	1.77	1.71	1.65
29	4.18	3.33	2.93	2.70	2.55	2.43	2.35	2.28	2.22	2.18	2.10	2.03	1.94	1.90	1.85	1.81	1.75	1.70	1.64
30	4.17	3.32	2.92	2.69	2.53	2.42	2.33	2.27	2.21	2.16	2.09	2.01	1.93	1.89	1.84	1.79	1.74	1.68	1.62
40	4.08	3.23	2.84	2.61	2.45	2.34	2.25	2.18	2.12	2.08	2.00	1.92	1.84	1.79	1.74	1.69	1.64	1.58	1.51
60	4.00	3.15	2.76	2.53	2.37	2.25	2.17	2.10	2.04	1.99	1.92	1.84	1.75	1.70	1.65	1.59	1.53	1.47	1.39
120	3.92	3.07	2.68	2.45	2.29	2.18	2.09	2.02	1.96	1.91	1.83	1.75	1.66	1.61	1.55	1.50	1.43	1.35	1.25
∞	3.84	3.00	2.60	2.37	2.21	2.10	2.01	1.94	1.88	1.83	1.75	1.67	1.57	1.52	1.46	1.39	1.32	1.22	1.00

TABLE A-10 (Continued)
1 Percent Level of Significance

ν_2 \ ν_1	1	2	3	4	5	6	7	8	9	10	12	15	20	24	30	40	60	120	∞
1	4,052.4	4,999.5	5,403.3	5,624.6	5,763.7	5,859.0	5,928.3	5,981.6	6,022.5	6,055.8	6,106.3	6,157.3	6,208.7	6,234.6	6,260.7	6,286.8	6,313.0	6,339.4	6,366.0
2	98.50	99.00	99.17	99.25	95.30	99.33	99.36	99.37	99.39	99.40	99.42	99.43	99.45	99.46	99.47	99.47	99.48	99.49	99.50
3	34.12	30.82	29.46	28.71	28.24	27.91	27.67	27.49	27.34	27.23	27.05	26.87	26.69	26.60	26.50	26.41	26.32	26.22	26.12
4	21.20	18.00	16.69	15.98	15.52	15.21	14.98	14.80	14.66	14.55	14.37	14.20	14.02	13.93	13.84	13.74	13.65	13.56	13.46
5	16.26	13.27	12.06	11.39	10.97	10.67	10.46	10.29	10.16	10.05	9.89	9.72	9.55	9.47	9.38	9.29	9.20	9.11	9.02
6	13.74	10.92	9.78	9.15	8.75	8.47	8.26	8.10	7.98	7.87	7.72	7.56	7.40	7.31	7.23	7.14	7.06	6.97	6.88
7	12.25	9.55	8.45	7.85	7.46	7.19	6.99	6.84	6.72	6.62	6.47	6.31	6.16	6.07	5.99	5.91	5.82	5.74	5.65
8	11.26	8.65	7.59	7.01	6.63	6.37	6.18	6.03	5.91	5.81	5.67	5.52	5.36	5.28	5.20	5.12	5.03	4.95	4.86
9	10.56	8.02	6.99	6.42	6.06	5.80	5.61	5.47	5.35	5.26	5.11	4.96	4.81	4.73	4.65	4.57	4.48	4.40	4.31
10	10.04	7.56	6.55	5.99	5.64	5.39	5.20	5.06	4.94	4.85	4.71	4.56	4.41	4.33	4.25	4.17	4.08	4.00	3.91
11	9.65	7.21	6.22	5.67	5.32	5.07	4.89	4.74	4.63	4.54	4.40	4.25	4.10	4.02	3.94	3.86	3.78	3.69	3.60
12	9.33	6.93	5.95	5.41	5.06	4.82	4.64	4.50	4.39	4.30	4.16	4.01	3.86	3.78	3.70	3.62	3.54	3.45	3.36
13	9.07	6.70	5.74	5.21	4.86	4.62	4.44	4.30	4.19	4.10	3.96	3.82	3.66	3.59	3.51	3.43	3.34	3.25	3.17
14	8.86	6.51	5.56	5.04	4.70	4.46	4.28	4.14	4.03	3.94	3.80	3.66	3.51	3.43	3.35	3.27	3.18	3.09	3.00
15	8.68	6.36	5.42	4.89	4.56	4.32	4.14	4.00	3.89	3.80	3.67	3.52	3.37	3.29	3.21	3.13	3.05	2.96	2.87
16	8.53	6.23	5.29	4.77	4.44	4.20	4.03	3.89	3.78	3.69	3.55	3.41	3.26	3.18	3.10	3.02	2.93	2.84	2.75
17	8.40	6.11	5.18	4.67	4.34	4.10	3.93	3.79	3.68	3.59	3.46	3.31	3.16	3.08	3.00	2.92	2.83	2.75	2.65
18	8.29	6.01	5.09	4.58	4.25	4.01	3.84	3.71	3.60	3.51	3.37	3.23	3.08	3.00	2.92	2.84	2.75	2.66	2.57
19	8.18	5.93	5.01	4.50	4.17	3.94	3.77	3.63	3.52	3.43	3.30	3.15	3.00	2.92	2.84	2.76	2.67	2.58	2.49
20	8.10	5.85	4.94	4.43	4.10	3.87	3.70	3.56	3.46	3.37	3.23	3.09	2.94	2.86	2.78	2.69	2.61	2.52	2.42
21	8.02	5.78	4.87	4.37	4.04	3.81	3.64	3.51	3.40	3.31	3.17	3.03	2.88	2.80	2.72	2.64	2.55	2.46	2.36
22	7.95	5.72	4.82	4.31	3.99	3.76	3.59	3.45	3.35	3.26	3.12	2.98	2.83	2.75	2.67	2.58	2.50	2.40	2.31
23	7.88	5.66	4.76	4.26	3.94	3.71	3.54	3.41	3.30	3.21	3.07	2.93	2.78	2.70	2.62	2.54	2.45	2.35	2.26
24	7.82	5.61	4.72	4.22	3.90	3.67	3.50	3.36	3.26	3.17	3.03	2.89	2.74	2.66	2.58	2.49	2.40	2.31	2.21
25	7.77	5.57	4.68	4.18	3.86	3.63	3.46	3.32	3.22	3.13	2.99	2.85	2.70	2.62	2.54	2.45	2.36	2.27	2.17
26	7.72	5.53	4.64	4.14	3.82	3.59	3.42	3.29	3.18	3.09	2.96	2.82	2.66	2.58	2.50	2.42	2.33	2.23	2.13
27	7.68	5.49	4.60	4.11	3.78	3.56	3.39	3.26	3.15	3.06	2.93	2.78	2.63	2.55	2.47	2.38	2.29	2.20	2.10
28	7.64	5.45	4.57	4.07	3.75	3.53	3.36	3.23	3.12	3.03	2.90	2.75	2.60	2.52	2.44	2.35	2.26	2.17	2.06
29	7.60	5.42	4.54	4.04	3.73	3.50	3.33	3.20	3.09	3.00	2.87	2.73	2.57	2.49	2.41	2.33	2.23	2.14	2.03
30	7.56	5.39	4.51	4.02	3.70	3.47	3.30	3.17	3.07	2.98	2.84	2.70	2.55	2.47	2.39	2.30	2.21	2.11	2.01
40	7.31	5.18	4.31	3.83	3.51	3.29	3.12	2.99	2.89	2.80	2.66	2.52	2.37	2.29	2.20	2.11	2.02	1.92	1.80
60	7.08	4.98	4.13	3.65	3.34	3.12	2.95	2.82	2.72	2.63	2.50	2.35	2.20	2.12	2.03	1.94	1.84	1.73	1.60
120	6.85	4.79	3.95	3.48	3.17	2.96	2.79	2.66	2.56	2.47	2.34	2.19	2.03	1.95	1.86	1.76	1.66	1.53	1.38
∞	6.63	4.61	3.78	3.32	3.02	2.80	2.64	2.51	2.41	2.32	2.18	2.04	1.88	1.79	1.70	1.59	1.47	1.32	1.00

If the computed statistic $F = s_1^2/s_2^2$, with the larger s in the numerator, exceeds the tabulated value of F at the specified level with ν_1, ν_2 degrees of freedom, we reject the null hypothesis that $\sigma_1 = \sigma_2$ (see figure).

Table adapted by permission of authors and publishers, from E. L. Crow, F. A. Davis, and M. W. Maxfield, *Statistics Manual* (New York: Dover Publications, Inc., 1960).

ν	5 Percent Level of Significance				1 Percent level of Significance				ν
	Total number of variables				Total number of variables				
	2	3	4	5	2	3	4	5	
1	.997	.999	.999	.999	1.000	1.000	1.000	1.000	1
2	.950	.975	.983	.987	.990	.995	.997	.998	2
3	.878	.930	.950	.961	.959	.976	.983	.987	3
4	.811	.881	.912	.930	.917	.949	.962	.970	4
5	.754	.836	.874	.898	.874	.917	.937	.949	5
6	.707	.795	.839	.867	.834	.886	.911	.927	6
7	.666	.758	.807	.838	.798	.855	.885	.904	7
8	.632	.726	.777	.811	.765	.827	.860	.882	8
9	.602	.697	.750	.786	.735	.800	.836	.861	9
10	.576	.671	.726	.763	.708	.776	.814	.840	10
11	.553	.648	.703	.741	.684	.753	.793	.821	11
12	.532	.627	.683	.722	.661	.732	.773	.802	12
13	.514	.608	.664	.703	.641	.712	.755	.785	13
14	.497	.590	.646	.686	.623	.694	.737	.768	14
15	.482	.574	.630	.670	.606	.677	.721	.752	15
16	.468	.559	.615	.655	.590	.662	.706	.738	16
17	.456	.545	.601	.641	.575	.647	.691	.724	17
18	.444	.532	.587	.628	.561	.633	.678	.710	18
19	.433	.520	.575	.615	.549	.620	.665	.698	19
20	.423	509	.563	.604	.537	.608	.652	.685	20
21	.413	.498	.552	.592	.526	.596	.641	.674	21
22	.404	.488	.542	.582	.515	.585	.630	.663	22
23	.396	.479	.532	.572	.505	.574	.619	.652	23
24	.388	.470	.523	.562	.496	.565	.609	.642	24
25	.381	.462	.514	.553	.487	.555	.600	.633	25
26	.374	.454	.506	.545	.478	.546	.590	.624	26
27	.367	.446	.498	.536	.470	.538	.582	.615	27
28	.361	.439	.490	.529	.463	.530	.573	.606	28
29	.355	.432	.482	.521	.456	.522	.565	.598	29
30	.349	.426	.476	.514	.449	.514	.558	.591	30
35	.325	.397	.445	.482	.418	.481	.523	.556	35
40	.304	.373	.419	.455	.393	.454	.494	.526	40
45	.288	.353	.397	.432	.372	.430	.470	.501	45
50	.273	.336	.379	.412	.354	.410	.449	.479	50
60	.250	.308	.348	.380	.325	.377	.414	.442	60
70	.232	.286	.324	.354	.302	.351	.386	.413	70
80	.217	.269	.304	.332	.283	.330	.362	.389	80
90	.205	.254	.288	.315	.267	.312	.343	.368	90
100	.195	.241	.274	.300	.254	.297	.327	.351	100
125	.174	.216	.246	.269	.228	.266	.294	.316	125
150	.159	.198	.225	.247	.208	.244	.270	.290	150
200	.138	.172	.196	.215	.181	.212	.234	.253	200
300	.113	.141	.160	.176	.148	.174	.192	.208	300
400	.098	.122	.139	.153	.128	.151	.167	.180	400
500	.088	.109	.124	.137	.115	.135	.150	.162	500
1,000	.062	.077	.088	.097	.081	.096	.106	.116	1,000

The critical value of r at a given level of significance, total number of variables, and degrees of freedom ν, is read from the table. If the computed $|r|$ exceeds the critical value, then the null hypothesis that there is no association between the variables is rejected at the given level. The test is an equal-tails test, since we are usually interested in either positive or negative correlation. The shaded portion of the figure is the stipulated probability as a level of significance.

Table reproduced with the permission of the authors and the publisher, from E. L. Crow, F. A. Davis, and M. W. Maxfield, *Statistical Manual* (New York: Dover Publications, Inc., 1960).

TABLE A-12
CONTROL CHART LIMITS FOR MEAN

[Factor A_w corresponds to 95 percent probability (z = 1.96);
factor A_A corresponds to 99.8 percent probability (z = 3.09)]

Sample size n....	2	3	4	5	6	7	8	9	10	11	12
Warning factor A_w	1.229	0.668	0.476	0.377	0.316	0.274	0.244	0.220	0.202	0.186	0.174
Action factor A_A	1.937	1.054	0.750	0.594	0.498	0.432	0.384	0.347	0.317	0.294	0.274

To obtain limits for a given sample size n, multiply mean range $\bar{R}$ by the appropriate value of A_w and A_A, then add to and subtract from mean $\bar{x}$.

Table adapted from Table G of O. L. Davies (ed.), *Statistical Methods in Research and Production* (Edinburgh: Oliver and Boyd, Ltd., 1958), by permission of the Imperial Chemical Industries, Ltd., and the publishers.

TABLE A-13
CONTROL CHART LIMITS FOR RANGE

[Factors D_{WU} and D_{WL} correspond to 95 percent probability;
factors D_{AU} and D_{AL} correspond to 99.8 percent probability]

Sample size n	2	3	4	5	6	7	8	9	10	11	12
Upper warning factor D_{WU}	2.81	2.17	1.93	1.81	1.72	1.66	1.62	1.58	1.56	1.53	1.51
Lower warning factor D_{WL}.....	0.04	0.18	0.29	0.37	0.42	0.46	0.50	0.52	0.54	0.56	0.58
Upper action factor D_{AU}	4.12	2.99	2.58	2.36	2.22	2.12	2.04	1.99	1.94	1.90	1.87
Lower action factor D_{AL}	0.00	0.04	0.10	0.16	0.21	0.26	0.29	0.32	0.35	0.38	0.40

To obtain limits, multiply mean range $\bar{R}$ by the appropriate value of D.

Table adapted from Table G of O. L. Davies (ed.), *Statistical Methods in Research and Production* (Edinburgh: Oliver and Boyd, Ltd., 1958), by permission of the Imperial Chemical Industries, Ltd., and the publishers.

TABLE A-14
RANDOM NUMBERS

53	74	23	99	67	61	32	28	69	84	94	62	67	86	24	98	33	41	19	95	47	53	53	38	09
63	38	06	86	54	99	00	65	26	94	02	82	90	23	07	79	62	67	80	60	75	91	12	81	19
35	30	58	21	46	06	72	17	10	94	25	21	31	75	96	49	28	24	00	49	55	65	79	78	07
63	43	36	82	69	65	51	18	37	88	61	38	44	12	45	32	92	85	88	65	54	34	81	85	35
98	25	37	55	26	01	91	82	81	46	74	71	12	94	97	24	02	71	37	07	03	92	18	66	75
02	63	21	17	69	71	50	80	89	56	38	15	70	11	48	43	40	45	86	98	00	83	26	91	03
64	55	22	21	82	48	22	28	06	00	61	54	13	43	91	82	78	12	23	29	06	66	24	12	27
85	07	26	13	89	01	10	07	82	04	59	63	69	36	03	69	11	15	83	80	13	29	54	19	28
58	54	16	24	15	51	54	44	82	00	62	61	65	04	69	38	18	65	18	97	85	72	13	49	21
34	85	27	84	87	61	48	64	56	26	90	18	48	13	26	37	70	15	42	57	65	65	80	39	07
03	92	18	27	46	57	99	16	96	56	30	33	72	85	22	84	64	38	56	98	99	01	30	98	64
62	95	30	27	59	37	75	41	66	48	86	97	80	61	45	23	53	04	01	63	45	76	08	64	27
08	45	93	15	22	60	21	75	46	91	98	77	27	85	42	28	88	61	08	84	69	62	03	42	73
07	08	55	18	40	45	44	75	13	90	24	94	96	61	02	57	55	66	83	15	73	42	37	11	61
01	85	89	95	66	51	10	19	34	88	15	84	97	19	75	12	76	39	43	78	64	63	91	08	25
72	84	71	14	35	19	11	58	49	26	50	11	17	17	76	86	31	57	20	18	95	60	78	46	75
88	78	28	16	84	13	52	53	94	53	75	45	69	30	96	73	89	65	70	31	99	17	43	48	76
45	17	75	65	57	28	40	19	72	12	25	12	74	75	67	60	40	60	81	19	24	62	01	61	16
96	76	28	12	54	22	01	11	94	25	71	96	16	16	88	68	64	36	74	45	19	59	50	88	92
43	31	67	72	30	24	02	94	08	63	38	32	36	66	02	69	36	38	25	39	48	03	45	15	22
50	44	66	44	21	66	06	58	05	62	68	15	54	35	02	42	35	48	96	32	14	52	41	52	48
22	66	22	15	86	26	63	75	41	99	58	42	36	72	24	58	37	52	18	51	03	37	18	39	11
96	24	40	14	51	23	22	30	88	57	95	67	47	29	83	94	69	40	06	07	18	16	36	78	86
31	73	91	61	19	60	20	72	93	48	98	57	07	23	69	65	95	39	69	58	56	80	30	19	44
78	60	73	99	84	43	89	94	36	45	56	69	47	07	41	90	22	91	07	12	78	35	34	08	72
84	37	90	61	56	70	10	23	98	05	85	11	34	76	60	76	48	45	34	60	01	64	18	39	96
36	67	10	08	23	98	93	35	08	86	99	29	76	29	81	33	34	91	58	93	63	14	52	32	52
07	28	59	07	48	89	64	58	89	75	83	85	62	27	89	30	14	78	56	27	86	63	59	80	02
10	15	83	87	60	79	24	31	66	56	21	48	24	06	93	91	98	94	05	49	01	47	59	38	00
55	19	68	97	65	03	73	52	16	56	00	53	55	90	27	33	42	29	38	87	22	13	88	83	34
53	81	29	13	39	35	01	20	71	34	62	33	74	82	14	53	73	19	09	03	56	54	29	56	93
51	86	32	68	92	33	98	74	66	99	40	14	71	94	58	45	94	19	38	81	14	44	99	81	07
35	91	70	29	13	80	03	54	07	27	96	94	78	32	66	50	95	52	74	33	13	80	55	62	54
37	71	67	95	13	20	02	44	95	94	64	85	04	05	72	01	32	90	76	14	53	89	74	60	41
93	66	13	83	27	92	79	64	64	72	28	54	96	53	84	48	14	52	98	94	56	07	93	89	30
02	96	08	45	65	13	05	00	41	84	93	07	54	72	59	21	45	57	09	77	19	48	56	27	44
49	83	43	48	35	82	88	33	69	96	72	36	04	19	76	47	45	15	18	60	82	11	08	95	97
84	60	71	62	46	40	80	81	30	37	34	39	23	05	38	25	15	35	71	30	88	12	57	21	77
18	17	30	88	71	44	91	14	88	47	89	23	30	63	15	56	34	20	47	89	99	82	93	24	98
79	69	10	61	78	71	32	76	95	62	87	00	22	58	40	92	54	01	75	25	43	11	71	99	31
75	93	36	57	83	56	20	14	82	11	74	21	97	90	65	96	42	68	63	86	74	54	13	26	94
38	30	92	29	03	06	28	81	39	38	62	25	06	84	63	61	29	08	93	67	04	32	92	08	09
51	28	50	10	34	31	57	75	95	80	51	97	02	74	77	76	15	48	49	44	18	55	63	77	09
21	31	38	86	24	37	79	81	53	74	73	24	16	10	33	52	83	90	94	76	70	47	14	54	36
29	01	23	87	88	58	02	39	37	67	42	10	14	20	92	16	55	23	42	45	54	96	09	11	06
95	33	95	22	00	18	74	72	00	18	38	79	58	69	32	81	76	80	26	92	82	80	84	25	39
90	84	60	79	80	24	36	59	87	38	82	07	53	89	35	96	35	23	79	18	05	98	90	07	35
46	40	62	98	82	54	97	20	56	95	15	74	80	08	32	16	46	70	50	80	67	72	16	42	79
20	31	89	03	43	38	46	82	68	72	32	14	82	99	70	80	60	47	18	97	63	49	30	21	30
71	59	73	05	50	08	22	23	71	77	91	01	93	20	49	82	96	59	26	94	66	39	67	98	60

This table is taken from Table XXXIII of Fisher & Yates: *Statistical Tables for Biological, Agricultural, and Medical Research* published by Oliver & Boyd Ltd., Edinburgh, by permission of the authors and publishers.

Index